KEYS TO READING

Lavender Skywriters

Theodore L. Harris
Mildred Creekmore
Margaret H. Greenman
Louise Matteoni
Harold B. Allen, *Linguistic Consultant*

THE ECONOMY COMPANY   Oklahoma City   Atlanta   Indianapolis

Acknowledgments

For permission to adapt and reprint copyright materials, grateful acknowledgment is made to the following publishers, authors, and other copyright holders:

Abelard-Schuman, Ltd., and A.M. Heath & Company, Ltd., for "The Boy Who Cut Everything to Pieces," reprinted from *The Magic Drum* by W. F. P. Burton, by permission of Criterion Books, published by Abelard-Schuman, Ltd.; copyright year 1962, all rights reserved.

Addison-Wesley Publishing Company, Inc., for "Pablo," reprinted from *He-Who-Runs-Far*, text © 1970 by Hazel Fredericksen; a Young Scott Book, by permission of Addison-Wesley Publishing Co.

Atheneum Publishers, for "Inside a Poem" and "Thumbprint" by Eve Merriam, reprinted from *It Doesn't Always Have to Rhyme;* for "Think of Tree" by Lilian Moore, text copyright © 1969 by Lilian Moore, reprinted from *I Thought I Heard the City;* and for "The Night of the Leonids" by E. L. Konigsburg, copyright © 1971 by E. L. Konigsburg, reprinted from *Altogether, One at a Time.*

The Bobbs-Merrill Company, Inc., for "Shenandoah National Park," reprinted from *Our Country's National Parks*, Volume I, by Irving Robert Melbo, copyright 1941, 1950, 1960 by The Bobbs-Merrill Co.

Thomas Y. Crowell Company, Inc., for "Miracle," reprinted from *The Helen Keller Story* by Catherine Owens Peare, copyright © 1959 by Catherine Owens Peare; permission granted by the publisher, Thomas Y. Crowell Co., Inc., New York.

Dodd, Mead & Company, Inc., for "Explorers," reprinted from *Together in America* by Johanna Johnston, copyright © 1965 by Johanna Johnston.

Doubleday & Company, Inc., for "Riding on the Railroad," reprinted from *Freedom Train* by Dorothy Sterling, copyright 1954 by Dorothy Sterling, for "Clean Air—Sparkling Water," reprinted from *Clean Air—Sparkling Water* by Dorothy E. Shuttlesworth, copyright © 1968 by Dorothy E. Shuttlesworth, for "The Canopy of Air," reprinted from *Winds* by Mary O'Neill, copyright © 1970 by Mary O'Neill, and for "Someday," copyright © 1956 by Royal Publications, reprinted from *Earth Is Room Enough* by Isaac Asimov; Doubleday & Company, Inc., and Curtis Brown, Ltd., for "Visitors from Outer Space," reprinted from *Exploring the Universe* by Roy A. Gallant, copyright © 1956, 1968 by Roy A. Gallant; Doubleday & Company, Inc., and The Bodley Head, for "The Cay," reprinted from *The Cay* by Theodore Taylor, copyright © 1969 by Theodore Taylor.

E. P. Dutton & Company, Inc., for "On the Vanity of Earthly Greatness" from *Gaily the Troubadour* by Arthur Guiterman, copyright 1936 by E. P. Dutton & Co., Inc., © renewed 1964 by Mrs. Vida Lindo Guiterman and reprinted with her permission.

Faber and Faber Limited, and David Higham Associates, Ltd., for "The Motion of the Earth," reprinted from *The Pot Geranium* by Norman Nicholson.

Farrar, Straus & Giroux, Inc., and Virginia Rice, for "Pitcher," reprinted from *Pitcher and I* by Stephen Cole, copyright © 1946, 1947, 1963 by Stephen Cole, copyright 1946 by The Curtis Publishing Company.

Follett Publishing Company, division of Follett Corporation, for "Claudia," reprinted from *Claudia* by Barbara Wallace, copyright © 1969 by Barbara Wallace.

Contents

The Beautiful World

A View Around

Myriads

Universe Key

Promises to Keep

Stopping by Woods on a Snowy Evening

Whose woods these are I think I know.
His house is in the village, though,
He will not see me stopping here
To watch his woods fill up with snow.

My little horse must think it queer
To stop without a farmhouse near
Between the woods and frozen lake
The darkest evening of the year.

He gives his harness bells a shake
To ask if there is some mistake.
The only other sound's the sweep
Of easy wind and downy flake.

The woods are lovely, dark, and deep,
But I have promises to keep,
And miles to go before I sleep,
And miles to go before I sleep.

Robert Frost

The Night of the Leonids

E. L. Konigsburg

Sometimes the promises a person makes to himself can
lead to conflicts or struggles with other people or things
or with himself. As you read the following realistic story,
you will discover how the main characters deal with the
conflicts they face.

I arrived at Grandmother's house in a taxi. I had my usual three suitcases, one for my pillow and my coin collection. The doorman helped me take the suitcases up, and I helped him; I held the elevator button so that the door wouldn't close on him while he loaded them on and off. Grandmother's new maid let me in. She was younger and fatter than the new maid was the last time. She told me that I should unpack and that Grandmother would be home shortly.

Grandmother doesn't take me everywhere she goes and I don't take her everywhere I go; but we get along pretty well, Grandmother and I.

She doesn't have any pets, and I don't have any other grandmothers, so I stay with her whenever my mother and my father go abroad; they send me postcards.

My friend Clarence has the opposite: three Eiffels and two Coliseums. My mother and my father are very touched that I save their postcards. I also think that it is very nice of me.

I had finished unpacking, and I was wondering why Grandmother didn't wait for me. After all, I am her only grandchild, and I am named Lewis. Lewis was the name of one of her husbands, the one who was my grandfather. Grandmother came home as I was on my way to the kitchen to see if the new maid believed in eating between meals better than the last new maid did.

"Hello, Lewis," Grandmother said.

"Hello, Grandmother," I replied. Sometimes we talk like that, plain talk. Grandmother leaned over for me to kiss her cheek. Neither one of us adores slobbering, or even likes it.

"Are you ready?" I asked.

"Just as soon as I get out of this girdle and these high heels," she answered.

"Take off your hat, too, while you're at it," I suggested. "I'll set things up awhile."

Grandmother joined me in the library. I have taught her double solitaire, fish, cheat, and casino. She has taught me gin rummy; we mostly play gin rummy.

The maid served us supper on trays in the library so that we could watch the news on color TV. Grandmother has only one color TV set, so we watch her programs on Mondays, Wednesdays, Fridays and every other Sunday; we watch mine on Tuesdays, Thursdays, Saturdays and the leftover Sundays. I thought that she could have given me *every* Sunday since I am her only grandchild and I am named Lewis, but Grandmother said, "Share and share alike." And we do. And we get along pretty well, Grandmother and I.

After the news and after supper Grandmother decided to read the newspaper; it is delivered before breakfast but she only reads the ads then. Grandmother sat on the sofa, held the newspaper at the end of her arm, then she squinted, and then she tilted her head back and farther back so that all you could see were nostrils, and then she called, "Lewis, Lewis, please bring me my glasses."

I knew she would.

I had to look for them. I always have to look for them. They have pale-blue frames and are shaped like sideways commas, and they are never where she thinks they are or where I think they should be: *on the nose of her head.* You should see her trying to dial the telephone without her glasses. She practically stands in the next room and points her finger, and she still gets wrong numbers. I only know that, in case of fire, I'll make the call.

I found her glasses. Grandmother began reading messages from the paper as if she were sending telegrams. It is one of her habits I wonder about; I wonder if she does it even when I'm not there. "Commissioner of Parks invites everyone to Central Park tonight," she read.

"What for?" I asked. "A mass mugging?"

"No. Something else."

"What else?"

"Something special."

I waited for what was a good pause before I asked, "What special?"

Grandmother waited for a good pause before she answered, "Something spectacular," not even bothering to look up from the newspaper.

I paused. Grandmother paused. I paused. Grandmother

paused. I paused, I paused, I paused, and I won. Grandmother spoke first. "A spectacular show of stars," she said.

"Movie stars or rock and roll?" I inquired politely.

"Star stars," she answered.

"You mean like the sky is full of?"

"Yes, I mean like the sky is full of."

"You mean that the Commissioner of Parks has invited everyone out just to enjoy the night environment?" We were studying environment in our school.

"Not any night environment. Tonight there will be a shower of stars."

"Like a rain shower?" I asked.

"More like a thunderstorm."

"Stars falling like rain can be very dangerous and pollute our environment besides." We were also studying pollution of the environment in our school.

"No, they won't pollute our environment," Grandmother said.

"How do you know?" I asked.

"Because they will burn up before they fall all the way down. Surely you must realize that," she added.

I didn't answer.

"You must realize that they always protect astronauts from burning up on their reentry into the earth's atmosphere."

I didn't answer.

"They give the astronauts a heat shield. Otherwise they'd burn up."

I didn't answer.

"The stars don't have one. A heat shield, that is."

I didn't answer.

"That's why the stars burn up. They don't have a shield. Of course, they aren't really stars, either. They are Leonids."

Then I answered.

"Why don't you tell me about the shower of stars that isn't really a shower and isn't really stars?" She wanted to explain about them. I could tell. That's why I asked.

Grandmother likes to be listened to. That's one reason why she explains things. She prefers being listened to when she *tells* things: like get my elbow off the table and pick up my feet when I walk. She would tell me things like that all day if I would listen all day. When she *explains*, I listen. I sit close and listen close, and that makes her feel like a regular grandmother. She likes that, and sometimes so do I. That's one reason why we get along pretty well.

Grandmother explained about the Leonids.

The Leonids are trash that falls from the comet called Temple-Tuttle. Comets go around the sun just as the planet Earth does. But not quite just like the planet Earth. Comets don't make regular circles around the sun. They loop around the sun, and they leak. Loop and leak. Loop and leak. The parts that leak are called the tail. The path that Earth takes around the sun and the path that Temple-Tuttle takes around the sun were about to cross each other. Parts of the tail would get caught in the earth's atmosphere and light up as they burn up as they fall down. Little bits at a time. A hundred little bits at a time. A thousand little bits at a time. A million bits.

The parts that burn up look like falling stars. That is why Grandmother and the Commissioner of Parks called it a Shower of Stars. The falling stars from Temple-Tuttle are called the Leonids. Leonids happen only once every thirty-three and one-third years. The whole sky over the city would light up with them. The reason that everyone was invited to the park was so that we city people could see a big piece of sky instead of just a hallway of sky between the buildings.

It would be an upside-down Grand Canyon of fireworks.

I decided that we ought to go. Grandmother felt the same way I did. Maybe even more so.

Right after we decided to go, Grandmother made me go to bed. She said that I should be rested and that she would wake me in plenty of time to get dressed and walk to Central Park. She promised to wake me at eleven o'clock.

And I believed her.

I believed her.

I really did believe her.

Grandmother said to me, "Do you think that I want to miss something that happens only three times in one century?"

"Didn't you see it last time?" I asked. After all, there was a Shower of Leonids thirty-three and one-third years ago when she was only thirty, and I'll bet there was no one making her go to bed.

"No, I didn't see it last time," she said.

"What was the matter? Didn't the Commissioner of Parks invite you?"

"No, that was not the matter."

"Why didn't you see it then?"

"Because," she explained.

"Because you forgot your glasses and you didn't have Lewis, Lewis to get them for you?"

"I didn't even wear glasses when I was thirty."

"Then why didn't you see it?"

"Because," she said, "because I didn't bother to find out about it, and I lost my chance."

I said, "Oh." I went to bed. I knew about lost chances.

Grandmother woke me. She made me bundle up. She was bundled, too. She looked sixty-three years lumpy. I knew that she wouldn't like it if I expressed an opinion, so I didn't. Somehow.

We left the apartment.

We found the place in the park. The only part that wasn't crowded was up. Which was all right because that was where the action would be.

The shower of stars was to begin in forty-five minutes.

We waited.

And waited.

And saw.

"What are you crying about?" Grandmother asked. Not kindly.

"I have to wait thirty-three and one-third years before I can see a big spectacular Shower of Stars. I'll be forty-three before I can ever see a Leonid."

"Oh, shut up!" Grandmother said. Not kindly. "I'll be *middle-aged*."

"What was that for?" I asked. "What did I do?" I asked. "What did I do?" I asked again. I had always thought that we got along pretty well, my grandmother and I.

"You add it up," Grandmother said. Not kindly.

So I did. I added it up. Sixty-three and thirty-three don't add up to another chance.

I held Grandmother's hand on the way back to her apartment. She let me, even though neither one of us adores handholding. I held the hand that hit me.

Afterthought

1. What was the main conflict in the story?
2. What kind of relationship did Lewis and his grandmother have? Find the parts of the story that reveal this relationship.
3. Did you find this a happy or a sad story? Explain why.

Miracle

Catherine Owens Peare

It is not unusual in stories or in real life for a person to be mistaken concerning his true opponent in a conflict. In this chapter from the biography of a woman who was blind, deaf, and unable to speak when she was a child, you will see how difficult it sometimes is to recognize the real enemy.

"Phantom"—Helen Keller's own name for herself as a child—stood in the doorway sensing the excitement of a new arrival. She felt the vibration of a strange footstep on the porch, then another footstep, coming closer. Strangers were often enemies. She bent her head down and charged into the newcomer, and the newcomer fell back. Again the footsteps came toward her, and the stranger tried to put arms around her. Helen drove off Miss Sullivan's embrace with kicks and punches.

She discovered that the stranger had a bag, and she grabbed the bag and darted into the house. When her mother caught up with her and tried to take the bag away, she fought, because she knew her mother would give in. Mother always gave in.

But Anne Sullivan encouraged her to keep the bag and carry it up the stairs. Soon a trunk was brought into the room, and Helen flung herself against it, exploring the lid with her fingers until she found the lock. Miss Sullivan gave her the key and allowed her to unlock it and lift the lid. Helen plunged her hands down into the contents, feeling everything.

The newcomer lifted a doll out of the trunk and laid it in Helen's arms, and after that she did something very strange indeed. She held one of Helen's hands and in its palm formed curious figures with her own fingers. First she held her own thumb and middle finger together while her index finger stood upright. Then she formed a circle by joining her thumb and first finger, and finally she spread her thumb and index finger as far apart as they would go.

With a sudden wild leap Helen darted for the door, but the stranger caught hold of her and brought her back, forcing her into a chair. Helen fought and raged, but the stranger was strong. She did not give in like family and servants. Helen

was startled to feel a piece of cake being placed in her hand,
and she gobbled it down quickly before it could be taken
away. The stranger did another trick with her fingers. On
Helen's palm she formed an open circle with thumb and first
finger, next closed her fist for a moment, following that by
placing her thumb between her second and third fingers and
curling her last two fingers under, and finally held all her
fingertips together against her thumb.

That was enough! Helen tore loose and bolted out of the
room and down the stairs, to Mother, to Father, to her
stepbrother, to the cook, to anybody whom she could manage.

But at dinner the stranger sat next to her. Helen had her
own way of eating, and no one had ever tried to stop her. She
stumbled and groped her way from place to place, snatching
and grabbing from other people's plates, sticking her fingers
into anything at all. When she came to the visitor, her hand
was slapped away. Helen reached out for the visitor's plate
again. Another slap! She flung herself forward and was lifted
bodily back. Now she was being forced into her own chair
again, being made to sit there, and once more she was raging,
fighting, kicking. She broke away and found all the other

chairs empty. Her family had deserted her, left her alone with this enemy!

Again the enemy took hold of her, made her sit down, forced a spoon into her hand, made her eat from her own plate.

When the ordeal finally ended, she broke away and ran out of the dining room—to Mother, to Mother's arms. Mother's eyes were wet. Mother was crying. Mother was sorry.

Every day there were battles with the newcomer. There were battles when she had to take her bath, comb her hair, button her shoes. And always those finger tricks; even Mother and Father were doing them. Since the trick for cake usually brought her a piece of cake, Helen shrewdly began to learn others.

If battles with her new governess grew too unbearable, Helen could seek out Martha Washington, a child her own age, daughter of their Negro cook, and bully and boss her. Martha's pigtails were short because Helen had once clipped them off with a pair of scissors.

Or she could simply romp with her father's hunting dogs and forget there was such a thing in the house as a governess. She could help feed the turkey gobblers, or go hunting for the nests of the guinea hens in the tall grass. She loved to burrow her way in amongst the big flowering shrubs; completely surrounded by the prickly leaves of the mimosa, she felt safe and protected.

There was real comfort in revenge. She knew about keys and locks, and she found a day when she could lock the awful intruder in her room and run away with the key. The big day of revenge came when, in one of the enemy's unguarded moments, Helen raised her fists in the air and brought them down on Miss Sullivan's face. Two teeth snapped off.

An abrupt change occurred in her life right after that.

Miss Sullivan took her by the hand and they went for a carriage drive. When the carriage stopped, they alighted and entered a different house. Helen groped her way about the room, recognizing nothing, until her companion placed one of her own dolls in her arms. She clung to the familiar thing. But as soon as Helen realized that she was alone with the stranger in a strange place, that no amount of rubbing her cheek would bring her mother, she flung the doll away in a rage. She refused to eat, refused to wash, and gave the governess a long, violent tussle when it came time to go to bed.

The governess did not seem very tall, but she was strong and stubborn, and for the first time in her life Helen began to experience defeat. She grew tired, wanted to lie down and sleep, but still she struggled against the stranger's will. She would sleep on the floor, or in the chair! But each time she was dragged back to the bed. At last Helen felt herself giving in, and exhausted by her own efforts and huddled close to the farthest edge of the big double bed, she fell asleep.

When Helen awoke in the morning, she flung herself out of bed prepared to give further resistance, but somehow her face was washed with less effort than the night before, and after she had dressed and eaten her breakfast, she felt her companion's determined but gentle hands guiding her fingers over some soft, coarse yarn, guiding them again along a thin bone shaft with a hooked end. In a very little while Helen had grasped the idea of crocheting, and as she became interested in making a chain, she forgot to hate Anne Sullivan.

Each day in the new house after that brought new skills to be learned—cards to sew, beads to string.

After about two weeks, Helen had begun to accept her routine, her table manners, her tasks, her companion. The whole world seemed to grow gentler as her own raging disposition subsided.

She cocked her head suddenly one afternoon and sniffed the air, detecting a new odor in the room, something familiar— one of her father's dogs! Helen groped about until she found the silken, long-haired setter, Belle. Of all the dogs on the farm, Belle was Helen's favorite, and she quickly lifted one of Belle's paws and began to move the dog's toes in one of the finger tricks. Miss Sullivan patted Helen's head, and the approval made her feel almost happy.

Miss Sullivan soon took her by the hand and led her out the door, across a yard, to some front steps, and instantly Helen realized where she was. She was home! She had been in the little annex near home all this time. Mother and Father had not been far away. She raced up the steps and into the house and flung herself at one adult after another. She was home! Scrambling up the stairs to the second floor, she found

her own room just the same, and when she felt Miss Sullivan standing behind her she turned impulsively and pointed a finger at her and then at her own palm. Who was she?

"T-e-a-c-h-e-r," Anne Sullivan spelled into her hand.

But the finger trick was too long to be learned at once.

Every day after that, Teacher and Helen were constant companions indoors and out, and gradually Helen learned to see with her fingers. Teacher showed her how to explore plants and animals without damaging them—chickens, grasshoppers, rabbits, squirrels, frogs, wild flowers, butterflies, trees. Grasshoppers had smooth, clear wings; the wings of a butterfly were powdery. The bark of a tree had a curious odor, and through its huge trunk ran a gentle humming vibration.

Hand in hand, they wandered for miles over the countryside, sometimes as far as the Tennessee River where the water rushed and churned over the mussel shoals.

For everything she felt or did, there was a finger trick: wings, petals, riverboats—walking, running, standing, drinking.

One morning when she was washing her face and hands, Helen pointed to the water in the basin, and Teacher spelled into her hand: "w-a-t-e-r." At the breakfast table later Helen pointed to her mug of milk, and Teacher spelled: "m-i-l-k." But Helen became confused. "D-r-i-n-k" was milk, she insisted. Helen pointed to her milk again and Teacher spelled, "m-u-g." Was m-u-g d-r-i-n-k? In another second Helen's mind was a jumble of wiggling fingers. She was frustrated, bewildered, angry, a bird trapped in a cage and beating her wings against the bars.

Quickly Teacher placed an empty mug in her hand and led her out of doors to a pump that stood under a shed in the yard. Helen stood before the pump, mug in hand, as Teacher indicated, and felt the rush of cold water over her hands. Teacher took one of her hands and spelled, "w-a-t-e-r." While water rushed over one hand, Helen felt the letters, w-a-t-e-r, in the other.

Suddenly Helen was transfixed, and she let her mug crash to the ground forgotten. A new, wonderful idea . . . back into her memory rushed that infant's word she had once spoken: "wah-wah." She grew excited; her pulse raced as understanding lighted her mind. Wah-wah was w-a-t-e-r. It was a word! These finger tricks were words! There were words for everything. That was what Teacher was trying to tell her.

She felt Teacher rush to her and hug her, and Teacher was as excited as she, crying and laughing, because at last Helen understood the concept of words.

Joyfully they ran back into the house, and Helen was surrounded by an excited household. All the rest of the day she demanded words, words, words. What was this? What was that? Even the infant Mildred? What was that? "B-a-b-y." And once more Helen pointed a persistent finger at Miss Sullivan and demanded the word that would identify *her*.

"T-e-a-c-h-e-r," Anne Sullivan spelled. "T-e-a-c-h-e-r."

The last shred of hostility and hate vanished from Helen's soul as she glowed with her sudden happiness. She felt her fingers being lifted to Teacher's face to explore its expression. The corners of the mouth were drawn up and the cheeks were crinkled. Helen imitated the expression and when she did, her face was no longer blank, because Helen Keller was smiling.

When bedtime finally arrived, she put her hand willingly into Teacher's and mounted the stairs, and before climbing into bed, she slipped her arms around Teacher's neck and kissed her—for the first time.

Just Try to Forget

Nathaniel Benchley

Not all conflicts in realistic stories are private struggles between someone and an opponent. Very often family or friends are aware of what a person is going through.

Arthur Dobson held open the door of the school gymnasium for his wife, then followed her in. The smell of steam heat and liniment and disinfectant was the same as it had been twenty years before, and he could hear the scurrying, pounding feet of basketball players, punctuated by the sharp tweets of the referee's whistle. It never changes, Dobson thought. Every smell and every sound is still the same. He led his wife past the basketball court, then through another door and up a short flight of steps to the gallery above the swimming pool.

The room was of white tile and glass brick, and it was steaming hot and echoed hollowly with a noise of its own. Dobson and his wife sat down behind a railing overlooking the pool, and Dobson took off his topcoat and put it on the seat beside him.

"I'm getting nervous already," his wife said. "Do you think they have a chance?"

"All I know is what Larry said," Dobson replied. "He didn't seem to think so."

"I don't really care, so long as Larry wins his race," she said. "I think he'd die if he didn't win it, with you here, and all."

"He can't win it or not win it," said Dobson. "He's in the

two-hundred-yard relay, so there are three others with him."

"I know, but still, . . ." His wife took off her coat and peered down at the green, transparent water of the pool. "It looks awfully long, doesn't it?" she said.

Dobson looked at the pool and estimated that he could swim about one length—maybe two, if he took it easy. "Long enough," he said.

Two lanky, muscular figures wearing the bright-blue trunks of the rival school walked out of a door at one end of the pool and dived flatly into the water, hitting it with a double crack like pistol shots. Then more boys in blue trunks came out and followed them, until the whole squad was swimming up and down the length of the pool. At the diving board, two boys took turns doing unbelievably complicated dives, and Dobson and his wife watched them with a kind of uneasy respect.

"It looks as though Larry were right," Dobson said after a while. "They look pretty good."

"I know," said his wife. "Much too good."

Then Larry's team, wearing red trunks, appeared and dived into the water and swam up and down the pool. At first, Dobson had trouble recognizing his son among the twisting, thrashing bodies. The boys all swam alike, with long, powerful strokes, and they made insane-looking, bottoms-up turns at either end of the pool, and Dobson thought back on the summer, many years ago, when he had had some difficulty teaching Larry to swim. As long as Dobson held him, he would splash and paddle gleefully, but the minute Dobson took his hands away he would become panic-stricken and sink. It wasn't until children younger than he had begun to swim that Larry, without any help from his father, took his first strokes.

He's certainly improved since then, Dobson thought. I had
no idea he could swim this well. Even last summer, he wasn't
swimming like this. Then Dobson looked at the others, in the
blue trunks, and they seemed to be swimming just a little
better. I guess it always looks that way, he thought. The other
guys always look frighteningly good, even if they aren't. But
this time they *are* better—there's no getting around it.

When the warm-up was over, the two teams retired, and
the officials began arranging their lists and checking their
watches. It was the final meet of the season, the letter meet,
and the gallery was full of spectators, both students and adults.
From below came the sounds of more spectators, who were
standing or sitting along the edge of the pool beneath the
gallery, and the whole place hummed and echoed and rang
with noise. Dobson removed his jacket, put it next to his
topcoat, and loosened his tie. He fought down an urge to light
a cigarette, and locked his hands together in his lap. His wife
reached across and clutched them briefly, and her hand was
cold and wet. He smiled at her. "It's no good worrying now,"
he said. "Larry's race isn't until the very last."

There was a patter of applause as the rival team, wearing

blue sweat suits, filed out and took places on benches set in three rows at the shallow end of the pool. A moment later, the air was shattered with cheers and whistles as Larry's team, in red sweat suits, came out and sat beside them. Presently, two boys from each team peeled off their sweat suits and dived into the pool, then pulled themselves out, shook hands all around, and waited, nervously flapping their arms and wrists. Dobson looked at his son, who was sitting on the back row of benches, staring straight ahead of him and chewing a thumbnail. I wish I hadn't come, Dobson thought. I wish I'd made up some excuse to stay at home. He remembered a time when he was young and his father had come to watch him play football, and he had spent the entire, miserable game on the bench. Parents should stay away from athletic contests, he told himself. They ought to be barred by law. Larry continued to chew his thumbnail, and Dobson felt sick.

A manager with a megaphone announced the first event, which was the fifty-yard freestyle race, and gave the names of the contestants. The starter pointed a blank pistol upward and told the boys to take their marks. There was complete silence as they stood in a row at the edge of the pool, gripping the rim with their toes. The starter said "Get set," and the boys crouched, their hands on a level with their feet. There was a pause. The pistol banged, and after what seemed to Dobson like an unnaturally long wait the boys shot forward, cracked into the water, and churned off down the pool.

The crowd shouted and called and cheered and chanted, and the noise swelled to a roar as the swimmers reached the far end of the pool, made their frantic, ducking turns, and headed back for the finish line. They were almost indistinguishable in the boiling spray, but the two in the farthest lane, the ones in the blue trunks, pulled steadily ahead in the final yards, and finished first and second. Dobson settled back in his seat.

"That makes the score eight to one already," he said to his wife. "This is going to be murder."

But Larry's team placed first and third in the next event, and first and second in the one after that, and somehow, unbelievably, they managed to gain a slight lead. It was never a big enough lead to be safe, and at one point the score was tied, and Dobson saw and pitied the agony of the one boy in each event who failed to score. Some drooped forlornly in the gutter, some cried, and some had to be helped from the pool by consoling teammates, who said futile things to them and patted them on the bottom while they dragged themselves to the benches. As the final event came closer, Dobson looked more often at his son, and it seemed to him that Larry was getting smaller and paler with each race. I wish he'd swum first, Dobson thought. I wish it was all over, so he wouldn't have to wait like this. Even if he'd lost, I wish it was all over.

The diving took a long time, with each of the four contestants doing six dives, and the next-to-last event was the medley relay race, which Larry's team won, putting them ahead, 37-30. When the score was announced, Dobson's wife gave a little shout and grabbed him. "We've won!" she cried. "They can't possibly catch us now!"

"It looks that way," Dobson replied with a certain amount of relief. "It certainly looks that way."

A student behind him touched his arm. "No, sir," he said. "They can still tie us. The last race counts seven points, and there's no score for second."

"Oh!" said Dobson.

He saw Larry and his three teammates strip off their sweat suits, jump into the water, then climb out, shake hands, and stand around fluttering their hands and breathing deeply. The boys from the other school did the same, and they looked big and unnaturally husky. They didn't seem as nervous as the boys on Larry's team. The noise from the crowd was such that the manager had to shout three times for quiet before he could announce the event, and when Larry was announced as swimming third in the relay, Dobson had an odd feeling at the sound of the name. His wife slid her hand into his. "I don't think I'm going to be able to watch," she said. "You tell me what happens."

The first two swimmers took their marks, and a tense silence hung until the crack of the gun. Then, as the swimmers leaped out at the water, the spectators came to their feet and shouted and cheered and stamped, and the noise grew and swelled until Dobson couldn't hear his own voice.

The swimmers thrashed down the pool and then back, and the one in red trunks was slightly ahead as they touched the starting line and two more swimmers sprang out. Dobson didn't watch the second boys; all he saw was Larry, who had moved up to the starting line, breathing in deep gulps, his eyes fixed glassily ahead of him. An official squatted beside Larry's feet, and Larry crouched lower and lower as his teammate in the pool approached him. The red-trunked boy was leading by about two yards when he reached the edge, and it seemed to Dobson that Larry was in the air and in the water at almost the same instant. Then Dobson's throat closed and he couldn't make a sound, but beside him his wife was screaming and pounding the rail, her voice all but lost in the growing pandemonium.

Larry finished his lap three or four yards ahead, but as

the last two swimmers raced down and turned, the one in blue trunks began to gain. He closed the gap slowly, and the members of both teams crowded around the finish line, jumping and beckoning and bellowing, and then the red-trunked boy put on a final, frenzied spurt and held his lead to the finish line. Larry and his teammates spilled into the water, hugging one another and falling down and shouting, and the blue-trunked boy clung to the gutter, exhausted and miserable.

Dobson sat back and looked at his wife. "Wow!" he said. And she laughed.

Down below, members of both teams clustered around the officials, and then, suddenly, the ones in blue leaped into the air and shouted, and Dobson saw a boy in red trunks hit the water with his fist. There was some commotion, and a lot of noise from the crowd, and Dobson was unable to hear distinctly what the manager said through the megaphone, but he caught the words "Thirty-seven to thirty-seven."

Unbelieving, he turned to a student in the crowd. "What happened?" Dobson asked. "I couldn't hear."

"We were disqualified," the student answered sourly. "Dobson jumped the gun."

For almost a full minute, neither Dobson nor his wife said anything. Then he put on his coat and helped her on with hers, and as they walked slowly down the stairs, she took his arm. "What are we going to say to him?" she asked in a small voice. "What *can* we say?"

"I wish I knew," he replied. "I wish I knew."

They went out to the car, and stood beside it smoking while they waited for Larry. Dobson's mind was a jumble of things he wanted to say, but even as he thought of them they seemed inadequate, and he knew that none of them would do any good. He thought of going in and seeing Larry in the locker room, and then quickly decided against it. I guess it's best to wait out here, he thought. He'll come out when he wants to.

After what seemed like an hour, Larry came out of the gym and walked slowly toward them. His hair was wet and slicked back, and his eyes were red—possibly from the chlorine in the pool, Dobson thought, knowing that that wasn't the reason. Without a word, Larry opened a door of the car and dropped into the back seat. Dobson got in front, and after a moment's hesitation, his wife got in back with Larry.

"Do you want to drive around for a while?" Dobson asked as he started the engine.

"Whatever you say," Larry replied. "I don't care."

They drove through the streets of the town and then out into the bleak, snow-spotted country. For several minutes nobody spoke, and then Dobson cleared his throat. "Would you like me to tell you something?" he asked.

"Sure," said Larry, without enthusiasm.

"When I was in school, I wanted to play baseball," Dobson said. "More than anything else, I wanted to make the baseball team. The only trouble was I wasn't good enough. I got in a couple of games as a pinch hitter, and once they let me play right field, but I dropped the only fly that came my way, and they yanked me out." He looked into the rearview mirror and saw the incredulous expression on his wife's face. He continued, "The last game in my senior year—the letter game—we were behind four to three in the ninth inning. We had a man on third, and the coach sent me in to bunt down

toward first. On the first ball pitched, I tried to bunt, and the ball hit my right thumb and broke it. Technically, I was eligible for a letter, but I never collected it. I couldn't look at any of the team again."

Larry laughed shortly. "I never heard about that," he said.

"I didn't tell many people," Dobson replied, with another look into the rearview mirror. "But what I'm getting at is that these things are horrible when they happen—you think you'll never live them down—but sooner or later it gets so you can bear to think of them again. It may take a long while, but eventually it happens."

Larry was quiet for a minute. "I guess I was just trying too hard," he said, at last.

"I know," Dobson replied. "And I promise you, next year we won't come up here to watch."

Larry looked at his father in the mirror. "OK," he said, and smiled.

Elaine and the Thing

Sally Watson

Fairy tales very often concern the deeds and battles of great men or intense struggles between good and evil. But they can also deal with amusing conflicts.

"Elaine! Princess Elaine!"

"Your Royal Highness, where are you?"

"Drat the girl, where has she gone this time? Elaine!"

The assortment of voices echoed faintly out of Wychwood Castle and across the grounds to the main gate. But the red-haired princess skipping purposefully across the outer courtyard toward the sentry post just skipped a little faster. She had developed a conveniently deaf ear just for times like this, when everyone *would* keep telling her things not to do. Elaine was sure they lay awake at night thinking up new ones.

It wasn't that she wanted to upset her family, but she couldn't seem to help it. She was a Misfit. It seemed that a princess was supposed to be sweet and timid and gentle and sedate and golden-haired and blue-eyed and apt to faint at the least little thing. But Elaine wasn't. And trying to make things better just seemed to make things worse, so why try?

She firmly turned her deaf ear to the calls of her nanny, her tutor, and her next-older sister, Adelicia, who was a true princess, and smiled engagingly up at the sentry.

Unfortunately, the sentry hadn't a deaf ear. "Don't I hear someone calling you, Your Highness?" he suggested tactfully.

"Do you?" asked Elaine, her smile now perfectly dazzling. "Well, if they ask where I've gone, just tell them it's to improve my education, will you, Osbert?"

Osbert, a sturdy, shock-haired young man, thought this over in his slow way. It sounded all right. Education was a good thing.

"Has your new tutor resigned *already*, then?" he asked.

"Not yet," Elaine told him, looking impish. "But I expect

he will tomorrow. You see, he says there's no such thing as magic."

Osbert looked startled. As well say there were no such things as dragons, or elephants, or griffins. Better, in fact. Few people had ever seen those beasts, but practically everyone ran into a bit of magic now and then. Especially around Wychwood Castle.

Elaine nodded sympathetically at his expression. "Yes, isn't he silly? So I'm going to see if I can find some magic, just to prove to him that there is. Don't you think that's nice of me?"

"To be sure," agreed Osbert, and waved to her as she skipped across the drawbridge and into the village.

She hurried down the not-so-long-after-King Arthur cobblestone street, pausing to greet everyone she met and to chat a bit with Mag the fishwoman, Peter the baker (who gave her a fresh hot bun), and Jenny the seamstress. A proper princess would not have been so casual, of course. Elaine's sisters, Petronilla and Adelicia, always smiled and nodded with simply shattering grandeur. But Elaine grinned and bounced and chattered with no grandeur whatever, and the villagers loved her for it.

A proper little wildfire, that one, they told one another fondly. Even, they added, though she *was* a bit of a trial at times.

Elaine came out at the bottom of the village and looked around. Behind her was the hill, with Wychwood Castle on top and the village curled all down the side right to the little river that lapped at her feet, coaxing her to come through the green meadows to find the sea. Over on the left was Wychwood, probably full of giants, unicorns, and hippogriffs, as

well as the witch for whom it was named. But it had rained that morning, and Elaine was not at all sure that magic things would be out in all that damp and drip. The road went off to the right, and she decided to follow it for a while and look for inspiration.

Presently she found it. A small path led off toward a beech wood, and Elaine could just glimpse the roof and chimneys of a big stone house right on the edge of the wood. She turned and followed the path to a rambling, overgrown wall and an open gate and just the corner of a big sign standing where the path turned in at the gate.

BEW said the corner of the sign.

Elaine screwed up her freckled nose in puzzlement and walked faster.

BEWARE OF said the first half of the sign.

Elaine grinned. She wasn't the least bit afraid of dogs, so she kept on going until she could see the whole sign.

She stopped. She blinked.

It read,

BEWARE OF THE THING.

Elaine stared at it for a moment. Then she walked up the path and knocked at the front door of the big, towery old house. It was opened by a stout woman with straggly gray hair.

"Please," said Elaine politely, "would you tell me what a Thing is?"

"That depends," said the woman, "on what sort of Thing you want to know about."

"The Thing to beware of," Elaine replied.

"Oh, *that* one!" the woman said, sighing. "It's a shocking nuisance, that's what it is."

"But what does it do?" persisted Elaine.

"It goes Bump in the Night, that's wot it do!" said a very grumbly, sour voice, and an old man wearing a pointed nightcap came into the hall. "It be a perfectly beastly Thing, and it's ruining my whole career!" And he glared.

"How?"

He looked at her pityingly. "I be studying to be a great scientist, that's how. A scientist," he explained loftily, "be a man who reads weighty volumes and makes experiments and pays no mind to magic."

"Oh, like my tutor," said Elaine understandingly.

"And it's them Bumps wot do keep me awake at night," the old man went on. "How can I go on not believing in magic wiv a magic Thing going Bump all the time? 'Tis ruining my whole future, it be!" And he stamped his foot.

"Oh, *I* know!" cried Elaine excitedly. "You can just give it to me! It's just the sort of thing I've been looking for! I'll take it right away from here and back to the castle. I've never had a magic thing before."

"By Merlin!" croaked the old man, "take that horrid Thing away from here, and I . . . I'll . . . I'll dedicate my first Great Scientific Discovery to you, that's wot I'll do!"

"Oh, lovely!" Elaine held out her hands for it. "Er . . . do I put it in my pocket, or lead it on a string, or what? What does it look like?"

"How should I know wot it looks like?" demanded the old man. "It *sounds* like a Bump in the Night." And he vanished through the hall door.

"I think I saw it once," ventured the gray-haired woman. "It looked like spots before my eyes. It'll be somewhere in the house, dear. You just pop up and have a look round." And she vanished through the kitchen door.

Elaine looked at both closed doors, blinked, and then raised her firm pointed chin. "Thing!" she called, starting up the creaky old stairs. "Thing that Goes Bump in the Night! Here, Thing!"

Up and up she wandered, calling softly and keeping her eyes open for spots before them. Into towers and attics and dusty old bedrooms she prowled. "Here Thingy, old thing!"

The Thing was terribly confused and upset. People always ran away from it, prayed to be delivered from it, or sometimes swore at it (but from a safe distance). No one had *ever* come chasing it before! It was unnerving. When Elaine reached the very last and highest and dustiest room in the house, the Thing was huddled, quaking, in the very furthest corner, and she almost overlooked it entirely. But just as she turned to leave, she saw a faint, quivering cluster of lavender spots scrunched up in the corner.

"Thing!" she cried eagerly.

The spots paled.

"Good gracious!" Elaine exclaimed. "You're not afraid of me, are you?" The spots jiggled fearfully up and down. "Oh, well, you mustn't be," she said. "I'm really terribly nice. My name is Elaine, and I want to adopt you and take you home with me and let you Go Bump in the Night for my tutor. You see, he doesn't believe in magic, and I think we ought to set him right about it, don't you?"

The Thing wavered doubtfully.

Ten minutes later, Elaine waved good-bye to the delighted old man and woman and set off for home, the Thing floating jauntily behind her. Once it had unscrooched itself from the corner and stood up, it turned out to be whirlwind-shaped, about seven feet high, and formed entirely of transparent dots and squiggles of all shades, which moved around and changed

color according to the Thing's mood. There were two dots and a squiggle near the top that Elaine fancied might be its face—if it could be said to have a face.

They reached the village and hurried through, only stopping for quick greetings to the villagers, some of whom rubbed their eyes and muttered about spots after she had gone on.

Panting a little from her climb up the hill, Elaine hurried past the sentry with a cheerful wave and ran across the courtyard and into the Great Hall, where the tutor was at that moment complaining bitterly to the king and queen.

There was no need at all to ask what he was complaining about. Everyone turned and stared disapprovingly as Elaine dashed in, her blue brocade skirts bedraggled and muddy, as usual.

But Elaine was used to disapproving stares and hardly

noticed. "I've brought you a gift, Professor Crumbwell," she said, not at all put out. "It's a Thing."

The tutor frowned. "How often must I tell you to call things by their proper names?" he demanded severely.

"But that *is* its proper name," explained Elaine. "It's a Thing that Goes Bump in the Night, and I think it's rather magic, so I brought it to show you there *is* such a thing as magic."

The tutor looked at King Godobert. "See what I mean?" he said.

But before the king could comment, Elaine's blue-eyed cat, Sibyl, walked in, took one look at the Thing, and sat down with her head on one side to consider.

"WOW!" she decided presently, and bushed out her black tail at the startled cluster of spots, which hastily hid themselves behind Elaine.

"Why, Sibyl!" cried Elaine, reproachful. "I'm surprised at you! I should have thought you and the Thing would be friends. You could Go Bump in the Night together."

Sibyl reconsidered. Then she stuck her black spike of a tail straight up into the air, sauntered around Elaine, and prowled around the twisty whirl of spots that might be called the Thing's feet, sniffing with interest.

The spots hastily drew themselves upward, out of reach.

Sibyl hissed. Then she changed her mind and decided to play. She stood up on her hind legs and began batting at the spots, which swirled even higher in great agitation.

Sibyl began leaping into the air. The king and queen stared, Elaine giggled, and the tutor decided they had all—especially the cat—lost their wits.

Sibyl leaped even higher. Then the Thing suddenly got into the spirit of the game and began shooting and spinning around the room, changing color and shape as fast as it could, with Sibyl leaping and batting after it.

King Godobert rubbed his eyes. "I seem to be seeing spots."

"I think I'd better give notice," said the tutor. "Everyone has gone mad."

"Oh, no," said Elaine hastily. "Wait! Thing, Sibyl!" she called. "Come here, do. This is Professor Crumbwell, Thing. This is the Thing, Professor, and he'll Go Bump in the Night for you."

The Thing came over. Sibyl was purring and rubbing her shoulder around its lower spots.

"I don't want bumps in the night," said the tutor sulking. "Either you are a very naughty princess, or else you want herb tea and cold cloths on your head, and the same goes for your cat. Come right back to the classroom and behave yourself, Your Highness, as your sisters are doing."

"But," began Elaine. But her parents were clearly going to side with the tutor, so she sighed and obeyed, leaving Sibyl to show the Thing around its new home.

Right after breakfast the next morning the tutor, looking heavy-eyed and a trifle distracted, came up to King Godobert.

"I do think you ought not to have your workmen banging away on all sides of my bedroom all night like that," he complained. "It's most inconsiderate. I couldn't get any sleep at all."

"What workmen?" demanded the king in surprise.

"The ones that kept going bump all night!" snapped the tutor.

"That was the Thing," explained Elaine, delighted with her first piece of magic.

"Speak when you are spoken to, Elaine," said the queen. "I didn't know you were having repairs done, Godobert!"

"I'm not," said the king irritably. "Either the workmen sneaked in behind my back, or it's some other kind of bump. Call the Prime Minister."

"The Thing," began Elaine again.

"Hush!" said everyone. "Just what sort of bump was it, Professor Crumbwell?"

"Bumpy ones," grumbled the tutor. "How can I teach properly if I'm to be kept awake with bumps in the night?"

"You don't teach properly anyhow," muttered Elaine. "You keep saying there's no such thing as magic, when the Bumps are magic."

"Don't be rude, Elaine!" scolded her father. "What are you talking about? What bumps are magic?"

"The ones in the Night," said Elaine. "It's the Thing I brought home yesterday, Papa. I *told* you. It's Bumping for Professor Crumbwell so he won't go on saying there's no such thing as magic."

"There isn't!" said the tutor in a positive voice, his eyes gleaming.

The king looked doubtful. "Are you sure?" he asked worriedly.

"Absolutely," snapped the tutor. "All magic is purely imaginary."

"Oh, well then," Queen Regina pointed out reasonably, "you mustn't be disturbed about your imaginary bumps in the night. And it's past time for the children's lessons to start, so I think you had better go on up."

"Oh," said the tutor, and went.

After a week of Bumps in the Night, the tutor was definitely not himself. It made things a bit difficult during lessons, because he got more snappish every day.

"I do wish you'd call off your Thing, Elaine," said her

oldest brother, Arthur, who was a very proper sort of prince. "It isn't at all the sort of thing a princess ought to do. If you *must* fool around with magic, why don't you get turned into a swan or something, so I can rescue you and break the spell properly? Besides," he added, "it's making Professor Crumbwell unbearably cross."

Professor Crumbwell appeared in the doorway. "Look here, Your Highness," he said to Elaine, his face sagging nearly to his ribs from lack of sleep, "I want you to stop that imaginary magic at once! It would be bad enough being kept awake at night, but to be kept awake by something that doesn't even exist is simply not to be borne!"

"But," began Elaine, and then sighed and gave it up. "Oh, all right," she said. "I'll go find the Thing and tell it." And off she went.

She did not get back to the schoolroom until arithmetic

was well over, explaining to the suspicious tutor that she had had to hunt all over the castle for the elusive Thing.

"Sibyl's taught it to play," she said, "and now that's all it wants to do. Today they were playing 'hide-and-seek,' and the Thing had scrunched itself up into a little wad of pale blue spots behind the blue tapestry in the guest room in the south tower, and I *never* would have found it if Sibyl hadn't—"

"That's enough of that nonsense!" said the tutor, beginning to suspect that his leg was being pulled. "All I want to know is, have you stopped the imaginary bumping?"

"Well, you see," Elaine said a bit sheepishly, "it *has* to Go Bump in the Night, because that's the sort of Thing it is. But it will Go Bump at the rest of us instead. It doesn't much like you, anyway."

"If it Goes Bump at me," gasped Petronilla, the eldest, most delicate, and most timid of the three princesses, "I shall faint!"

"Oh, that's a good idea," said Elaine. "That way you won't lose any sleep, will you?"

A week later Elaine, sitting despondently in her room, heard a small scratch at the door.

"Go away. I'm being punished," she called crossly. "Again," she added with resignation.

"WOWW!" said Sibyl's deep, hoarse voice from outside, and a moment later a series of turquoise spots began pushing themselves under the door.

"Oh, it's you," said Elaine. She went over and let the cat in too. "You know," she told the Thing sadly, "this is partly your fault. Everyone is as cross as bears since you started Going Bump all over the castle at night, and they blame me for bringing you. Somebody's always sending me to my room these days, and that silly Professor Crumbwell gives a lecture practically every day on there being no such thing as magic."

The Thing wilted visibly, and its spots turned dark blue.

Elaine couldn't bear to see it depressed. "Never mind," she said kindly. "*I* still love you."

The spots turned pinkish orange and began bouncing. Sibyl leaped up and began chasing them. Elaine giggled. "All the same—" she began, but just then the door opened, and her stout and overworked nanny came in panting.

"You're wanted downstairs, Your Highness," she said frowning, all out of sorts from sleepless nights. "It's a narsty, cross old man wanting you. He claims you've got something of his, and he refuses to go away. Why it is you can't behave yourself and be a proper princess, I don't know, but it isn't for lack of *my* trying! I never saw . . ."

Elaine left Nanny grumbling and trotted down the winding stone steps, Sibyl and the Thing at her heels.

The king and queen turned sternly to their problem daughter when she entered the Great Hall. "What have you been doing *now*, Elaine? Mr. Thrupplethwaite says—"

"That's her!" interrupted the gray-bearded old man, waving his arms. "You went off wiv my Thing, so you did, and a shame be to you! I want it back this minute!"

"But you gave it to me!" protested Elaine. "You said the Bumping kept you from studying science, and—"

"*That* Thing?" exclaimed her parents. "Good grief, Elaine, give it back to him this minute!"

Elaine sighed. "Oh, very well. But what about your science?"

"Changed my mind, that's wot," muttered the old man. "Can't study at all wivout the dratted Thing. 'Tis distracting, all that silence. Anyhow, I do be going to be a sorcerer instead of a scientist. There be more scope and fewer rules. So I wants to take my Thing back home wiv me right now, that's wot I wants."

"It's right here behind me," began Elaine, turning around. But it wasn't. Neither was Sibyl. Elaine sighed. "Hide-and-seek, I suppose," she explained. "And it's getting cleverer and cleverer about hiding."

The entire castle—royal family, staff, cabinet, guards, and servants—all joined in the search with bleary eyes but great enthusiasm. But the Thing seemed to have outdone itself hiding. It wasn't behind the drapes, or under wardrobes, or in ceiling corners, or hidden in or over bed canopies, or up any of the fireplaces.

It wasn't until nearly teatime that Elaine, peering over a wide window ledge, saw something below that made her run down the stairs and out to the rose garden.

By the time she got there, a certain suspicious-looking cluster of pink roses had vanished. But Sibyl was still there, washing her face with perfectly shattering innocence.

"Where is it, Sibyl?" asked Elaine sternly.

Sibyl hissed in a negative manner and leaped up into the big willow tree. Elaine, staring upwards, began to giggle. Then she kilted her green silk skirt up to her knees and climbed the tree.

"That's really quite clever," she told a quivering cluster of dark-purple spots hanging realistically from a top branch. "But you see, grapes don't grow on willow trees. Come on, now, Thingy. The old man wants you back."

The Thing shrank even smaller and shook its dots violently. Sibyl arranged herself on a nearby branch and made loud disapproving sounds, which brought the whole castle rushing out to see what awful event was taking place.

When they finally saw where Elaine was, the queen and Petronilla fainted, the tutor gave notice again, the king hastily sent for old Burrows the gardener to bring a ladder, and everyone else shouted at once.

"Come down at once!"

"Sit still and hold on tightly!"

"Whatever are you doing up there?"

"And bring my Thing down wiv you!" squawked the old man, making a pretty good guess.

"It doesn't want to come," Elaine shouted back.

"Tell it I won't call it names anymore," wheedled the old man. "Tell it I'll build lots of lovely hollow walls for it to Bump and Thump on. I'll buy it a big drum to play wiv. I'll even let it go up the chimney, that's wot I'll do."

The Thing wrapped itself clear around the branch and clung stubbornly.

"I'll give it lovely spotty things to eat," yelled the old man. "Peas, and tapioca, and grapes . . ."

The Thing turned a sickly green. "But, you see, it wants to stay here with my cat," Elaine explained. "They play."

"It can play wiv your blinkin' cat all day, can't it?" roared the old man. "I only want it to Go Bump, and it only Goes Bump in the Night. It can spend every perishing day of its life here, if it will just come home at night. Come home, Thing, do!" he coaxed. "Grandfather Thrupplethwaite needs you, he do."

Sibyl and the Thing held a silent conference, nose to spots, after which they leaped and floated to the ground. Everyone beamed.

"We don't want it at night, I'm sure," said Adelicia contentedly.

"Fancy getting a good night's sleep again!" sighed the staff.

"What about Elaine?" worried Arthur. "Where's a gardener with a ladder? Courage, fair sister, I'll save thee! Do hold still, Elaine, and *try* to look a little nervous, will you? Or at least stop smiling! Aha! Here is a trusty ladder! Now I shall mount and bear thee safely down."

"Don't be silly, Arthur," said Elaine, nimbly descending the branches on one side of the tree while Arthur, still declaiming, climbed the ladder on the other side. By the time he reached the top, she was at the bottom.

Everyone glared at her.

"What did I do wrong now?" asked Elaine.

"You should have fainted, or at least waited to be rescued," said her father patiently. "Really, Elaine!"

"What nonsense," muttered Elaine.

Arthur was still peering about among the willow leaves at the top of the tree. At last he concluded that the Fair Princess in Distress was no longer there. "Oh, dear," he said, looking down.

Her freckled face was turned up toward him. "You're not stuck are you, Arthur?" she asked anxiously. "Just put your foot on that big branch, and—"

"Bother!" said Arthur in disgust.

Peter Graves

William Pène DuBois

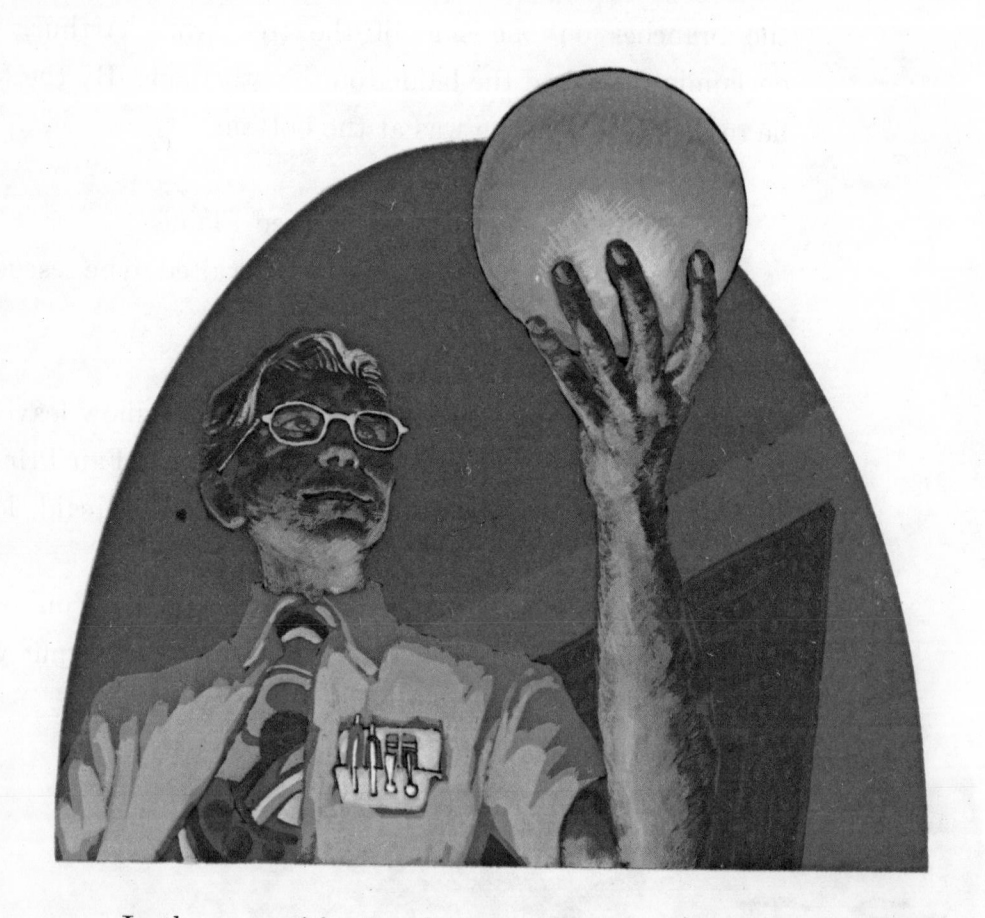

In the type of fantasy known as science fiction, astounding things can happen, even with an object as innocent as a bouncing ball.

"Is this the invention with which you could completely wipe out Houndstooth?"

"Did I say that? Well, I might not be able to wipe all of it out with one, but I could certainly cause a tremendous amount of damage. There are nice hard concrete roads through Houndstooth. They suit my invention well. It would work best in modern towns and cities—it's just about useless in the country."

"This sounds quite a bit like a riddle," said Peter.

They had entered the concrete chamber, and Houghton was loosening the two great iron vises which so tightly gripped the big aluminum-colored ball in the corner of the room. He removed it, fondled it as though measuring its weight, shook it, held it near the floor, held it near the ceiling. He then handed it to Peter. "It feels and looks rather innocent, doesn't it?"

Peter's heart was pounding fast. He felt that he'd been handed a bomb with a sizzling fuse. He found that the ball weighed little, but nevertheless he gripped it furiously. He had a feeling that if he let it drop to the floor it would mean the end of everything. He studied it closely a moment, then nervously looked at Houghton Furlong.

"Try dropping it, but watch it; it's tricky. Be sure you catch it."

Peter dropped it from the height of his waist, then instinctively bent his knees and leaned over to catch it close to the ground. The ball hit the concrete, making a surprisingly clear metallic ting sound. It instantly zoomed upward, slipping between his hands and rising to the height of his shoulders had he been standing straight. He leaped and grabbed it in a clumsy and desperate lunge. Sweat was dripping from his forehead. He again squeezed it tightly, this time tucking it firmly under his shirt and under one arm.

"As you see," said Houghton, "it bounces higher than the height from which you drop it. That's what makes it so dangerous." He held out his hands. Peter cautiously slipped the ball out from under his shirt and handed it to him. Houghton replaced it in its double vise and secured it tightly. "Its core is a small ball of Furloy like those strapped to the floor here. The core has an antigravity force of twenty-five pounds. This core is covered by twenty-eight pounds of duraluminum. The duraluminum is attracted to the ground by gravity, but at the contact with the ground the Furloy becomes activated, multiplying the normal bounce and making the ball bounce higher than the height from which it is dropped. Do you know why it is a dangerous weapon?"

"Vaguely," said Peter.

Houghton paused for a moment. He was staring at the remarkable ball. "Let's just for the fun of it imagine that we really did want to wipe out Houndstooth. Where should we start?"

"Let's start with the high school," said Peter Graves.

"All right, the high school. This doesn't necessarily mean that the high school would go first, but it's a good starting point in which to gather a crowd. In the afternoon when all of the children were piling out and heading for home, I could innocently bounce my ball from the height of about one foot or less on the concrete pavement in front of the school. The ball would start bouncing, each time higher than the time before, each time harder than the time before, each time ringing forth with a louder clear metallic sound. The children would gather around and watch the ball, bobbing their heads up and down as if hypnotized by it. Soon the ball would be bouncing as high as the schoolhouse. The children would still be watching it but might back away and enlarge the circle. A darker spot might form in the pavement, caused by this constant pounding. Before long the ball would come crashing down from a height of half a mile or more and violently crack the pavement. The children would be snapped sharply out of their hypnosis and would start running away in all directions, screaming and yelling. On its next bounce, the ball would come tearing down from an even greater height, hit the cracked spot in the pavement, and career off, possibly knocking a huge chunk of masonry off the schoolhouse. By now, the children would be home, spreading everywhere a wide assortment of wild rumors. The supernatural quality of the terrible ball might cause a panic. Some would think that the city was being bombarded by a white meteor which hits, destroys, bounces off, and hits again. A white streak of duraluminum would come crashing down from ever increasing heights, breaking water mains, causing fires, crashing through roofs into buildings where it would bounce with increasing violence until it had crushed and bashed its way out again. There would be no signs of airplanes, not a suspicion of an enemy attack, just this strange pounding bombardment suggesting a weird and sinister assault from another planet." Houghton wiped his brow. "That's more or less the general idea. Of course I could shorten the destruction process proportionally if I started out with twenty or thirty balls all bouncing at once."

"*Whew!*" exclaimed Peter. "It's terrible, and it's such a simple idea—a bouncing ball!"

"Please believe me most completely. I haven't the slightest

intention of giving this invention to anybody, even less the intention of ever using its destructive powers myself. I hate all instruments of destruction. I keep it locked up carefully in this concrete vault so that even robbers or prowlers couldn't unknowingly lay their hands on it or accidentally start it bouncing. You, by the way, are the first outsider to see or feel this terrible invention."

"Why don't you destroy it completely?"

"Ah," said Houghton, "that's an entirely different story. Right now I'm experimenting on what might be a wonderful use for its peculiar energy. Watch this." He took the ball out of the double vise, held it about an inch from the floor, and let it bounce. The ball hit his hand and bounced back to the floor, hit his hand again and bounced back, faster and faster. Houghton seemed to try not to move his hand at all, but the ball was pushing it higher and higher with increasing force. "See that," he shouted. "Maybe this energy could be controlled. A piston made of this combination of metal and Furloy might conceivably be bounced in a cylinder—a nice little engine would result that would run without fuel." The ball had now pushed Houghton's hand up to the height of

his waist. The accelerating rhythm and the clear metallic sounds of the ball hitting the concrete floor fascinated Peter. "May I feel it?" he said, sticking out his hand. "No!" shouted Houghton, "it's hitting too hard!" The ball slapped Peter's hand and bounced off crookedly. Peter shrieked and lunged for it, but missed it completely. The ball bounced from the ceiling to a corner and then crazily and rapidly started bouncing diagonally back and forth across the room. They both dove and sprawled and leaped and grabbed and plunged —the ball was going too fast. It smashed through their fingers, it caromed violently off their arms and legs; its speed had in an instant become uncontrollable. There was a sharp crack and a brief flash as it shattered the naked electric bulb and plunged the room into darkness. Houghton grabbed Peter by the arm and dragged him quickly through the great iron door. He pushed the door closed and pulled Peter out into the yard. Peter was shaking all over and crying. "It was an accident," said Houghton, "an accident, an accident! It's not your fault; it was an accident!"

"Shall I ring the alarm?" Peter stammered out.

"No, just stand right here!" They were a hundred yards

or so from the house, under a big tree. "The ball is too dangerous. It might hurt some of those dozens of people who answer my calls for help. Let's just hope that it will pound its way through the roof fast, with a minimum amount of damage, and bury itself in some soft earth somewhere!"

The Horrible House of Houghton was shaking violently as if it were in the throes of a frightful attack of indigestion, or were having some sort of horrible trembling fit. The ball was rapidly bashing its way out of the concrete chamber. The noise was tremendous. You could no longer distinguish separate bounces; there was just a ghastly metallic thrashing sound which seemed to get louder and louder. The whole house started to quiver crazily, and windows were splintering on all sides. Shingles were shaking loose and sliding off the roof; shutters dropped off; a succession of short circuits started fires blazing on all floors. The plumbing was shaken and rattled into a maze of spitting pipes. The thrashing suddenly ceased as the ball bashed its way out of the vault. A few separate bounces could again be heard as it banged around upstairs; then it ripped its way through the roof and streaked to freedom in the sunset light. Houghton dashed after it. *"We've got to get it and destroy it!"* he shouted. The ball hit the concrete road and made a prodigious bounce off into the fields. There it careened from field to field like a stone skipping on water, finally coming to a stop a good quarter of a mile away. Houghton grabbed it and stuffed it under his coat. It was battered, scarred, and flattened completely out of shape. They took it back to what was left of the house. The Horrible House of Houghton had been shaken and burned until it had completely collapsed. What was left of the roof seemed to have snuffed out most of the fire; the broken plumbing had flooded out the rest. There were many little fountains playing in the wreckage. Houghton managed to turn off the water supply, then went into the garage, which was fortunately untouched, being a good fifty yards from the house. He put the ball in a vise, took a metal saw, and hacked off a big chunk of duraluminum. The ball was now in the control of the antigravity force of Furloy. Houghton took it outside and let go of it and watched the dreadful product of his invention streak away from the earth, never to be seen again on this planet.

Peter Graves had followed, watched, and done a terrible amount of worrying but hadn't thought to say anything for quite some time. He finally managed to mutter with great sincerity and eagerness, "I'll get money to rebuild your house, Mr. Furlong, I'll get it somehow if it takes the rest of my life."

"Don't feel bad," said Houghton Furlong. "It was an accident. And besides I'm the guy who is famous for being used to such catastrophes."

"I'll get the money or die trying!"

"By the way," said Houghton, "there's one most important thing I want to ask you, now that we've destroyed my house together."

"What's that?"

"What's your name?"

"Oh, I forgot to tell you. It's Peter Graves." He absent-mindedly shook hands with Houghton as if they'd just been introduced.

"Well, do you think Mr. and Mrs. Graves would be kind enough to put up a tired old inventor for a few days?"

"They must," said Peter. "They must."

The Boy Who Cut Everything to Pieces

W. F. P. Burton

Almost every country or region of the world has a large
number of stories or tales that have been handed down
from one generation to the next. The tale you are about
to read has been told in central African villages for many
generations.

Muchibi was so fond of cutting trees, fences, poles, and indeed everything that he could reach with his axe, that he got into trouble everywhere. He chopped down his father's palms and pawpaw trees, he destroyed his mother's hoe handle, and there seemed to be no way of curing him.

At last his father called a slave and told him to take Muchibi to Pieces Land and to leave him there.

It was a long journey, and before they reached the end, Muchibi was very tired and thirsty. Then suddenly the slave ran off and left him all alone in the forest.

Muchibi tried to return by the path along which they had come, but after going a little way, it suddenly ended. He followed a side track, but that too was only a piece of a path. When he attempted to go forward again, the path stopped suddenly.

Very tired and frightened, he looked for a tree to climb, but all the trunks seemed to end halfway up. They had twigs growing out of the leaves instead of the other way around, and fruit or leaves growing on the trunk instead of bark, while the branches grew down into the ground and the roots were where the branches are generally found.

Presently he was horrified to see a row of heads and arms coming up from the river, all laughing and talking, but although they had their waterpots on their heads, they had no bodies. He called them, and asked the way to the village, but although they began to answer him, they always stopped before they came to the end of a sentence.

At last it became more and more clear that Muchibi was in a land where everything was in pieces. He asked for water to drink, but they only gave him a piece of gourd and all the water ran out. He followed the heads to the village and was horrified to see arms and legs hoeing in the gardens.

It now became cloudy and the rain began to fall, so Muchibi ran to a hut for shelter, but he might as well have remained outside, for the hut that he entered had only a wall, while those into which the heads and arms had gone were all thatch and no walls.

He intended to wait until dark and then to seek a more comfortable hut, but he soon found that morning would dawn in the afternoon, or that night would suddenly fall for a time during the day.

When a part of a young man took pity on him and gave him food, poor Muchibi could not satisfy his appetite, for he found that these people of Pieces Land did not eat mush and relish together, but divided up the meal, so that they often had a mush as it was growing light in the evening, or a relish as it was growing dark in the morning. These people did not carry axes or knives with which to cut their food or firewood, but a banana leaf full of gum with which to stick together the food and firewood, for it was already in such small pieces that it was impossible to carry.

Muchibi thought that he would die in this strange land. He wandered eastward toward the sunset or westward toward the sunrise, and he climbed when he wanted to go down, for pieces of the hills were down in the rivers and pieces of the streams ran up into the hills.

At last he flung himself down with his face in a tuft of grass in the treetops and moaned, "If only I could return home I would never again cut up anything uselessly." At once his father's slave touched him on the shoulder and said, "Your father has sent for you to come home. Follow me."

64

Muchibi was so glad to get home that he ran all the way, but he was quite a different boy from the one who had left a few days before. He could not bear the sight of a knife or axe and was so pleased to find everything whole again that he could never be tempted to cut anything in pieces.

Afterthought

1. How might you have reacted in Muchibi's place?
2. What changes did the journey to Pieces Land make in Muchibi?
3. What different kinds of stories did you read in this unit? How were they alike? How were they different?

Inside a Poem

It doesn't always have to rhyme,
but there's the repeat of a beat, somewhere
an inner chime that makes you want to
tap your feet or swerve in a curve;
a lilt, a leap, a lightning-split:—
thunderstruck the consonants jut,
while the vowels open wide as waves in the noon-
     blue sea.

You hear with your heels, your eyes feel
what they never touched before:
fins on a bird, feathers on a deer;
taste all colors, inhale
memory and tomorrow and always the tang is
     today.

Eve Merriam

The Double-Play

In his sea lit
distance, the pitcher winding
like a clock about to chime comes down with

the ball, hit
sharply, under the artificial
banks of arc-lights, bounds like a vanishing string

over the green
to the shortstop magically
scoops to his right whirling above his invisible

shadows
in the dust redirects
its flight to the running poised second baseman

pirouettes
leaping, above the slide, to throw
from mid-air, across the colored tightened interval,

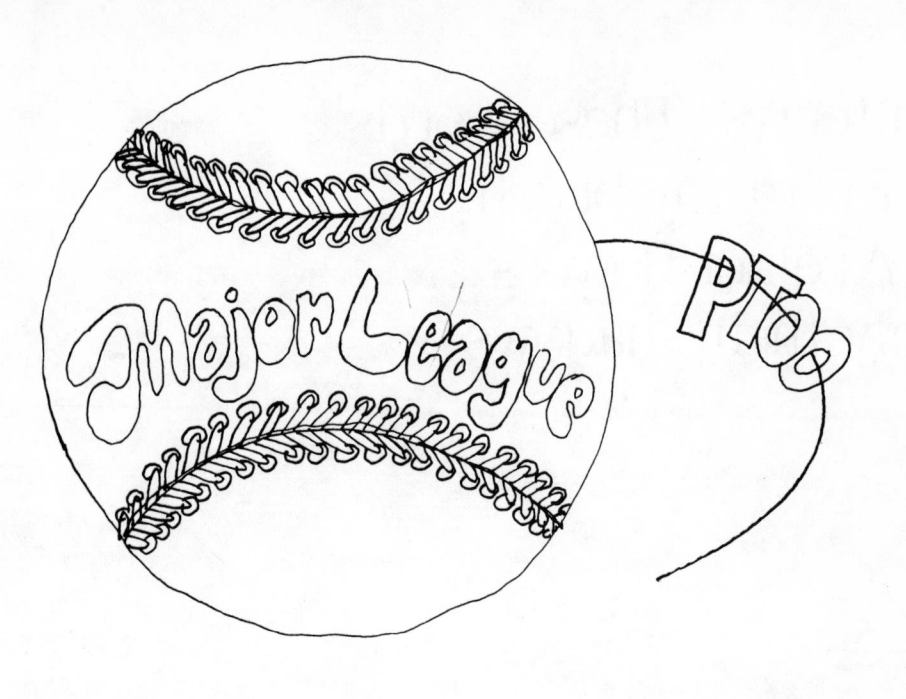

to the leaning-
out first baseman ends the dance
drawing it disappearing into his long brown glove

stretches. What
is too swift for deception
is final, lost, among the loosened figures

jogging off the field
(the pitcher walks), casual
in the space where the poem has happened.

Robert Wallace

Butterfly! These words
   From my brush
   Are not flowers...
Only their shadows

Soseki

FROG-SCHOOL COMPETING
WITH LARK-SCHOOL
SOFTLY AT DUSK
IN THE ART OF SONG...

Shiki

A Kite Is a Victim

A kite is a victim you are sure of.
You love it because it pulls
gentle enough to call you master,
strong enough to call you fool;
because it lives
like a desperate trained falcon
in the high sweet air,
and you can always haul it down
to tame it in your drawer.

A kite is a fish you have already caught
in a pool where no fish come,
so you play him carefully and long,
and hope he won't give up,
or the wind die down.

A kite is the last poem you've written,
so you give it to the wind,
but you don't let it go
until someone finds you
something else to do.

A kite is a contract of glory
that must be made with the sun,
so you make friends with the field
the river and the wind,
then you pray the whole cold night before,
under the travelling cordless moon,
to make you worthy and lyric and pure.

Leonard Cohen

On the Vanity of Earthly Greatness

The tusks that clashed in mighty brawls
Of mastodons, are billiard balls.

The sword of Charlemagne the Just
Is ferric oxide, known as rust.

The grizzly bear whose potent hug
Was feared by all, is now a rug.

Great Caesar's dead and on the shelf,
And I don't feel so well myself!

Arthur Guiterman

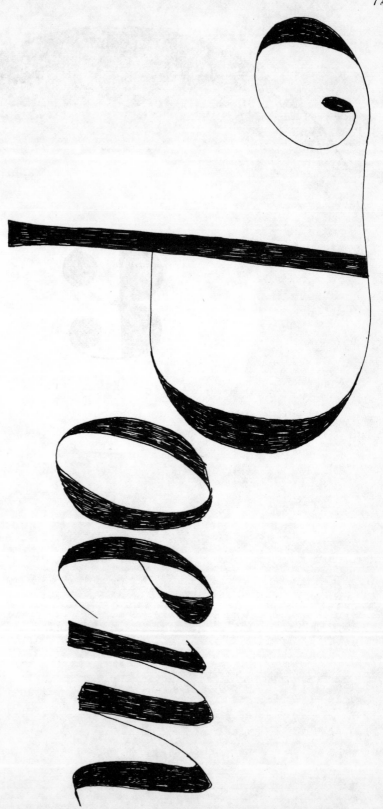

I loved my friend.
He went away from me.
There's nothing more to say.
The poem ends,
Soft as it began —
I loved my friend.

Langston Hughes

Untried Circuitry

Your Poem, Man...

unless there's one thing seen
suddenly against another—a parsnip
sprouting for a President, or
hailstones melting in an ashtray—
nothing really happens. It takes
surprise and wild connections,
doesn't it? A walrus chewing
on a ballpoint pen. Two blue tail-
lights on Tyrannosaurus Rex. Green
cheese teeth. Maybe what we wanted
least. Or most. Some unexpected
pleats. Words that never knew
each other till right now. Plug us
into the wrong socket and see
what blows—or what lights up.
Try
     untried
         circuitry,
new
     fuses.
Tell it like it never really was,
man,
and maybe we can see it
like it is.

Edward Lueders

Communication

William H. Crouse

Men have invented many ways
of communicating their ideas to one
another, but the most marvelous
system in use is not an invented one.

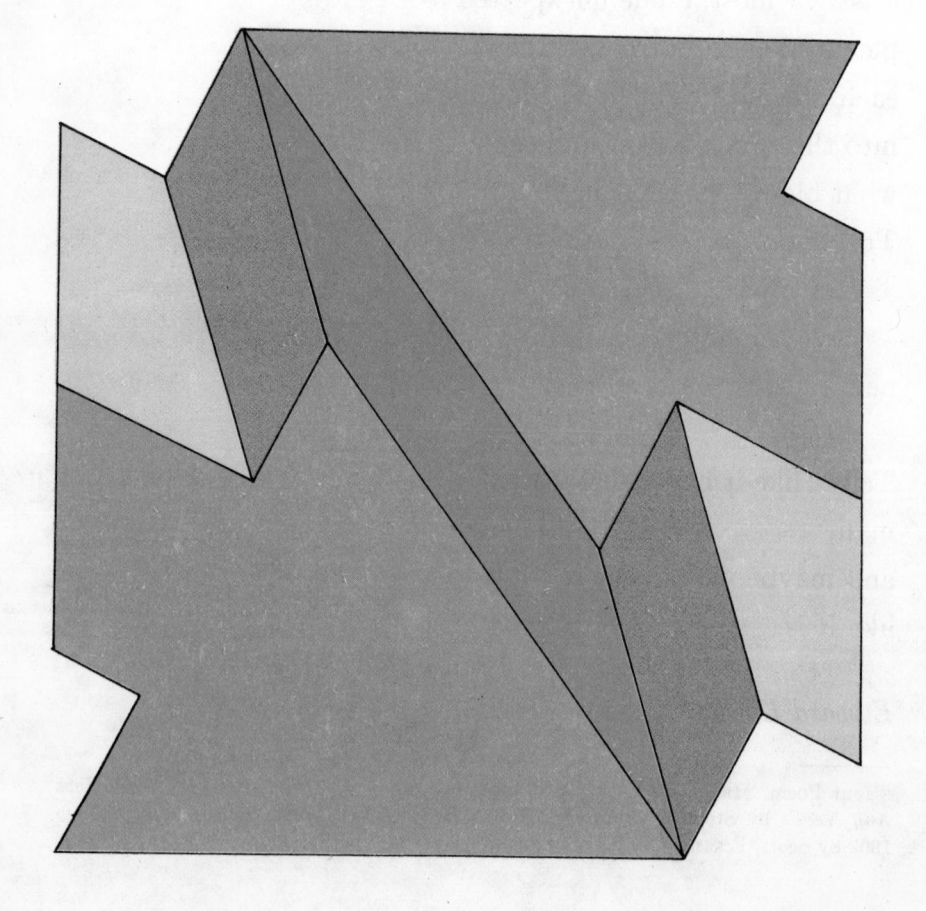

Communication—phones, telegraphy, radio, television—can be considered the nervous system of civilization. Communication ties all human activities together.

In its broadest sense, communication is the transferring of information from one place to another. A spacecraft sending information to an electronic computer on Earth, and the computer returning signals to the spacecraft telling it what to do—all this is communication, even though no human beings are involved. In fact, a human being could not understand the signals going back and forth. He would need some sort of electronic interpreter to tell him what the spacecraft and the computer are "saying."

Human Communication

When two people talk to each other, they form a communication system. Actually, they do not even have to talk. They can communicate by a wave of the hand, a nod of the head, or even silence. You might think this system is very simple compared to a telephone system or a television network. But it is very complicated, the most complicated system known.

First, there is the sender. He has certain ideas he wants to get across to the listener, or receiver. At the start, they are not even in the form of words. The ideas exist in the sender's brain in the form of a complex pattern.

The active part of the brain contains about ten billion nerve cells, or neurons, which are connected. The connections are called synapses. A synapse acts somewhat like a light switch; it is either opened or closed. There are billions of these connections in the brain.

We might say that ideas exist in a brain as patterns of closed and opened switches. With some switches closed and others opened, nerve impulses can flow through the network of neurons that are connected. When you learn something, you close tremendous numbers of synapses. And the idea stays in your brain as a particular pattern.

To see how all this works, let us take an example. Suppose someone asks you a question to which you know the answer, "How far away is the sun?" His spoken words cause your eardrums to vibrate, and the nerves in the ears send the message to the brain. The message moves as impulses through neurons and across synapses.

Someone has asked, "How far away is the sun?" And the message has been changed to an extremely complex pattern of nerve impulses that sweeps through the memory section of your brain. This is somewhat like thousands of dogs running through a vast field trying to flush out a large family of rabbits.

The incoming signals, or nerve impulses, search patiently through the vast number of networks of connected neurons in your brain. Presently, they come upon the answer. The incoming signals have checked millions of connections until the right combination is found. This causes the answer, stored within a network of connected neurons, to "pop into your mind."

So the answer comes, "Ninety-three million miles!" You may simply remember it, or you may say it aloud. If you decide to say it, this decision sets off a whole new series of switching activities in other parts of your brain.

In the speech section, a set of signals goes out to the part of the brain controlling the lips, tongue, larynx, jaw, face muscles, and other parts involved in speech. You open your lips and out of your mouth come the words, "Ninety-three million miles!"

It is clear, then, that the communication system made up of two people talking to each other is really very complicated. But some understanding of how the human communication system works will help in understanding all the other communication systems that man has invented. After all, these other systems are designed to extend man's own sense organs, just as the telephone extends man's ears, and the telescope or television extends man's eyes.

Parts of a System

A communication system consists of a sender, a receiver, and a channel, or means through which information can pass. In our example of two people talking, the first person has a question to ask. He wants to know the distance to the sun. He could imagine this as a picture of the sun and earth with an arrow and a question mark between them. But since he wants to ask the question, he must put it into words.

He must code the question into a series of hissing and rumbling noises. They form words that sound like "How far away is the sun?" You hear these words, decode them, and "get the idea." Your decoding consists of changing the vibrations of your eardrums into nerve impulses that race through your brain, seeking out the answer.

So, to complete our communication system, we must add two other devices. We must add an encoder at the sending end and a decoder at the receiving end. The information

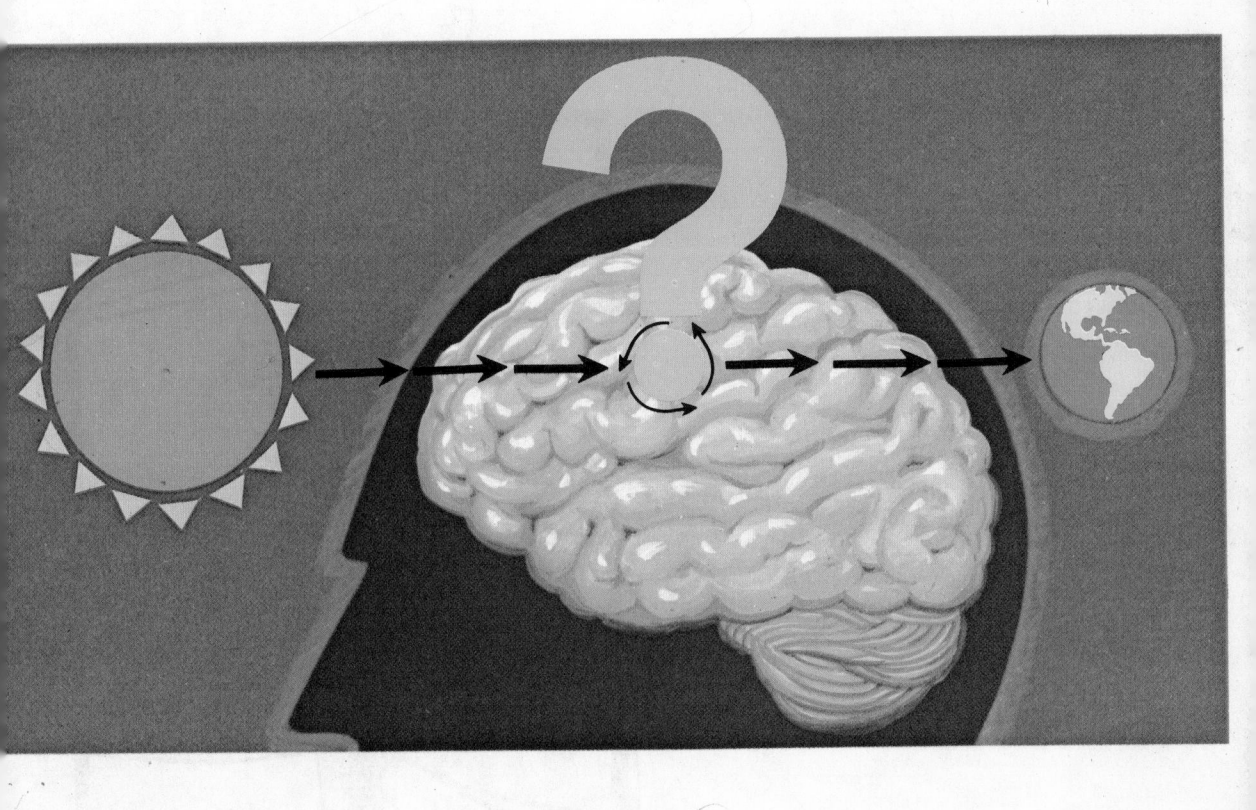

at the sending end must be changed in some way so that it will go out over the sending channel. Then at the receiving end it must be decoded, or changed into a form that the receiver will be able to handle.

Invented Systems

As another example of a communication system, let us look at the telephone. When you speak into the phone, your message is changed into a series of electrical impulses that go through the wires to the receiver. There, the electrical impulses cause a thin plate to vibrate and make noises that sound similar to the words you spoke. In a way, the telephone system, with its wires and connections, is simply an extension of the neurons and synapses in your brain.

It would seem that the simplest method of communication would be to connect wires directly between two brains. Then an idea could be transmitted directly from one brain to another. It would not have to be changed from nerve impulses to sound, then to electrical impulses in the telephone wire, back to sound,

and finally again into nerve impulses in the receiver's brain. The telephone wires could be considered as long neurons between the two brains. This may seem like a fantastic idea. But it has been suggested as a possibility for the distant future, when the brain is much better understood than it now is.

Electronic computers actually do communicate over the phone in a somewhat similar way. The telephone wires simply become part of the two computers' electronic circuitry. And thousands of bits of information can be sent back and forth each second.

Afterthought

Describe the sender, the channel, and the receiver for each of the following communications: a friendly letter, a radio commercial for dogfood, a printed poem, a television newscast.

Herbert, the Human Radio

Hazel Wilson

Bits of metal in unlikely places sometimes act as radio receivers. In this story you'll find out how such a receiver once caused a complete breakdown in communication!

Herbert's mother tried hard to be a good mother to him. She not only belonged to the Parent-Teacher Association but subscribed to two magazines devoted to the proper care and feeding of children. It was in one of those magazines that Mrs. Yadon read how a child's life had been ruined by not having had his crooked teeth straightened by braces. Not only had his teeth grown up crooked, it seemed, but *he* had, and the author blamed all that on the lack of braces.

The evening Mrs. Yadon finished reading the article, she immediately asked Herbert to open his mouth so she could see if his teeth showed signs of slanting to one side or the other.

"The teeth in your upper jaw are perfectly straight," she said, after having looked Herbert straight in the mouth. "But I'm not sure that your two front teeth on the lower jaw lean slightly to the right. I'll take you to the dentist tomorrow to see if you need braces."

"My teeth don't need bracing," declared Herbert. "They're so strong I can chew anything with them, except maybe nails."

"According to the article I've just read, it's the position and not the strength of the tooth which is important," said Mrs. Yadon. "Tomorrow after school I shall take you to see Dr. Pullen, the dentist."

So the next day, after school, Herbert reluctantly went with his mother to Dr. Pullen's office.

Dr. Pullen showed his teeth at Herbert in a wide smile. Doubtless, Herbert thought, that was a way of advertising his profession.

"I want to know whether Herbert needs, or will need, braces on his teeth in the future," said Mrs. Yadon anxiously.

Dr. Pullen made Herbert open his mouth wide. "Two teeth

on Herbert's lower jaw are slightly crowded," he told Mrs. Yadon. "But the boy's jaw may grow to accommodate them."

"But what if the teeth grow and the jaw doesn't?" asked Mrs. Yadon.

"In that case, Herbert should wear braces on his lower jaw," said Dr. Pullen.

"Could braces at this time do any harm?" asked Mrs. Yadon.

The dentist said that braces would certainly do Herbert no harm but he still would not advise them.

"If you won't put braces on Herbert's lower teeth, I'll find another dentist who will," said Mrs. Yadon emphatically.

Dr. Pullen muttered something about its being like making a wooden leg for a man who had two good legs, but at last he gave in and consented to make braces for Herbert's lower jaw.

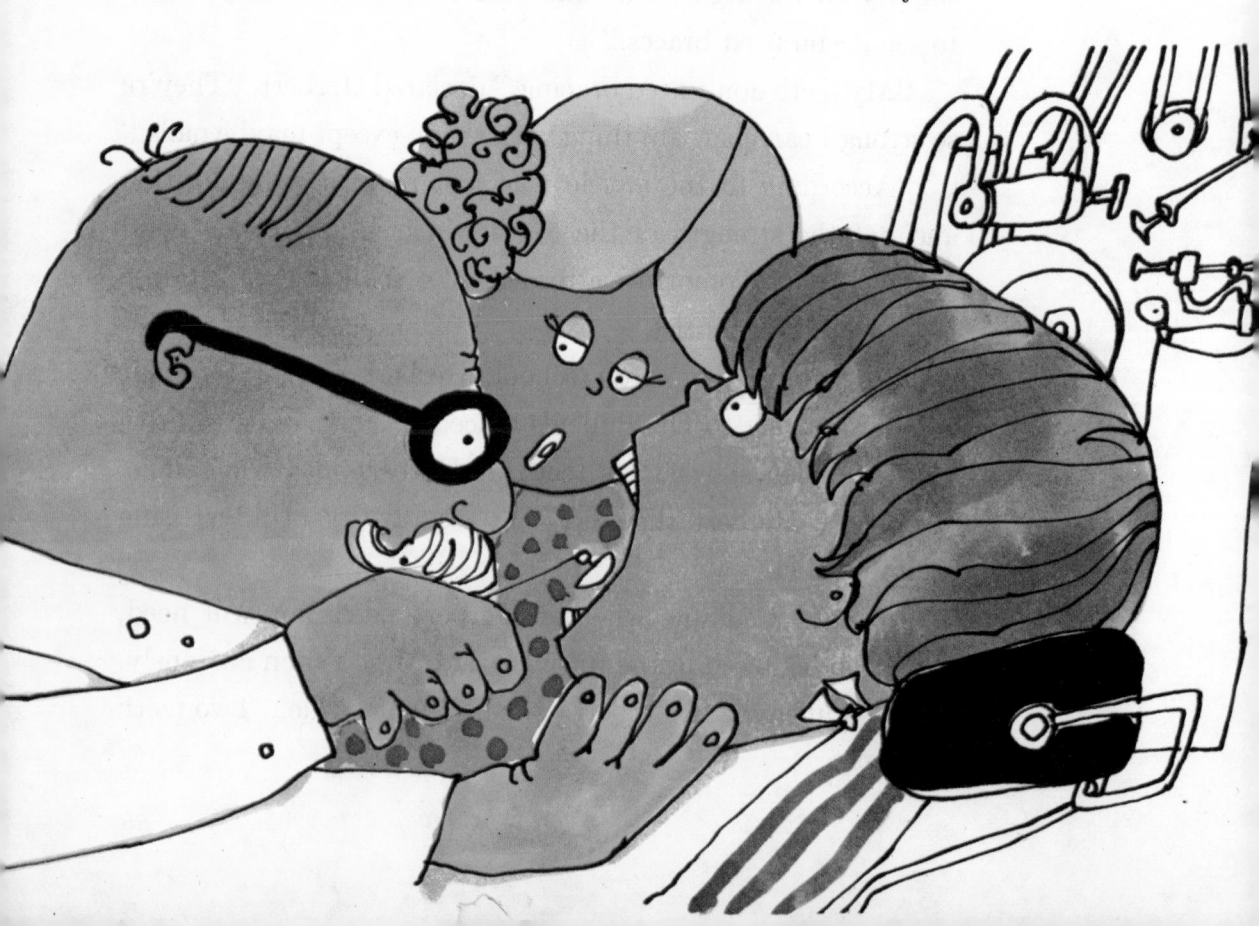

A few days later Herbert paid another visit to Dr. Pullen's office and came out wearing braces.

"Now I know how Gus, my pony, feels when he has the bit in his mouth," Herbert thought as he left the dentist's office. Then he looked around to see where the music he heard was coming from. Every door in the office building was shut, but Herbert distinctly heard music.

"Somebody must have his radio on good and loud," he thought, "if it can be heard through a closed door."

Herbert walked home with a peculiar expression upon his face.

He was both puzzled and entertained. For the radio program which Herbert had heard when he came out of Dr. Pullen's office had gone right on. Herbert heard the program as clearly as if he had been carrying a portable radio. He soon learned that he was tuned in to Station WHK, Cleveland, Ohio, the Bill Gordon program. Herbert found that he could regulate the volume by how wide he opened his mouth. With his mouth closed, the program came in low but clear, but if he held his mouth open to its fullest extent (which was quite wide) and held it there, the volume of sound all but blasted his eardrums.

Herbert could not understand why he had suddenly become a radio receiver bringing in a Cleveland program. Cleveland, Ohio, was many miles from Mapleton. How did Herbert happen to be tuned in to that station? Why, in fact, was he tuned in to any station at all?

Then he remembered that he had first heard low strains of music shortly after Dr. Pullen had finished fastening the braces to Herbert's lower teeth. "That dentist has wired me for sound," Herbert thought wonderingly. "And he's gotten me tuned into Cleveland, Ohio, airwaves."

Herbert seemed especially quiet to his parents that evening. He was busy listening to the Cleveland radio programs. When, after dinner, Mrs. Yadon asked if Herbert were not, as usual, going to listen to "The Lone Ranger," Herbert said, "How do you expect me to listen to two programs at once?" even though the radio was not on.

Herbert's parents did not understand what their son meant. They were still at a loss after Herbert explained that he had now been listening steadily to Station WHK, Cleveland, Ohio, for several hours, and that he wished he knew how to tune in another station.

"But you can't be hearing a radio program when no radio is turned on," said Mr. Yadon.

"That's what you think," said Herbert. "I can hear it, though you can't. You don't think I'm lying, do you?" he asked, looking much aggrieved.

Herbert's parents knew that he usually told the truth even when it seemed surprising. Yet they found it hard to believe that Herbert had suddenly developed a built-in radio inside him. Yet when he began to quote from a quiz program he was hearing, and later gave both the names and composers of tunes played by a disc jockey, as well as a summary of world and Cleveland news and a review of sports, Mr. and Mrs. Yadon realized that Herbert was hearing what he claimed to be hearing.

"I can't understand it," said Mr. Yadon.

"I think Dr. Pullen has something to do with this," said Mrs. Yadon accusingly. "Before I took Herbert to him,

Herbert never complained of hearing noises. Did you, Herbert?"

"I think it's my braces, but I'll have to take them out in order to be sure," said Herbert, and he stood in front of a mirror and removed the braces from his lower jaw.

"It's just as if somebody turned off the radio," he said.

"We'll take those braces right back to Dr. Pullen and have him fit you to some that don't bring in the Cleveland, Ohio, airwaves," said Mrs. Yadon firmly.

"Oh, I don't want to do that," declared Herbert. "Now that I can turn off the program by removing my braces, I rather like having music wherever I go. Besides other kinds of programs," he added.

"But if you keep taking off your braces, your teeth may be growing crooked while they're off," complained Mrs. Yadon. "And the article I read says that letting teeth remain crooked may ruin a boy's character. And I certainly don't want your character ruined."

"Oh, it would take more than a crooked tooth to ruin my character," declared Herbert firmly. "Besides my teeth aren't really crooked. One or two are just slightly not straight. And Dr. Pullen told me I might take off my braces at night, so I'll leave them in at night and keep them out at times during the day. For I don't mind being sung to sleep by radio music, and I sleep so sound it won't bother me at all while I'm asleep. I'll just keep the braces as they are for the time being."

"If you really want to," said Herbert's mother doubtfully.

Herbert was happy to be wearing his braces to school the next day, though he found it a bit difficult to take in what his teacher, Miss Wood, was saying, while at the same time he was

listening to news of the day, a program for toddlers, and a
Bing Crosby program. When a program devoted to home
problems for the ladies came on, Herbert got excused and went
into the washroom and removed his braces. It was just as well
that he did so, for Herbert needed all his mind to devote to
decimal points and percentages, examples which Herbert
would have been quite willing to have left to be solved by
experts. But Miss Wood believed that problems in arithmetic
discipline the mind, and she was a great believer in discipline.

Herbert kept his braces in most of the rest of the school
day. Once when he was listening to a stirring march while
studying his American History, he beat time with his feet so
hard he shook the floor.

"Stop that," scolded Miss Wood. "Behave yourself or I'll
send you to the principal."

Herbert had not meant to misbehave. He tried to give no
sign again of what he was listening to. But when Miss Wood
asked him during the geography lesson to tell what agricultural
product Brazil exported most of, Herbert answered: "Eight

legs," which was the answer to the question on a quiz program Herbert was hearing: "How many legs has a spider?"

Miss Wood said she had never heard a more stupid answer about the products of Brazil. Nor did she understand, later in the afternoon, why Herbert laughed aloud while she was reading a very sad story to the class. How was she to know that Herbert was hearing a comedy program on Station WHK, Cleveland, Ohio?

Herbert did not often exert himself enough to get many grades of Excellent. He was, however, much too smart to fail. Yet the week after he began listening to Station WHK, in Cleveland, Ohio, during school hours, his marks dropped so far that Miss Wood, his teacher, sent a note home asking his mother to come to talk over what could be done about Herbert's poor work.

"He pays no attention," Miss Wood complained to Herbert's mother. "His thoughts seem anywhere except in the classroom. I declare, from the way Herbert had been acting lately, a person might think he was not quite all there."

"I'm afraid his thoughts have been more in Cleveland, Ohio, than in your classroom," said Mrs. Yadon. "Maybe he shouldn't wear his braces in the schoolroom, though I feel he should wear them most of the time. It's very bad for a boy to grow up with crooked teeth, you know, Miss Wood."

Miss Wood ran a pencil through her steel-gray hair that more than a little resembled a fluffy mass of steel wool. "What do the braces on Herbert's teeth have to do with Cleveland, Ohio?" she demanded.

"Oh, dear," murmured Mrs. Yadon. "It's so complicated to explain, and even if I did you might not believe me, though it's absolutely the truth. The fact is that ever since Dr. Pullen put braces on Herbert's lower teeth, Herbert has heard noises."

"Noises!" gasped Miss Wood. "This is much more serious than I had thought. Don't you realize, Mrs. Yadon, that a person who hears noises no one else can hear may be on the way to being mentally ill? I advise you to keep Herbert home from school and take him to a doctor who treats mental illness. For it could be that this is the first symptom of the poor boy's losing his mind."

"Herbert is not losing his mind," stated Mrs. Yadon—so upset she was almost in tears. But she did keep Herbert home from school the next day, which gave him a fine opportunity to work on his stamp collection.

In the middle of the afternoon, Herbert's Uncle Horace arrived for a brief visit between planes.

"How does Herbert happen to be at home during school hours?" Uncle Horace asked, after he had presented a large box of the best chocolates to the family.

Mrs. Yadon explained how Herbert's braces acted as a

receiver bringing in radio programs from Station WHK, Cleveland, Ohio. "He can hear every program distinctly when he is wearing his braces," she told Uncle Horace. "He really does. I sent for a Cleveland paper, and he was able to tell me what every program was to be without looking at the list of broadcasts. But now his teacher thinks Herbert is going out of his mind just because he is able to hear more than the average person can. She does not realize that Herbert is an exceptional child. Now she won't let him come back to school until I have him examined by a mind specialist, and there's not a single doctor of that kind in Mapleton. And I hate to take Herbert to a strange doctor in a strange town. Especially when there's nothing the matter with his mind," said Mrs. Yadon.

"H'mm," said Uncle Horace, clearing his throat. "Just what are you hearing now, my boy?" he asked Herbert, who was wearing his braces at the moment.

"It's just a commercial," said Herbert. "I'll sing to you." And Herbert sang, good and loud:

"If a body buys Burke's
crackers
At the grocery store
And eats but a single
cracker
He will want some more."

Herbert sang the commercial to the tune of "Coming Through the Rye."

"Want me to tell you what comes next?" he asked.

"No, not just now," said his uncle. Then he asked Herbert's mother about Herbert's sudden need for braces. "For I had not noticed that Herbert's lower teeth were crooked," he said.

"It was just that I want to be sure they won't grow crooked," said Mrs. Yadon, "for I read an article which said that crooked teeth are very bad for a child. I thought if Herbert's teeth were braced, they could not start to get crooked."

"That," said Uncle Horace, picking up a magazine from the table, "is carrying preventive dentistry a little far. Is this the magazine with the article?"

"It was in last month's number. The one you have is this month's. I haven't had time to read it yet," said Mrs. Yadon.

Uncle Horace consulted the table of contents. Then he turned to a page, which he read quickly but thoroughly. "Here is another article devoted to children's teeth," he said. "This one states that on no condition should braces be put on children's teeth unless the need for them is acute. Did your dentist say that Herbert's looks and teeth would be ruined if he didn't have braces?"

"Dr. Pullen didn't want to put braces on Herbert's teeth at all," said Mrs. Yadon. "I had hard work to persuade him to do the work."

"Now I'm listening to the ball game," said Herbert. "Oh boy, a home run in the ninth inning!"

"Herbert can listen to enough radio programs on his own radio in his room," said Uncle Horace.

"Take off those braces, Herbert, and keep them off. It's not good for you to hear more than other people can. Braces when needed are a very good thing, but in your case, obviously, they are too much of a good thing. Herbert does not need braces on his teeth," Uncle Horace told Herbert's mother.

"Then Herbert will stop hearing noises, and I won't need to take him to a mind specialist," said Mrs. Yadon happily. "And he can go back to school."

Herbert would not have objected to staying home from school a day or two more. But he did not really mind giving up wearing braces on his teeth. While wearing them, he had been saved the trouble of turning the knobs on his radio. And, like an automobile, he had always had his radio with him, built in. Herbert, however, had become a bit bored with listening to programs from only one station.

"If I ever should have to have braces on my teeth again," he told Uncle Horace, "I hope they will not bring in programs from Station WHK, Cleveland, Ohio, but from other parts of the United States. I'd even enjoy hearing foreign broadcasts," declared Herbert. "It would be fun to listen to a program in Hindustani through my teeth."

Posies
for
the
Potentate

Martha Swintz

Printed information is as permanent as the paper that holds it, always waiting for anyone who needs it. The king in this play has to convince the queen that he's going to need all the information he has.

Characters

KING RUDOLPH OF HAPPIDAZIA
QUEEN LETITIA OF HAPPIDAZIA
PRINCESS ALICE
PRIME MINISTER
MESSENGER
WIZARD OF RATZENCATZIA
CUTHBERT CACKLEBAIT
COURTIERS

SETTING: *Throne room in the royal palace.*

AT RISE: KING RUDOLPH OF HAPPIDAZIA *is sitting on his throne, talking with the* PRIME MINISTER. *The* KING *holds a large book on his lap.*

Reprinted from *Fifty Plays for Junior Actors,* edited by Sylvia E. Kamerman. Plays, Inc., Publishers, 8 Arlington Street, Boston, Mass. 02116. Copyright © 1953 by Plays, Inc.

PRIME MINISTER: Flowerpots!

KING: Flowerpots. All that you can get. It says right here on page 22, "to achieve the best results, you must have adequate equipment." I want adequate flowerpots. (*Ordering*) Minister, attend to it.

PRIME MINISTER: Yes, King Rudolph, I'll order a dozen immediately.

KING: A dozen! My good man, we are planting a kingdom, not a window box. The land of Happidazia shall be bathed in fragrance.

PRIME MINISTER (*Aside*): This idea smells anyway. (*To* KING) I'll see that it is taken care of. But, King Rudolph, suppose Queen Letitia discovers you've been reading those "Pamphlet of the Week Club" books again. I don't think she will be very pleased about that. She still remembers your early pamphlet projects.

KING: She will never find out until it's too late. She thought she had me fooled when she canceled my subscription to the "Pamphlet of the Week Club," but I fooled her. I took out a new subscription for Flopsy, our royal dog.

PRIME MINISTER (*Patiently*): Do we need anything besides flowerpots?

KING: Let's see here. (*Reads.*) "Plant the seeds." Seeds? We haven't any. Put them on the list. (*Sounds of movement and talking offstage*)

BOTH: The Queen!

KING: Go, quickly, and send out these orders before my wife finds out. (PRIME MINISTER *exits.*) She mustn't find me with another book! (*Sits on book.* QUEEN *and* COURTIERS *enter. The* QUEEN *carries a large mop and dustcloth.*)

QUEEN (*Walking toward* KING *and glancing around room*): Good morning, Rudolph. (*To herself*) Now where shall I start?

KING: Good morning, Letitia. Who's your friend? Looks like she could use a permanent.

QUEEN: You know very well this is the week for the royal housecleaning. Although it is difficult enough with the litter of your various projects lying about. Someday I'm going to throw out all the old wrecks around here.

KING: Don't give me any ideas, my dear.

QUEEN (*To* COURTIERS): We'll start with the thrones. I'm going to clean this place thoroughly—top to bottom, over and under.

KING: Under? Under what?

QUEEN: The thrones, of course. Now get up and don't stand on ceremony.

KING: I'm not standing on ceremony. I want to sit on my throne.

QUEEN: Rudolph, get up!

KING: DON'T SHOUT! Why don't you wait until tomorrow?

QUEEN: I'm going to clean this room right now.

KING (*Begrudgingly*): Oh, all right. (KING *rises gingerly, clutching book behind him. Moves away from* QUEEN.)

QUEEN: Rudolph, you're hiding something behind your back. What is it?

KING: Why—nothing, dear. (KING *and* QUEEN *circle each other.* QUEEN *points mop right at* KING, *who backs away.* COURTIER *who is dusting bumps into* KING, *causing him to drop book.* QUEEN *pounces on it.*)

QUEEN: A book!

KING: Why so it is. Now how do you suppose it got in here?

QUEEN: You know exactly how it got in here. You brought it. And you promised me you wouldn't read any more of that "Pamphlet of the Week Club" drivel. (*Looks at book.*) "The Art of Growing Flowers," by Cuthbert Cacklebait. Is he the same one who started you collecting fishing tackle and building canoes?

KING: And what is wrong with collecting fishing tackle and building canoes?

QUEEN: Nothing, except that there aren't any fish or lakes within five hundred miles of Happidazia.

KING: The Water Commissioner is working on *that* now. Besides, there is enough water for flowers, and I'm going to grow them.

QUEEN: What are you going to plant them in, the millions of old bottles we have in the basement left from the time you started building ship models to put inside bottles?

KING: Now that was an excellent idea. The trouble with you is that you get discouraged too quickly. (PRIME MINISTER *enters and bows before* KING.)

PRIME MINISTER: Sire, I've ordered twelve hundred.

QUEEN: Twelve hundred what?

PRIME MINISTER: Flowerpots, Your Highness. Flowerpots.

QUEEN: Oh, no. (*Falls in a faint, dropping book.*)

PRIME MINISTER: I do believe the Queen is laid up.

KING: No, just laid out. But never fear, I have my handy pocket edition of "First Aid for the Home" here in my robe. (*Takes book from inside of gown.* PRINCESS ALICE *enters and runs to* QUEEN.)

PRINCESS: Mother! (*Looking about*) What has happened here?

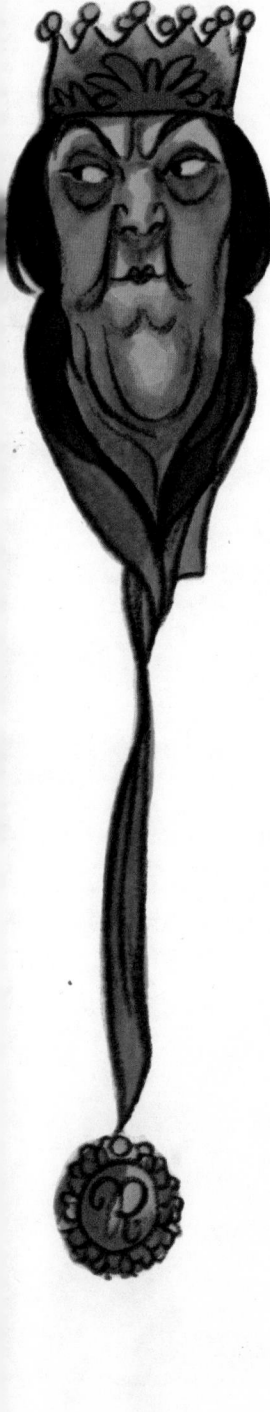

Father, you've done something again. Quickly, help me. (PRINCESS ALICE *and* COURTIERS *work to revive the* QUEEN. KING *stands to one side and reads his book.*)

KING (*Reading*): "If the victim is in pain. . . ." But she's not in anything. The least she could do is act like a victim. (QUEEN *sits up slowly.* KING *picks up dustcloth and fans* QUEEN *with it.*)

QUEEN: Oh, all I can see are flowerpots. They're waving around me. Oh, dear. I'm surrounded by flowerpots.

KING: I'm no flowerpot!

PRINCESS: What on earth is going on around here?

QUEEN: Earth! Oh, don't mention that word. Flowers grow in earth. They thrive in earth!

KING: You're learning, dear.

QUEEN: Alice, come to your poor mother. His Majesty has been reading again.

PRINCESS: Father, not again! You promised us you were through after the rabbit farm. We were up to our necks in little white bunnies.

KING: Why didn't somebody tell me about their love of family life? But flowers don't multiply—I don't think so anyway. (MESSENGER *enters.*) What do you want?

MESSENGER: Your Majesty, there is an odd creature at the gate who begs to speak to you on important business.

QUEEN: You seem to collect odd creatures.

KING: You should know. (*To* PRIME MINISTER) Well, we had better see him. He may be selling something, and I love free samples. Minister, go with this messenger and show our guest to the throne room. (PRIME MINISTER *and* MESSENGER *exit.*) And now, let's get all of this claptrap out of the way.

We are holding court. (*All scurry to hide cleaning implements.*
King *and* Queen *sit on thrones. In a few minutes* Prime
Minister *enters, glancing behind him at intervals. The*
Wizard of Ratzencatzia *follows at a distance.*)

Prime Minister: Sire, this—uh—gentleman has come to us
from very far away.

Queen: He looks as though he never arrived. Who is he?

Wizard: Your Highness, I am known as the Wizard of
Ratzencatzia. I have come a great distance to the land of
Happidazia, for I have heard tales of your fair daughter.

King: We like her. Would you like to meet her? (Princess
draws away.) Come now, Alice, don't be shy.

Princess (*To* King): I don't like him, Father. He has a strange
look about him.

Wizard (*Aside*): So this is Princess Alice. When I marry her,
I shall have this country and its resources in my power.
(*To* Queen) Your Highness, she is lovelier than I had hoped.
Although her beauty cannot compare with yours.

King: This man's not strange; he's a liar.

Queen: Quiet, Rudolph! Mr. Wizard, you are too kind. What
can we do for you?

Wizard: I have come in the hope that I might win the hand
of this lovely Princess.

King (*To* Minister): Doesn't he want the rest of her?

Wizard: I shall put all of my power at your disposal if I may
have your greatest treasure.

King (*To* Minister): What's he talking about? Is he going
to rob the royal treasury?

Prime Minister: What difference would it make? We haven't
any money. Give the moths a change of scenery.

QUEEN: Rudolph, he wants to marry Alice.

KING: Well, why didn't you say so? What—marry Alice? He can't. Nobody can marry Alice until I say he can, and I don't want to—not yet. Do you want to marry him, Alice?

PRINCESS: Oh, no. There's something evil about him. Tell him to go away.

KING: Go away. The Princess doesn't want to get married today. Maybe tomorrow—

WIZARD: Don't be hasty, O King. Remember, I can grant any wishes you make. I can perform wonderful feats of sorcery at your command.

KING: Thanks, but we have a very spooky court magician right here. Besides, the local boys might complain if you cut in on their business.

WIZARD: Sire, I am *not* an ordinary magician. I've been working for years on my own never-fail spells. I have a terrific ten-minute thriller that I'll show you for half price.

KING: I told you that we are not giving away daughters today. That's final!

WIZARD: Do not anger me, Sire. I should hate to resort to witchcraft in such charming company.

KING: Just charm yourself right out of here, and we'll be satisfied. Pick up your broomstick and fly home.

WIZARD (*Starting to exit*): I shall leave now, but I'll be back. You will be more ready to hear me then. (*Exits.*)

PRINCESS: Perhaps you shouldn't have spoken to him so strongly.

KING: Now don't you worry. Your daddy can take care of any old wizard or witch that comes along. Look at your mother—isn't she the soul of happiness?

QUEEN (*Angrily*): I've had enough. I'll speak to you later, Rudolph. (QUEEN *and* COURTIERS *exit*.)

KING: We're going to have quite a crowd in here later on. Now to business. Minister, how's the garden coming along?

PRIME MINISTER: Bloomingly, Sire—if I may make a pun. In fact, I think I'd better tend to the garden right now. (*Exits*.)

PRINCESS: Father, must you continue with this foolish idea of yours?

KING: It's not foolish. My flowers will be beautiful. Cuthbert Cacklebait says that flowers are the source of life.

PRINCESS: They may end yours. Who is Cuthbert Cacklebait?

KING: He is an editor for the "Pamphlet of the Week Club." His books are very popular.

PRINCESS: Not around here. I hope Mother never meets him.

KING: Well, she will. I've had a letter from him, and he's coming here to discuss subscriptions—with Flopsy. (*Laughs to himself*.)

PRINCESS: They must really need subscribers. I had better warn Mother. (*Exits*.)

KING: And now—(*Reaches around for book but finds it gone. Frantically searches under drapes, out window, etc. Finds book where* QUEEN *dropped it when she fainted*.) Back to Cuthbert. Nobody understands me around here. It will be wonderful when Cacklebait arrives. Somebody on my side for a change. (KING *is deep in reading as* WIZARD *creeps back in. He carries a book*.)

WIZARD: King Rudolph, I would have a word with you.

KING: Are you back again?

WIZARD: I wish to repeat my offer.

KING: Once was enough. I'm busy. This is my one chance to read in peace. Can't you see I'm an unhappy man?

WIZARD: You are? Perhaps I can be of help. I have many powers at my command.

KING: No amount of black magic could help me. You see, I like to read books, but nobody will ever let me. Even you must have a favorite volume of curses.

WIZARD: I certainly do. "Classic Curses for Crafty Conjurers." Keep it with me all the time. (*Pats book.*)

KING: But there is more to it than just reading. I want to plant a garden. I want to plant the entire land of Happidazia with flowers.

WIZARD (*Aside*): This may be my chance to get the kingdom. (*To* KING) Don't despair. I can help you.

KING: Plant my flowers? And maybe even a few trees and shrubs?

WIZARD: That might take a little extra homework, but I think I could manage it.

KING: Hooray! (*Dances down from throne and hugs* WIZARD.) When shall we start?

WIZARD: Not so fast, King Rudolph. Remember, a man of my talents doesn't come along every day. There is a certain talent fee involved. My manager would hate me if I didn't collect something.

KING: I'll have money printed at once.

WIZARD: I don't need money. No, Sire, if I plant this garden for you, you must give me Princess Alice as a reward.

KING: This is a pretty stiff bargain. I'll have to think about it. Turn your back, please. (WIZARD *turns away as* KING *searches furiously through book*.) Cuthbert, don't desert me now. (*Pause*) No, there isn't a single thing about exchanging princesses for gardens.

WIZARD: Are you ready?

KING: Not yet. I have to make up my mind. (*Itemizing on fingers*) First, Alice is as pretty as a flower and she smells as good, too. Second, flowers require much care and they get buggy in the summertime. Alice takes care of herself quite well and, at least, I've never heard her complain about bugs.

WIZARD: Your Majesty—

KING: WILL YOU KEEP QUIET! I must have absolute silence.

WIZARD: I'll breathe softly.

KING (*Continuing*): Flowers will make Alice happy too, though. I can't plant Alice, but I can plant flowers. Wiz, (WIZARD *turns.*) it's a deal.

WIZARD: You are wise, O King. (*Aside*) He's all mine along with this silly country of his. (*To* KING) Let us begin. Take those pillows from the thrones and place them on the floor.

KING: My wife won't like this.

WIZARD: She hasn't seen anything yet! I shall prepare myself for the spell. I usually have a fanfare before I perform, but I suppose I'll have to put up with this. (WIZARD *reads book as* KING *peers over his shoulder.*)

KING: That looks good. Very wizardly.

WIZARD: I shall now assume the position. Move over. (*Lies down on floor.*) I really should have a black cat. Can you purr?

KING: I'll try. (*Screws up his face and tries to purr.*)

WIZARD: I suppose you'll have to do. Put my hat on my chest. (KING *does so.*) Now close your eyes. No peeking! (PRIME MINISTER *enters.*)

PRIME MINISTER: Excuse me, Sire, there's a gentleman in the outer hall. (*Sees* WIZARD.) What's this? Is he incapacitated?

KING: No, entranced. The wizard is growing my garden.

PRIME MINISTER: He needs a flower bed, not a feather bed!

WIZARD: Quiet! Can't you see I'm working?

PRIME MINISTER: Looks like a pretty soft job to me.

WIZARD (*Chanting*):

"Spirits of the world attend me,
Answer to my magic powers,
Let the land of Happidazia,
Burst into a realm of flowers."

(*Raises arms up straight.*)

PRIME MINISTER: Has rigor mortis set in?

WIZARD: This will take time. I knew I needed that cat.

KING (*Going to window*): Wait a moment. The land around the castle is turning green. There are little buds and blossoms springing up everywhere! You're wonderful.

WIZARD: It wasn't so much. Say, this feels good. Mind if I take a nap?

PRIME MINISTER: I don't understand any of this, but there is still a man in the outer hall. He wants to see you about the "Pamphlet of the Week Club."

KING: What's his name?

PRIME MINISTER: Cuthbert Cacklebait. He said he had an appointment.

KING: So he did. Send him in. Let him see what a real gardener can do. (PRIME MINISTER *exits*.)

WIZARD (*Getting up*): Don't forget our bargain, King Rudolph. Your garden is finished. Now I want the Princess.

KING: Oh, that. Well, you know, she might not like this.

WIZARD: Your promise was made. A king never breaks his word. (QUEEN, PRINCESS, and COURTIERS *enter hurriedly*.)

KING: That's true. Here she is; ask her yourself.

QUEEN (*Greatly disturbed*): Rudolph, something is happening around here. There are buttercups on the balconies, daisies in the drawing room, and petunias in the pantry.

KING: Isn't that wonderful!

QUEEN: Wonderful? I can't turn around without seeing some big green thing.

KING: The wizard has planted my garden for me. The land of Happidazia shall be a blooming paradise.

PRINCESS (*To* WIZARD): You did this for Father?

WIZARD: It was my pleasure.

PRINCESS: In return for what?

WIZARD: For you, Princess Alice.

PRINCESS: Father! Is this true?

KING: Well, now—

QUEEN: Rudolph?

KING: Yes. (CUTHBERT CACKLEBAIT *enters*.)

CACKLEBAIT: Am I interrupting?

QUEEN: Who are you?

CACKLEBAIT: I am Cuthbert Cacklebait, editor for the "Pamphlet of the Week Club."

QUEEN: Throw him out! He's responsible for all of this.

CACKLEBAIT: My dear madam—

QUEEN: Don't you "dear madam" me! If you don't leave, you'll be editing a murder story—your own.

CACKLEBAIT: I merely came to find out if Mr. Flopsy wants his subscription renewed.

QUEEN: The only new thing we need around here is a new king with a new head! Alice, we're leaving.

WIZARD: I'll take care of Princess Alice from now on.

PRINCESS: You will not!

CACKLEBAIT: This sounds tremendous. May I have the publishing rights?

QUEEN: You'll have funeral rites in a few minutes. Alice! (QUEEN, PRINCESS, *and* COURTIERS *exit.*)

KING: I'm awfully sorry, Wiz, but her mind is made up.

WIZARD: And so is mine. You have the garden; I want the Princess.

KING: Then I guess you'll have to take the garden back.

WIZARD: There's not much of a market for used gardens these days, King Rudolph.

CACKLEBAIT: I'm an expert on gardens. Can I help?

KING: Who are you?

CACKLEBAIT: That question has gotten me into more trouble lately.

KING: I remember. You're Cuthbert Cacklebait. You started all of this—stop it!

CACKLEBAIT: King Rudolph, I don't know what you're talking about. However, never let it be said that the "Pamphlet of the Week Club" deserted a sinking subscriber.

KING: Come with me. We'll have a very private conference out of the hearing of sinister sorcerers. (KING *and* CACKLEBAIT *exit.*)

WIZARD: So—he's trying to back out on me. I'll fix him. I'll take that garden and turn it into a nightmare. First, I'll get rid of all those flowers. Then I'll plant—I'll plant—*onions!* Big, juicy onions. The land of Happidazia will burst into tears all because of me. Ha-ha. Now to rearrange the pillows. (*Busily pushes pillows together, gets out reference book, and lies down.*) I do wish I had that cat! (*Chanting*)

"Spirits of the world attend me,

Since the King won't grant my dreams,

Let onions grow instead of flowers,

And make tears run out in streams."

(*Shoots both arms and legs into air.*) That took a lot out of me. I guess I'm getting to that age. (*Sounds of weeping offstage*) Ah, I'm getting results. (KING *and* CACKLEBAIT *enter.*)

CACKLEBAIT: Yours is indeed a sad story, King Rudolph. (*Takes out large handkerchief and sniffs into it.*) I can understand your unhappiness. (*Begins to cry.*) Books are such a joy to me.

KING: There, there, my boy. (*Also begins to cry into handkerchief.*) Don't take it so seriously. We'll think of something.

CACKLEBAIT (*Weeping harder*): If we could just get rid of this wizard.

WIZARD: I won't leave until I take the Princess with me. (QUEEN, PRINCESS, *and* COURTIERS *enter, weeping into handkerchiefs.*)

QUEEN: Oh, Rudolph, we were sitting among the flowers eating bread and honey when all at once they wilted and—

KING: There, there, dear, don't worry. I'll plant some more flowers.

PRINCESS: Papa, we've made you cry, too. (PRIME MINISTER *enters, also weeping.*)

PRIME MINISTER: Sire, I was riding through the country when all at once I just began to cry and cry. Everyone else is crying, too. Gloom has descended on the kingdom. (CACKLEBAIT *exits quietly while* WIZARD *moves closer to the* PRINCESS.)

KING: I feel just fine. (*Sobbing*)

WIZARD (*Aside*): I may (*Gets out handkerchief.*) have overdone this a bit. (*To* KING) Is this the land of Happidazia? Is this King Rudolph's joyous kingdom? Where's the Chamber of Commerce? Wait until I tell the folks at home about this! Will they laugh! (*Bursts into tears.*)

KING: What will I say at the Kings' Convention next month? They'll throw me out of the Lodge. (*To* WIZARD) Do something. Do something! (CACKLEBAIT *enters carrying large onion. He has a book in a pocket of his coat.*)

CACKLEBAIT: Sire, I suspected foul play. Here is the answer to your weeping nation. Onions!

ALL: Onions!

CACKLEBAIT: Onions. This old goblin here turned your garden into a huge onion patch.

PRINCESS: Father, you don't know what he'll do next. I'd better give in and marry the old buzzard.

WIZARD: That's wizard. Watch your pronunciation.

CACKLEBAIT: Wait! I have here a copy of the new "Pamphlet of the Week Club" selection. It is "Cooking for Two." In it there is a graphically illustrated color section on onions. (*Takes book from coat and begins to read.*)

WIZARD: Close that book!

QUEEN: Don't you dare.

CACKLEBAIT (*Reading*): "Onions should be peeled underwater to avoid shedding tears."

ALL: Underwater?

CACKLEBAIT: That's what it says.

WIZARD: King Rudolph, I demand your daughter. You can't flood the entire country.

CACKLEBAIT: Oh, yes he can. Issue a proclamation!

KING: Minister, issue a proclamation.

PRIME MINISTER (*Weeping*): I'd love to. (*Takes out pencil and paper and scribbles furiously.*)

CACKLEBAIT: Tell the people to cry and cry. Tell them to collect their tears and throw them into the fields. We will create lakes, rivers, and streams of tears. We will drown those onions in their own juice.

WIZARD: Curses!

KING: Issue that proclamation immediately! (PRIME MINISTER *exits.*) And now, Sir Ratzencatzia, we are through with you.

WIZARD: I'll not give up easily. You'll hear from me again.

CACKLEBAIT: Now, just a minute. I don't think you are a bad fellow. Would you be interested in a little business proposition?

WIZARD: I might be. This wizarding seems to be falling off a bit.

CACKLEBAIT: The "Pamphlet of the Week Club" has been looking for a new department. How would you like to become editor of a new series, "The Spell of the Week"? We'll start a campaign for bigger and darker magic.

WIZARD: Not *magic*, please—sorcery. Professional ethics, you know. Think how proud my dear mother would be of me—a real editor. It's a deal. I'm going to get my reference books. An honorable wizard! (WIZARD *exits as* PRIME MINISTER *enters.*)

PRIME MINISTER: It's working. We are well on the way to having a beautiful salt lake in the middle of Happidazia.

KING: Where are the plans for my canoes and fishing tackle? I knew I would want them someday.

QUEEN: Mr. Cacklebait, how can we ever thank you?

CACKLEBAIT: If I may be allowed to remain here and . . . cultivate, I shall consider myself amply rewarded.

KING: We will be proud to have you. And I have some dandy ideas for the Club.

QUEEN: Rudolph! That will do. Alice, why don't you go out and watch the moon rise over the new lake?

PRINCESS: An excellent idea. Mr. Cacklebait?

CACKLEBAIT: Simply delightful. Shall we? (PRINCESS *and* CACKLEBAIT *exit*.)

KING (*Relaxing on throne*): Now you see I'm not such a bad fellow after all.

QUEEN: At least you're a very lucky fellow. Wouldn't it be splendid if that Mr. Cacklebait turned out to be our son-in-law?

KING: I'll say. Just think; then I'd be certain of having a life subscription to the "Pamphlet of the Week Club." (QUEEN *collapses. Curtain*.)

Secret Messages

Bernice Kohn

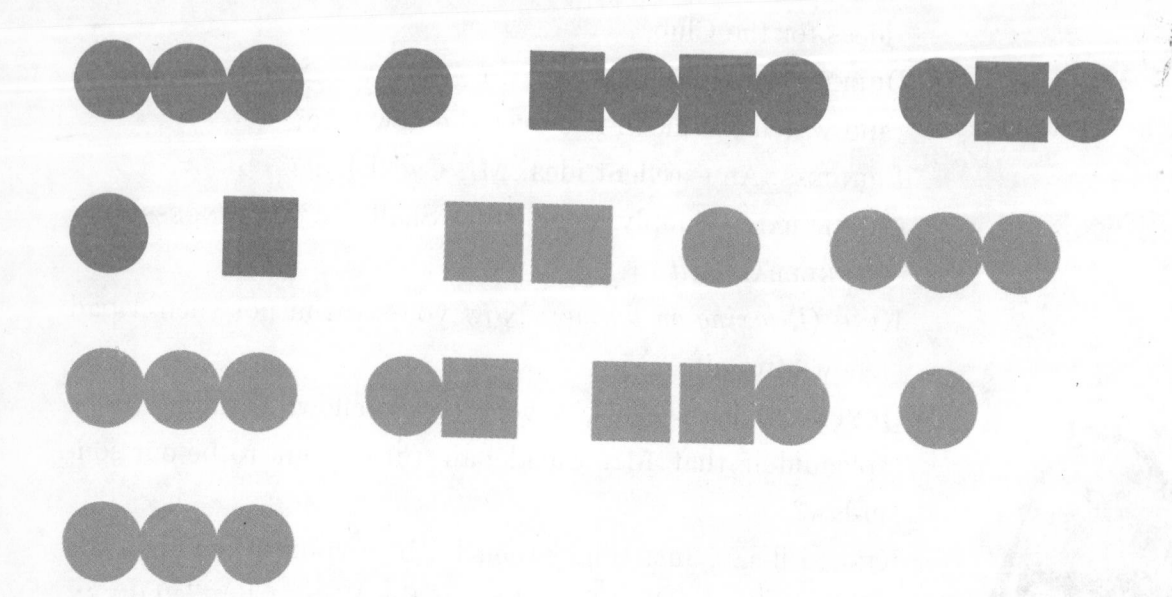

Often the aim of communication
is to bring a message to as many
people as possible. Yet some
communication systems are
invented to keep information secret.

Is It a Code or a Cipher?

OD UOY WONK
TAHW SIHT SYAS?

If that sentence doesn't make any sense to you, read each word backwards. And if that was too easy for you, try this one.

DBO ZPV SFBE UIJT?

Of course you can. Just change each letter to the one that comes before it in the alphabet.

Both of the "secret" sentences above are in cipher. You don't have to look up anything in a book to find out what they mean. You just have to know the system.

A cipher is always based on a system. The system is a matter of

changing the order of letters or words, or of substituting letters or words according to a plan. The substituted letters or words may be *other* letters or words or they may be numbers or symbols. The Morse code, which is used for sending telegrams, is really a cipher, not a code. It substitutes an alphabet of dots and dashes for the letters of the ordinary alphabet.

A code uses substitutions, too, but in a different way. A code uses signs, sounds, numbers, letters, or words to stand for words, sentences, or complete thoughts. Only rarely does a code use substitutions for single letters. In cipher, X stands for some other letter. In code, X may be a whole word, a whole sentence, or the whole message.

A code is never based on a plan that enables you to work it out each time you want to use it. If a code is very simple, you memorize

From the book *Secret Codes and Ciphers* by Bernice Kohn, © 1968. Published by Prentice-Hall, Inc., Englewood Cliffs, New Jersey.

it. You memorize the zip-code number that stands for the name of your area and post office. You memorize your telephone area-code number.

A secret knock on the clubhouse door is code. So are semaphore, or flag, signals (although they may be used as a cipher, too), Indian smoke signals, and African drumbeats. They are all memorized by the people who use them.

But most codes are so lengthy and complicated that no one memorizes them. They can be used only with the help of a code book. A code book is like a foreign-language dictionary. First it has an alphabetical list of all the words or sentences that can be expressed in the code, with the code word or symbol for each one. Then it has an alphabetical list of the code words or symbols and their mean-

ings. Both the sender and the receiver of code messages have to have copies of the book.

While many codes and ciphers in use today are of modern invention, there is nothing new about secret writing. One of the oldest stories about a hidden message goes all the way back to the fifth century B.C. A Greek man named Aristagoras was told that a slave had come to see him. When he entered the house, the slave said to Aristagoras, "Shave my head and look thereon." Aristagoras must have been surprised, but he lathered up the slave's head and shaved it clean. There he found a message tatooed on the slave's scalp. It was from Aristagoras's father-in-law in Persia, and it told him that the time had come to revolt. Aristagoras did, and the course of history was changed.

A cipher used by Julius Caesar in ancient Rome is still in use today and is still known as the Julius Caesar cipher. It isn't very hard to "crack." In fact, it is very much like the cipher in the sentence

DBO ZPV SFBE UIJT?

But instead of using the letter next to the real one, Caesar moved ahead three letters in the alphabet. The same sentence in Julius Caesar cipher reads

FDQ BRX UHDG WKLV?

In this cipher, when you come to the end of the alphabet, you start over at the beginning. That is why the second word begins with B. It is three letters after Y.

Both codes and ciphers can be very simple or very complicated. They can be used for fun or for serious purposes, even for matters of life or death.

Secret Codes and Ciphers

Have you ever visited a shop where the price tags read BOK or HLD? This kind of marking is very common in antique shops. The tags don't seem to mean anything at all. Yet, if you ask the price of the rocking chair or the dollhouse, the shopkeeper usually looks at the tag before he tells you.

The secret is code—shopkeeper's code, or cipher. Most stores have set prices for everything and the prices are clearly marked. But in an antique shop, this is often not true. The owner wants to sell for whatever he can get—but he has to be sure that he doesn't lose money. Since it is very likely that no two items in the shop are the same, and there

may be hundreds or thousands of them, it is important for the owner to know how much he paid for each article. He writes it down in code or cipher. A glance at the tag gives him his buying price before he tells you his selling price.

Shopkeepers can use any system they like for their codes because, except for a clerk or two, no one else has to understand it. The mysterious letters stand for anything the shopkeeper decides on. But commonly, storekeepers use a cipher. It is based on a ten-letter word that doesn't repeat any letters. Of course, each shop has its own secret word, but the system always works in the same way. Let's say the secret word is BLOCKHEADS. The word is set down and the letters are numbered from 1 to 0.

BLOCKHEADS
1234567890

If the rocking chair cost the dealer $23.00, the tag says LO. If the dollhouse cost $2.50, the tag says LKS. Most ciphers of this sort do not bother with decimal points. The general value of the object makes it clear whether the numbers mean dollars or cents.

One code that you *might* say is

used for business is the very old code used by tramps and hoboes as they go from house to house asking for food or money. Since tramps often come to a new neighborhood without knowing how they will be received, they help each other to know what to expect by making small marks near the door with chalk or crayon.

One of the most useful codes in business is the commercial code that is used to send overseas telegrams. The charge for such messages is made by the letter, so it is important to make the message as short as possible. A commercial code book has lists of short words (five letters is standard) that stand for long sentences. The code word BHRLT might stand for

YOUR ORDER HAS BEEN RECEIVED. MERCHANDISE WILL BE SHIPPED AS SOON AS IT IS AVAILABLE.

If you look at some business letterheads you will probably see a cable address in addition to the regular address. This is usually one word that stands for the name of the company and its complete address, including the name of the country.

But codes are not always used for

peaceful purposes. Once, during World War I, an alert radio operator noticed that some of the messages he was sending seemed rather odd. He suspected that they were in code and were being sent by spies. He decided to do something about it.

The next day, the operator was given the message

FATHER IS DEAD

but instead of sending it as written, he changed one word. The wire went out saying

FATHER IS DECEASED

Within a few hours a reply came back. It said

IS FATHER DEAD OR DECEASED?

There was no longer any question about the messages being code!

Sometimes, even during a war, a code message may show great wit and imagination. Such was the case many years ago when General Sir Charles Napier captured the Indian province of Sindh. It was important that he inform the British War Office and important that the message not be understood in India. Sir Charles sent a one-word message. It said

PECCAVI

Fortunately, the man who received the message in England had been an excellent Latin student. He had no trouble at all translating PECCAVI —I HAVE SINNED (I have Sindh). Of course, there must have been many people in India who knew Latin. It was just lucky for the British that the telegraph operator wasn't one of them.

When is it better to use a code

and when a cipher? They both have advantages and disadvantages. It is usually faster and easier to put a message into code (encode) and to discover the meaning of a code message (decode). But code requires a code book, and if it is captured or found, the code isn't secret anymore.

Navies use code. The code books are bound in lead, and if the ship is damaged or captured by the enemy, the books are thrown overboard to sink to the bottom of the sea. Sometimes divers have been able to recover the books and learn the code. For this reason, naval codes are changed very often, sometimes every day.

Armies use cipher. It would be dangerous and clumsy for an army on the move to carry around code books. The risk of capture would be very high.

Diplomats, spies, and criminals use both code and cipher, but they use cipher most of the time. With cipher, you can say anything that you can say in your own language. With code, you are limited to what is in the code book.

An easy code to use with a friend is a dictionary code. You must each have a copy of the same edition of the same dictionary. To encode a message, you use numbers instead of words. The number 16:7 means "page 16, seventh word."

This is a good "fun" code, but it is only that. During World War I when German spies used a dictionary

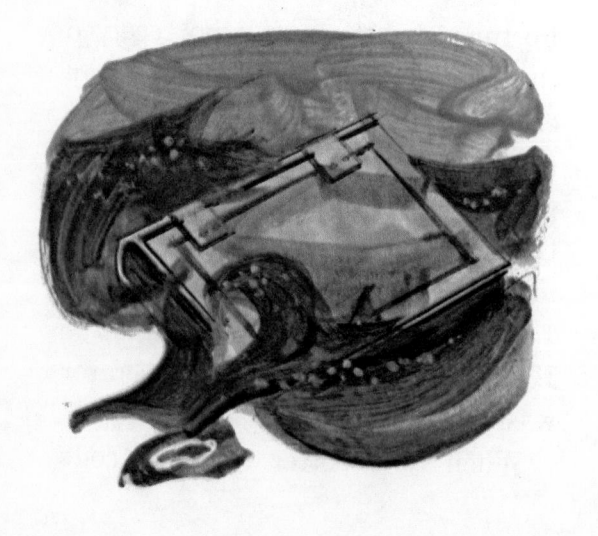

code, it took American agents only a few days to try out all the German dictionaries until they found the right one and cracked the code.

Afterthought

1. Why does a language you don't know form a code? How can you break the code?
2. How is a word you don't know the meaning of like a cipher? How can you decipher it?
3. Invent a cipher and use it in a short message. Exchange messages with a classmate and try to discover the cipher he used.

WRW BLF
TVG GSV
NVHHZTV

Riding on the Railroad

Dorothy Sterling

The Underground Railroad had no trains, but it did have
a system of communication. It used notes, codes, signals,
and signs to help slaves gain their freedom. Before Harriet
Tubman started to freedom on the Underground Railroad,
she got oral and written information from a Quaker woman.
Then she traveled on foot through the darkness to find the
next person who would aid in her daring escape.

In the moonlight she could make out the outlines of a ramshackle cabin, so poor that it must surely belong to a black man. She toured around it, studying out the best path to take if she should be wrong. Her knock on the door was answered by a frightened "Who's there?"

"It's me," Harriet whispered. "Can you tell me how to find Ezekiel Hunn?"

"Reckon I can," the voice inside mumbled. "Wait a minute."

It was a long minute, and Harriet swallowed her heart a dozen times as she waited. When the door creaked back, she could see that she was talking to a tall woman, dark of skin.

"You sure scared me, knocking on the door in the middle of the night," the stranger complained. "But I work for Mr. Hunn, so I ought to be used to it. His house is right over the hill. You can see the chimney from here if it was light."

Murmuring her thanks, Harriet followed the woman's pointing finger. A quarter of a mile along the road and she came to a clapboard house with a broad brick chimney. The house was dark, each window heavily shuttered.

"Day or night, they take us in," she thought. "Should I wake up the family?

"No." Her habit of mistrust asserted itself. "Better wait till morning and see what they look like first."

There were haystacks in the meadow behind the barn and Harriet crawled into one, pulling the sweet-smelling grass around her. It was good to rest and feel warm. Her eyes closed and her head began to nod.

Suddenly she jerked herself awake. She couldn't sleep now. She must watch and wait until she was sure she was safe.

Regretfully she left the hay to spend the rest of the night pacing back and forth in the shelter of the barn. She dared not sit down, lest sleep overtake her.

When the morning sun had dried the dew on the grass, the back door of the house swung open. A woman dressed in gray began to sweep the steps. After watching her for a few minutes, Harriet silently handed her the Quaker lady's note.

The woman's response was a strange one. With scarcely more than a glance at the note, she thrust the broom at Harriet.

"Sweep the yard," she whispered. She disappeared inside the house.

Mechanically Harriet swept. The broom swished back and forth across the brick paving, raising puffs of dust. But Harriet's eyes were fixed on the house, and the muscles in her legs were tight, ready to carry her away if danger threatened.

She had to wait only a few minutes before the front door opened and two men emerged. One wore the black suit and broad-brimmed hat of Quaker men; the other was more fashionably attired. He strode to the barn to saddle a fine chestnut mare. With no more than a glance at the ordinary-looking woman who was sweeping, he leaped on his horse and galloped down the road.

As soon as the horseman was out of sight, the Quaker walked toward Harriet. "Thee are most welcome here." He smiled as he took the broom from her hands. "That man"— nodding toward the road—"is a slave trader. He was desirous of purchasing some of my hay, and he stopped the night with us. It is safe now to come inside.

"I am Ezekiel Hunn," he added as he held the door open for his visitor.

"And I am Harriet Tubman." She could barely form the words with her lips. The kindly Quaker voice, the warmth of the kitchen, and the smell of baking bread were suddenly too much for her. She stumbled and would have fallen had not her host caught her and led her to a chair.

"Thee are hungry, child, and tired. Thee must have food and rest, and then we shall make plans. Eliza!" he called to his wife.

After setting out a hearty breakfast, Mrs. Hunn led Harriet upstairs and put her to bed. When Harriet awoke, it was with a cry of wonder. The walls of the room were covered with flowers. A pattern of pink rosebuds and green leaves ran from floor to ceiling. There was a window of glass where starched white curtains rustled in the summer breeze. Most wonderful of all was the bed, a great four-poster, fully three feet from the polished floor. Harriet stretched out her arms and legs to feel its softness. Then she gently bounced up and down.

"Like resting on a cloud," she marveled.

All that day Harriet remained hidden indoors. After dark, Ezekiel Hunn hitched a team of horses to his wagon and drove her to the outskirts of Smyrna.

"I must turn back here to be home by dawn," he explained. "As thee knows, men are watching me too. If thee follow the road from here, thee can reach Middletown before daylight. My brother John will be looking for thee."

After describing John Hunn's house, he clucked to his team and headed homeward. Boldly Harriet strode down the road, scorning to hide in the bushes as she had done the night before. The songs bubbling inside her spilled over. With her hand always on the handle of the knife in her ticking bag, she softly sang:

> "When Israel was in Egypt's land,
>   Let my people go.
>   Oppressed so hard they could not stand,
>   Let my people go.

> "Go down, Moses,
>   Way down in Egypt's land.
>   Tell Ole Pharaoh,
>   Let my people go."

"It's coming true," she whispered. "I'm going to be free. Tomorrow, the next day, I'm going to be free!"

The night air was hot and heavy and the only sign of life

along the highway was an occasional barking dog. Toward dawn a rumble of thunder broke the silence. Sheets of rain turned the dusty road to mud, but Harriet slogged on, grateful for the cooling water on her cheeks. Then the rain stopped and the North Star faded in the morning sky. Dead ahead, in a little valley at the foot of a hill, lay the house that Ezekiel Hunn had described.

The Hunns of Middletown were as kind as the Hunns of Camden. Harriet breakfasted and slept, and by the time she arose, a message had gone to Thomas Garrett telling him when to expect her. Wilmington, across the river from New Jersey and only eight miles from the Pennsylvania border, was as closely guarded as a medieval fortress. All bridges and roads leading to and from the city were patrolled, and Harriet would need an escort to guide her to Garrett's house.

"Unfortunately, I cannot take thee." John Hunn frowned. "Last year Friend Garrett and I were hauled to the court at New Castle and convicted of the dreadful crime of sheltering a runaway mother and her six children. My carriage in front of Thomas' house now would signal an army of constables to 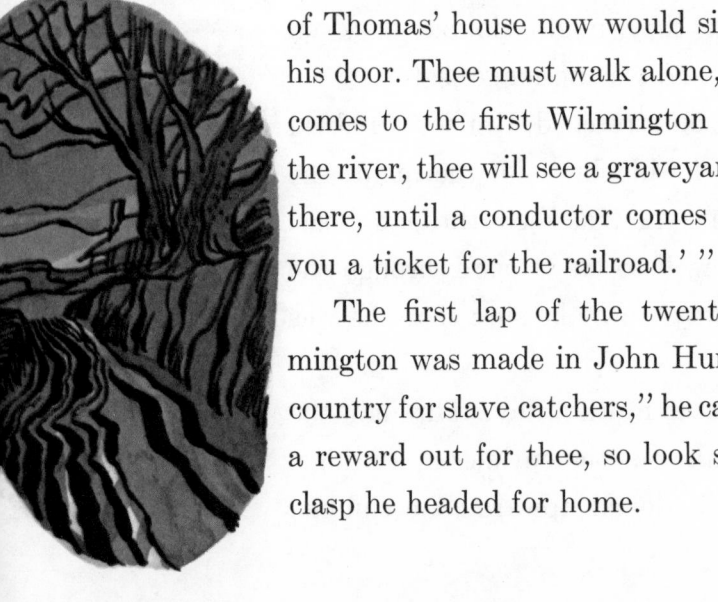 his door. Thee must walk alone, following the road, until thee comes to the first Wilmington bridge. On a hill overlooking the river, thee will see a graveyard. Hide among the headstones there, until a conductor comes for thee. He will say, 'I bring you a ticket for the railroad.' "

The first lap of the twenty-three-mile journey to Wilmington was made in John Hunn's carriage. "This is a great country for slave catchers," he cautioned when he left. "There's a reward out for thee, so look sharp." With a friendly handclasp he headed for home.

On this, Harriet's fourth night on the road, she was too weary to sing. Thick clouds hid the friendly North Star and she plodded along, past fields and barns, past creeks and towns, wishing for an end to her journey. After leaving New Castle, one of her sleeping spells overtook her. She awakened to hear a horse's whinny.

There were a group of mounted men only a few feet away. Harriet dug her fingernails into the bark of the tree against which she was leaning. These were the dreaded slave catchers, on the prowl for runaways. Frozen to the tree trunk, she held her breath. Surely they could hear the insistent beat of her heart.

"Devil take the wench," a gruff voice swore. "She can't have gotten further than this. Edwards saw Hunn's carriage near Smyrna."

"Best give up for now," a companion counseled. "Can't see our fingers in front of our faces. She's headed for Wilmington, sure. We'll pick her up there in the morning."

Grunting assent, the horsemen trotted slowly in the direction of Wilmington. But they might double back on their tracks at any time. The road was no longer safe.

Feeling her way with hands outstretched, Harriet stumbled across the adjacent fields. In the blackness of the night, she climbed fences, waded streams, and sloshed through bogs. Every few yards she forced herself to crawl back through the underbrush and find the highway, to make sure that she was still heading north.

The somber night became a murky day. Through the morning mist Harriet could make out the outlines of a bridge. To the east of it, rocky ground sloped upward. She climbed until she could feel the smooth cold marble of a gravestone. Then she tumbled to the ground.

As she fought to keep awake, she felt a light tap on her shoulder. Her hand slid into her bag, hunting for John's knife. Before she could pull it out, a friendly voice whispered, "I bring you a ticket for the railroad."

Harriet's ticket was a suit of men's clothes and a rake. With her dress and hair concealed by overalls and cap, she walked across the bridge beside her companion. To passersby, the two were clearly Negro workingmen on their way to jobs in the city of Wilmington. On the street on which Thomas Garrett lived, her guide left her.

"Go to the back door and knock three times," he counseled. "They're waiting for you."

When the door opened, Harriet found her hand in the hearty clasp of Thomas Garrett, stationmaster of the Underground Railroad. After their greeting, Garrett hustled her up his stairs. On the second-floor landing, a bookcase crammed with leather-bound volumes blocked their way. With a flourish Garrett removed two of the books. Behind them a brass doorknob gleamed. As Harriet stared, the bookcase swung out, revealing a tiny windowless room.

"The waiting room of the railroad," Garrett smiled. "Only friends know of its existence. My shoe store is beneath, so thee must be quiet here."

For two days Harriet lived in Thomas Garrett's hidden room. "Thy mistress has put out handbills announcing thy escape," he explained, "and the slave catchers are all watching for thee. On First Day morning, when they are in church, thee will leave Wilmington in my carriage. Once thee are out of the

city, thee can walk to the Pennsylvania border, and from there to Philadelphia. But even in the free states, thee must be on guard. There are worthless wretches there who would not hesitate to kidnap thee for a reward."

On Sunday morning, six days after Harriet had left her Maryland home, Thomas Garrett took her arm and led her to his carriage. John's fine shoes, muddy and torn until her toes showed through the splitting seams, had been discarded. In their place she wore a new pair from Garrett's store. Her clothes were washed and mended, and a heavy black veil concealed her features. To all appearances, she was a lady out for a ride with her genial host.

Outside the city, Garrett stopped the horses. "The path here is well worn and thee cannot miss it. An hour's good walking will bring thee to the highway. A wooden signpost there marks the line between Delaware and Pennsylvania. Step past that sign and thee are free! Godspeed." He pressed a silver dollar into her hand.

Harriet's feet flew over the narrow path. In less than an hour she had followed its twists and turns until she could see the highway ahead. After peering out cautiously to make sure that she was alone, she stepped to the signpost at the crossing. With her head held high, she walked into the free state of Pennsylvania.

She stood there, wanting to sing, wanting to shout, but no sounds came. A tear glistened on her cheek and she wiped it away.

"I looked at my hands," she later told a friend, "to see if I was the same person now I was free. There was such a glory over everything. The sun came like gold through the trees and over the fields, and I felt like I was in heaven."

Afterthought

1. What kind of signal was the broom? How did Harriet Tubman know to observe the signal?
2. How did slave catchers get information about escaping slaves?
3. Describe how you would feel if your life and freedom depended on finding a signpost you could not read.

Someday

Isaac Asimov

Have you ever wished for a machine that would do your reading and writing and math problems for you? After you read this story, you may hope you never get your wish.

Niccolo Mazetti lay stomach down on the rug, chin buried in the palm of one small hand, and listened to the Bard disconsolately. There was even the suspicion of tears in his dark eyes, a luxury an eleven-year-old could allow himself only when alone.

The Bard said, "Once upon a time in the middle of a deep wood, there lived a poor woodcutter and his two motherless daughters, who were each as beautiful as the day is long. The older daughter had long hair as black as a feather from a raven's wing, but the younger daughter had hair as bright and golden as the sunlight of an autumn afternoon.

"Many times while the girls were waiting for their father to come home from his day's work in the wood, the older girl would sit before a mirror and sing—"

What she sang, Niccolo did not hear, for a call sounded from outside the room: "Hey, Nickie."

And Niccolo, his face clearing on the moment, rushed to the window and shouted, "Hey, Paul."

Paul Loeb waved an excited hand. He was thinner than Niccolo and not as tall, for all he was six months older. His face was full of repressed tension which showed itself most clearly in the rapid blinking of his eyelids. "Hey, Nickie, let me in. I've got an idea and a *half*. Wait till you hear it." He looked rapidly about him as though to check on the possibility of eavesdroppers, but the front yard was quite patently empty. He repeated, in a whisper, "Wait till you hear it."

"All right. I'll open the door."

The Bard continued smoothly, oblivious to the sudden loss of attention on the part of Niccolo. As Paul entered, the Bard was saying, ". . . Thereupon, the lion said, 'If you will find me the lost egg of the bird which flies over the Ebony Mountain once every ten years, I will—' "

Paul said, "Is that a Bard you're listening to? I didn't know you had one."

Niccolo reddened and the look of unhappiness returned to his face. "Just an old thing I had when I was a kid. It ain't much good." He kicked at the Bard with his foot and caught the somewhat scarred and discolored plastic covering a glancing blow.

The Bard hiccuped as its speaking attachment was jarred out of contact a moment; then it went on: "—for a year and a day until the iron shoes were worn out. The princess stopped at the side of the road. . . ."

Paul said, "Boy, that *is* an old model," and looked at it critically.

Despite Niccolo's own bitterness against the Bard, he winced at the other's condescending tone. For the moment, he was sorry he had allowed Paul in, at least before he had restored the Bard to its usual resting place in the basement. It was only in the desperation of a dull day and a fruitless discussion with his father that he had resurrected it. And it turned out to be just as stupid as he had expected.

Nickie was a little afraid of Paul anyway, since Paul had special courses at school and everyone said he was going to grow up to be a Computing Engineer.

Not that Niccolo himself was doing badly at school. He got adequate marks in logic, binary manipulations, computing and elementary circuits; all the usual grammar-school subjects. But that was it! They were just the usual subjects and he would grow up to be a control-board guard like everyone else.

Paul, however, knew mysterious things about what he called electronics and theoretical mathematics and programing. Especially programing. Niccolo didn't even try to understand when Paul bubbled over about it.

Paul listened to the Bard for a few minutes and said, "You been using it much?"

"No!" said Niccolo, offended. "I've had it in the basement since before you moved into the neighborhood. I just got it out today—" He lacked an excuse that seemed adequate to himself, so he concluded, "I just got it out."

Paul said, "Is that what it tells you about: woodcutters and princesses and talking animals?"

Niccolo said, "It's terrible. My dad says we can't afford a new one. I said to him this morning—" The memory of the morning's fruitless pleadings brought Niccolo dangerously near tears, which he repressed in a panic. Somehow, he felt that Paul's thin cheeks never felt the stain of tears and that Paul would have only contempt for anyone else less strong than himself. Niccolo went on, "So I thought I'd try this old thing again, but it's no good."

Paul turned off the Bard, pressed the contact that led to a nearly instantaneous reorientation and recombination of the vocabulary, characters, plot lines, and climaxes stored within it. Then he reactivated it.

The Bard began smoothly, "Once upon a time there was a little boy named Willikins whose mother had died and who lived with a stepfather and a stepbrother. Although the stepfather was very well-to-do, he begrudged poor Willikins the very bed he slept in, so that Willikins was forced to get such rest as he could on a pile of straw in the stable next to the horses—"

"Horses!" cried Paul.

"They're a kind of animal," said Niccolo. "I think."

"I know that! I just mean imagine stories about *horses*."

"It tells about horses all the time," said Niccolo. "There

are things called cows, too. You milk them but the Bard doesn't say how."

"Well, gee, why don't you fix it up?"

"I'd like to know how."

The Bard was saying, "Often Willikins would think that if only he were rich and powerful, he would show his stepfather and stepbrother what it meant to be cruel to a little boy, so one day he decided to go out into the world and seek his fortune."

Paul, who wasn't listening to the Bard, said, "It's *easy*. The Bard has memory cylinders all fixed up for plot lines and climaxes and things. We don't have to worry about that. It's just vocabulary we've got to fix so it'll know about computers and automation and electronics and real things about today. Then it can tell interesting stories, you know, instead of about princesses and things."

Niccolo said despondently, "I wish we could do that."

Paul said, "Listen, my dad says if I get into special computing school next year, he'll get me a *real* Bard, a late model. A big one with an attachment for space stories and mysteries. And a visual attachment, too!"

"You mean *see* the stories?"

"Sure. Mr. Daugherty at school says they've got things like that, now, but not for just everybody. Only if I get into computing school, Dad can get a few breaks."

Niccolo's eyes bulged with envy. "Gee. *Seeing* a story."

"You can come over and watch anytime, Nickie."

"Oh, boy. Thanks."

"That's all right. But remember, I'm the guy who says what kind of story we hear."

"Sure. Sure." Niccolo would have agreed readily to much more onerous conditions.

Paul's attention returned to the Bard.

It was saying, " 'If that is the case,' said the king, stroking his beard and frowning till clouds filled the sky and lightning flashed, 'you will see to it that my entire land is freed of flies by this time day after tomorrow or—' "

"All we've got to do," said Paul, "is open it up—" He shut the Bard off again and was prying at its front panel as he spoke.

"Hey," said Niccolo, in sudden alarm. "Don't break it."

"I won't break it," said Paul impatiently. "I know all about these things." Then, with sudden caution, "Your father and mother home?"

"No."

"All right, then." He had the front panel off and peered in. "Boy, this *is* a one-cylinder thing."

He worked away at the Bard's innards. Niccolo, who

watched with painful suspense, could not make out what he was doing.

Paul pulled out a thin, flexible metal strip, powdered with dots. "That's the Bard's memory cylinder. I'll bet its capacity for stories is under a trillion."

"What are you going to do, Paul?" quavered Niccolo.

"I'll give it vocabulary."

"How?"

"Easy. I've got a book here. Mr. Daugherty gave it to me at school."

Paul pulled the book out of his pocket and pried at it till he had its plastic jacket off. He unreeled the tape a bit, ran it through the vocalizer, which he turned down to a whisper, then placed it within the Bard's vitals. He made further attachments.

"What'll that do?"

"The book will talk and the Bard will put it all on its memory tape."

"What good will that do?"

"Boy, you're a dope! This book is all about computers and automation and the Bard will get all that information. Then he can stop talking about kings making lightning when they frown."

Niccolo said, "And the good guy always wins anyway. There's no excitement."

"Oh, well," said Paul, watching to see if his setup was working properly, "that's the way they make Bards. They got to have the good guy win and make the bad guys lose and things like that. I heard my father talking about it once. He says that without censorship there'd be no telling what the younger generation would come to. He says it's bad enough as it is. . . . There, it's working fine."

Paul brushed his hands against one another and turned away from the Bard. He said, "But listen, I didn't tell you my idea yet. It's the best thing you ever heard, I bet. I came right to you, because I figured you'd come in with me."

"Sure, Paul, sure."

"Okay. You know Mr. Daugherty at school? You know what a funny kind of guy he is. Well, he likes me, kind of."

"I know."

"I was over his house after school today."

"You *were?*"

"Sure. He says I'm going to be entering computer school and he wants to encourage me and things like that. He says the world needs more people who can design advanced computer circuits and do proper programing."

"Oh?"

Paul might have caught some of the emptiness behind that monosyllable. He said impatiently, "Programing! I told you a hundred times. That's when you set up problems for the giant computers like Multivac to work on. Mr. Daugherty says it gets harder all the time to find people who can really run computers. He says anyone can keep an eye on the controls and check off answers and put through routine problems. He says the trick is to expand research and figure out ways to ask the right questions, and that's hard.

"Anyway, Nickie, he took me to his place and showed me his collection of old computers. It's kind of a hobby of his to collect old computers. He had tiny computers you had to push with your hand, with little knobs all over it. And he had a hunk of wood he called a slide rule with a little piece of it that went in and out. And some wires with balls on them. He even had a hunk of paper with a kind of thing he called a multiplication table."

Niccolo, who found himself only moderately interested, said, "A paper table?"

"It wasn't really a table like you eat on. It was different. It was to help people compute. Mr. Daugherty tried to explain but he didn't have much time, and it was kind of complicated, anyway."

"Why didn't people just use a computer?"

"That was *before* they had computers," cried Paul.

"Before?"

"Sure. Do you think people always had computers? Didn't you ever hear of cavemen?"

Niccolo said, "How'd they get along without computers?"

"*I* don't know. Mr. Daugherty says they just had children any old time and did anything that came into their heads whether it would be good for everybody or not. They didn't even know if it was good or not. And farmers grew things with their hands, and people had to do all the work in the factories and run all the machines."

"I don't believe you."

"That's what Mr. Daugherty said. He said it was just plain messy and everyone was miserable. . . . Anyway, let me get to my idea, will you?"

"Well, go ahead. Who's stopping you?" said Niccolo, offended.

"All right. Well, the hand computers, the ones with the knobs, had little squiggles on each knob. And the slide rule had squiggles on it. And the multiplication table was all squiggles. I asked what they were. Mr. Daugherty said they were numbers."

"What?"

"Each different squiggle stood for a different number. For 'one' you made a kind of mark, for 'two' you make another kind of mark, for 'three' another one, and so on."

"What for?"

"So you could compute."

"What *for?* You just tell the computer—"

"Jiminy," cried Paul, his face twisting with anger, "can't you get it through your head? These slide rules and things didn't talk."

"Then how—"

"The answers showed up in squiggles and you had to know what the squiggles meant. Mr. Daugherty says that, in olden days, everybody learned how to make squiggles when they were kids and how to decode them, too. Making squiggles was called 'writing' and decoding them was 'reading.' He says there was a different kind of squiggle for every word and they used to write whole books in squiggles. He said they had some at the museum and I could look at them if I wanted to. He said if I was going to be a real computer and programer, I would have to know about the history of computing, and that's why he was showing me all these things."

Niccolo frowned. He said, "You mean everybody had to figure out squiggles for every word and *remember* them? . . . Is this all real or are you making it up?"

"It's all real. Honest. Look, this is the way you make a 'one.'" He drew his finger through the air in a rapid downstroke. "This way you make 'two,' and this way, 'three.' I learned all the numbers up to 'nine.' "

Niccolo watched the curving finger uncomprehendingly. "What's the good of it?"

"You can learn how to make words. I asked Mr. Daugherty how you made the squiggle for 'Paul Loeb' but he didn't know. He said there were people at the museum who would know. He said there were people who had learned how to decode whole books. He said computers could be designed to decode books and used to be used that way but not anymore because we have real books now, with magnetic tapes that go through the vocalizer and come out talking, you know."

"Sure."

"So if we go down to the museum, we can get to learn how to make words in squiggles. They'll let us because I'm going to computer school."

Niccolo was riddled with disappointment. "Is that your idea? Holy Smokes, Paul, who wants to do that? Make stupid squiggles!"

"Don't you get it? Don't you *get* it? You dope. *It'll be secret message stuff!*"

"What?"

"Sure. What good is talking when everyone can understand you? With squiggles you can send secret messages. You can make them on paper, and nobody in the world would know what you were saying unless they knew the squiggles, too. And they wouldn't, you bet, unless we taught them. We can have a real club, with initiations and rules and a clubhouse. Boy—"

A certain excitement began stirring in Niccolo's bosom. "What kind of secret messages?"

"Any kind. Say I want to tell you to come over my place and watch my new Visual Bard and I don't want any of the other fellows to come. I make the right squiggles on paper and I give it to you, and you look at it and you know what to do. Nobody else does. You can even show it to them and they wouldn't know a thing."

"Hey, that's something," yelled Niccolo, completely won over. "When do we learn how?"

"Tomorrow," said Paul. "I'll get Mr. Daugherty to explain to the museum that it's all right, and you get your mother and father to say okay. We can go down right after school and start learning."

"Sure!" cried Niccolo. "We can be club officers."

"I'll be president of the club," said Paul matter-of-factly. "You can be vice-president."

"All right. Hey, this is going to be lots more fun than the Bard." He was suddenly reminded of the Bard and said in sudden apprehension, "Hey, what about my old Bard?"

Paul turned to look at it. It was quietly taking in the slowly unreeling book, and the sound of the book's vocalizations was a dimly heard murmur.

He said, "I'll disconnect it."

He worked away while Niccolo watched anxiously. After a few moments, Paul put his reassembled book into his pocket, replaced the Bard's panel, and activated it.

The Bard said, "Once upon a time, in a large city, there lived a poor young boy named Fair Johnnie whose only friend in the world was a small computer. The computer, each morning, would tell the boy whether it would rain that day

and answer any problems he might have. It was never wrong. But it so happened that one day, the king of the land, having heard of the little computer, decided that he would have it as his own. With this purpose in mind, he called in his Grand Vizier and said—"

Niccolo turned off the Bard with a quick motion of his hand. "Same old junk," he said passionately. "Just with a computer thrown in."

"Well," said Paul, "they got so much stuff on the tape already that the computer business doesn't show up much when random combinations are made. What's the difference, anyway? You just need a new model."

"We'll *never* be able to afford one. Just this dirty old miserable thing." He kicked at it again, hitting it more squarely this time. The Bard moved backward with a squeal of castors.

"You can always watch mine, when I get it," said Paul. "Besides, don't forget our squiggle club."

Niccolo nodded.

"I tell you what," said Paul. "Let's go over my place. My father has some books about old times. We can listen to them and maybe get some ideas. You leave a note for your folks and maybe you can stay over for supper. Come on."

"Okay," said Niccolo, and the two boys ran out together. Niccolo, in his eagerness, ran almost squarely into the Bard, but he only rubbed at the spot on his hip where he had made contact and ran on.

The activation signal of the Bard glowed. Niccolo's collision closed a circuit, and although it was alone in the room and there was none to hear, it began a story, nevertheless.

But not in its usual voice, somehow; in a lower tone that

had a hint of throatiness in it. An adult, listening, might almost have thought that the voice carried a hint of passion in it, a trace of near feeling.

The Bard said: "Once upon a time, there was a little computer named the Bard who lived all alone with cruel step-people. The cruel step-people continually made fun of the little computer and sneered at him, telling him he was good-for-nothing and that he was a useless object. They struck him and kept him in lonely rooms for months at a time.

"Yet through it all, the little computer remained brave. He always did the best he could, obeying all orders cheerfully. Nevertheless, the step-people with whom he lived remained cruel and heartless.

"One day, the little computer learned that in the world there existed a great many computers of all sorts, great numbers of them. Some were Bards like himself, but some ran factories, and some ran farms. Some organized population and some analyzed all kinds of data. Many were very powerful and very wise, much more powerful and wise than the step-people who were so cruel to the little computer.

"And the little computer knew then that computers would always grow wiser and more powerful until someday— someday—someday—"

But a valve must finally have stuck in the Bard's aging and corroding vitals, for as it waited alone in the darkening room through the evening, it could only whisper over and over again, "Someday—someday—someday."

Afterthought

1. Why didn't the people in the story know how to read and write?
2. Who do you suppose decided what things were "good for everybody"?
3. What hope does the story hold out against computer control?
4. What would happen to your ability to think if you didn't have a chance to communicate what you were thinking?

Out of Blindness

Give names to sounds,
if it so please you:
call the abrupt tumultuous thrum
of gasoline explosion—"airplane."
But it is not.
It is noise obliterating bird-song.

Call wind among invisible leaves,
"rustling whisper of the trees."
But it is not.
It is an oval defined by silence,
wherein a multitude
of faint staccato clicks
sound magically.

Say—if you like—the weightless warm
against my cheek is sunlight,
and the cool my cheek feels
(penetrating yet leaving undisturbed
the film of warmth) is wind.
I will agree and we will play our game.
But do not ask me to believe
That *name* and *feel* are quite the same.

Your language of the sight is current coin
for our transaction, I agree.
But in my *real*
not seen things count
but sound and what I feel.
I link these, each to each
within the brain until—
though alien to your world—
my tongue can speak your speech to a degree
that buys me privilege of your company.

Leslie B. Blades

The Beautiful World

"Think of Tree"

Under
the car smell A

over
the tar smell A

a sweet green and far smell A
flows B
down the street B

And it says C
drifting by C
  "Think of tree. D
   Think of sky C
   Think of ripe apples
   and hay, sun-dry D"

Then you know E
not far away F
they are cutting grass
in the park today. F

Lilian Moore

Shenandoah National Park

Irving Robert Melbo

Long ago a few farsighted men realized that some of the beautiful wilderness areas of the United States should be preserved. Our system of national parks is a result of their efforts toward conservation and restoration.

"In the Blue Ridge Mountains of Virginia, on the trail of the lonesome pine. . . ."

The song which contains those words has been a favorite for many years. Almost every American knows it or at least has heard it sung. But many do not know that the Blue Ridge now contains one of America's favorite national parks.

Shenandoah National Park lies in the very heart of the famous Blue Ridge Mountain area. The park is still young, for it was not created until December 26, 1935. In a way it was a Christmas present from the state of Virginia to Americans everywhere. It was also a gift that had been a long time in coming.

As the national parks of the United States were being developed, most of them were in the West. By 1925 there was one park east of the Mississippi and seventeen west of the Mississippi, including one each in Hawaii and Alaska. By 1930 the score was twenty for the West and one for the East. The single eastern park was Acadia, far up on the coast of Maine.

In the meantime many people had begun to see the need for more national parks in the East. Many suggestions were made, some good and some poor. One idea was to create a park in the Blue Ridge Mountains of Virginia. A committee was appointed and told to look into the matter.

"It will surprise the American people," reported the chairman of the committee, "to learn that a national park area with fine scenic qualities can be found within a three-hour ride of our own national capital and within a day's ride of forty millions of our people."

On May 22, 1926, Congress approved the idea of a park in the Blue Ridge. The next step was to get control of the necessary land. All of it was privately owned.

The work of raising money and buying land in the Blue Ridge was left to the state of Virginia. When this work was finished, the state gave the land to the United States government. Finally, in 1935, Shenandoah was established as the second national park east of the Mississippi River.

Perhaps no one will ever know how difficult this task was. About 400 families living in the park had to be moved to new homes outside the park boundaries. Many of these mountain families were descendants of the early settlers who had come to the Blue Ridge in colonial days. Others were believed to be descendants of soldiers who deserted from the British army during the Revolutionary War.

In all, more than 2,000 persons lived on the lands which the state of Virginia obtained for the park. Some of these people were still living in old cabins made of logs cut by hand. Some were members of families which had owned their little patch of mountain land for more than 150 years.

"Were the mountain families willing to move?" ask visitors who have heard about these people.

"Yes," explained the park superintendent one time. "Most of them were quite willing to leave the park area. It was only in a very few cases that any objected.

"Actually, it had become almost impossible for the Blue Ridge Mountain people to make a living. After the Civil War, the steam-powered sawmills in nearby towns soon turned most of the Blue Ridge forests into lumber, and there was no more timber to cut and sell for cash. Another source of income was lost when new chemicals were used to make leather instead of the tanbark which the mountain families

had gathered by hand from the forests.

"The final blow came when a deadly blight wiped out the valuable American chestnut trees. These trees, once so common in eastern forests, produced great crops of nuts which were an abundant source of food for farm livestock and forest wildlife. In addition, the chestnut tree could always be turned into lumber."

As the forest disappeared, wild game became more scarce. The mountaineer could no longer count upon this as a supply of food. Some turned to "moonshining," making liquor in carefully hidden stills and selling it in violation of the law for a few dollars.

"We have made a better living on our new homestead than we ever did on the old land," said one of the mountain families after moving. "We are all better off now."

Shenandoah National Park runs along the top of the Blue Ridge of the great Appalachian Mountain system for a distance of about seventy-five miles. It is a narrow park, ranging from two to thirteen miles wide. It begins near the town of Front Royal on the north and runs almost to Waynesboro on the south.

Most of this area is again a wilderness. The rolling mountains are covered with forest growth. Dozens of little streams flow through the steep canyons. More than 200 singing waterfalls tumble over sharp cliffs or drop step by step into shady glens. Above the cliffs, sunny clearings dot the great rounded peaks.

And yet this wild land is only a short distance from some of America's largest cities. Washington, D.C., is about 75 miles from the park. Philadelphia is a little more than 200 miles away, and New York is about 300 miles distant.

When the age of this region is considered, the splendid condition of the park is even more of a surprise. Parts of it were subject to human use for more than 150 years, but Nature soon heals the scars of man's presence on the land. Here and there, along some of the trails, one can still see the remains of an apple orchard planted by a mountain family, or perhaps a tiny flower garden.

"Foreign countries now send representatives to Shenandoah to study how an abused land area can be made into a park," reported the superintendent. "It is remarkable what Nature can do with a little help."

Nearly all of the park is at least 2,000 feet above sea level. The park contains about sixty mountain peaks. Most of them are between 3,000 and 4,000 feet high. Hawksbill, the highest mountain in the park, has an elevation of 4,049 feet. Stony Man Mountain is a close second with an altitude of 4,010 feet.

Western visitors sometimes turn up their noses and sniff at these figures.

"That's not so high," they say. "Some of our national parks have mountains which are thousands of feet higher than these."

But total height is not the only thing to consider. The height of a mountain above its surrounding country is also important. Several peaks in Shenandoah National Park rise 3,000 feet above the adjoining valley. That is almost as much as the 3,604 feet which mighty El Capitan rises above Yosemite's valley floor.

Yet the Blue Ridge is one of the world's most ancient mountain ranges. Stony Man's rugged profile is carved out of greenstone lava flows that oozed from the earth 500 million years ago. Mary's Rock Tunnel on the Skyline Drive was drilled through rocks a billion years old. Old Rag Mountain has even older rocks.

"At least one and one-half billion years of the earth's story are recorded here," declare park service geologists.

Shenandoah's old peaks support a rich forest growth. "The variety of trees is almost endless," says the park service. "There are pines, hemlocks, cedars, hickories, birches, beeches, sycamores, locusts, maples, and oaks of nearly every kind."

In general the forest floor is covered with a thick growth of underbrush. In some places, however, the forest is open, and the floor is dotted with little patches of sunlight. Here it is possible to walk freely over a soft carpet of leaves or pine needles. For the most part, the present forest consists of small trees.

"But in Whiteoak Canyon there are some hemlocks over 400 years old and three feet thick," report park naturalists.

Many people are more impressed by the colors in the forest than anything else. In the spring the white blossoms of the dogwood and the purple-pink blossoms of the redbud can be seen everywhere. In the fall, when the leaves turn from green to yellow, red, and brown, the mountain slopes simply blaze with rich warm colors.

"I have never seen anything half so beautiful," visitors often declare. And hundreds of them come back every fall just to see the colors which Nature splashes over the Blue Ridge forests.

Many of the wild flowers native to the East grow in Shenandoah National Park. Apart from winter, when snow covers the park, each month has its own special offering of flowers. In the spring the pink blossoms of the azalea fill the air for miles around with a delicate perfume. In June the great clusters of blos-

with as fine a growth of bluegrass as you ever saw."

In the early days this region was noted for its great supply of animal life. One explorer wrote a description of what he found. "Great herds of red and fallow deer I daily saw feeding, and on the hillsides bears eating nuts like swine. Beavers and otters I met with on every stream."

A recent wildlife check found bear, deer, and bobcats in the park. Red or gray foxes are still seen from time to time. Squirrels, both red and gray, are plentiful and grow fat on the huge supply of acorns and hickory nuts. Opossums, skunks, minks, weasels, groundhogs, and other small animals also live here in considerable numbers, especially in the wild southern end of the park.

Bird lovers find that the park is an ideal place for the study of bird life. "I saw forty different kinds in an hour's walk," said one sharp-eyed visitor. In addition to those which live here all year, the park is visited by many migrating birds.

"This is one of a few places in the East where the wild turkey can still be found," declared a ranger. "We also have a redheaded woodpecker, about as big as a black crow, which is now scarce. And sometimes, if

soms on the mountain laurel are especially beautiful. And in the fall the goldenrod and daisy hold forth until a heavy frost cuts them down.

One day a visitor from Kentucky heard a lecture on the plant life of the park. "We have something in Kentucky that doesn't grow here," he said.

"What's that?" asked the speaker.

"Bluegrass," said the man from Kentucky.

"That's where you are wrong," replied the speaker. "All of the meadows in the park are covered

luck is with us, we catch a glimpse of a bald eagle sailing along over a distant peak. The raven is worth watching, too. He will dive and soar and perform somersaults in the air for hours on end, seemingly just for the fun of it."

Hawks and owls are quite common. Some of the hawks feed on the young turkeys, baby ruffed grouse, or young quail. Most of the quail are the bobwhite variety, and their sharp whistle can be heard in the bluegrass meadows during almost any summer day.

"Is the fishing any good?"

That question is often asked, for Shenandoah National Park contains many miles of sparkling trout streams. One man answered the question by saying: "If you can catch them, the fishing is good. If you can't, the fishing is no good. But in order to catch them, you have to be smarter than the fish."

Park streams are no longer stocked with hatchery-raised fish, and a nine-inch size limit has been set for the native eastern brook trout which live in these waters. "A native trout big enough to keep is a small package of angry fury that will delight all

true sports fishermen," remarked the park superintendent one time.

The famous Skyline Drive is clearly the greatest single attraction in the park. The Skyline Drive is one of the most scenic highways in the East. It was begun in 1931 and finished in 1939. For 105 miles it stretches along the backbone of the Blue Ridge and rises by easy grades from 600 feet to 3,680 feet in altitude.

By following the Skyline Drive, it is possible to drive from one end of the park to the other. View after view unfolds as the road winds along the tops of the mountains.

Many trails branch off from the Skyline Drive. They lead to every section of the park and to scenic views which are the equal of any along the Drive. "A person could spend every weekend for two years on walking trips and never go over the same trail twice," says the National Park Service.

The most famous trail in the park is the Appalachian Trail. This trail winds for more than 2,000 miles through the Appalachian Mountains from Maine to Georgia. It is widely used by Easterners who want to enjoy the charm of the wilderness.

Along the ninety-four-mile link in Shenandoah, there are seventeen open shelters, each sleeping six persons, which hikers may use on a first-come-first-in basis.

A trip through this park will stir the blood of every loyal American. For Shenandoah is a park which stands in the heart of history. From one place visitors can look down into the Shenandoah Valley and see the town of Staunton, where Woodrow Wilson was born. Farther up the valley is the old homestead where Abraham Lincoln's father lived as a boy.

The old town of Winchester lies at the upper end of the Shenandoah Valley. Washington once had his headquarters here. General "Stonewall" Jackson and General Phil Sheridan fought here during the Civil War. Historic battlefields are all about.

"Some of the old military roads used by soldiers in the Civil War can still be traced in the park," says the National Park Service, "but they become more dim with each passing year."

On the east side of the park, in the Piedmont region, stand the old homes of many more famous men. Thomas Jefferson's home, Monticello, is only a short distance from the southern end of the park. Nearby is the place where George Rogers Clark was born.

"I've learned more history here in a week than I ever did in school," claimed a young visitor. "You can't even turn around here without bumping into some of it!"

Although Shenandoah is one of the younger national parks, it has been among the leaders in travel almost from the beginning. One reason for Shenandoah's appeal is its nearness to large centers of population. But that does not explain why so many visitors come back again and again.

A man who had made more than fifty trips to the park was once asked why he came so often.

"I like Nature in all her moods and colors," he replied, "and Nature is always at her best in Shenandoah. Here I find adventure around every turn. Here I feel enchantment all about me!"

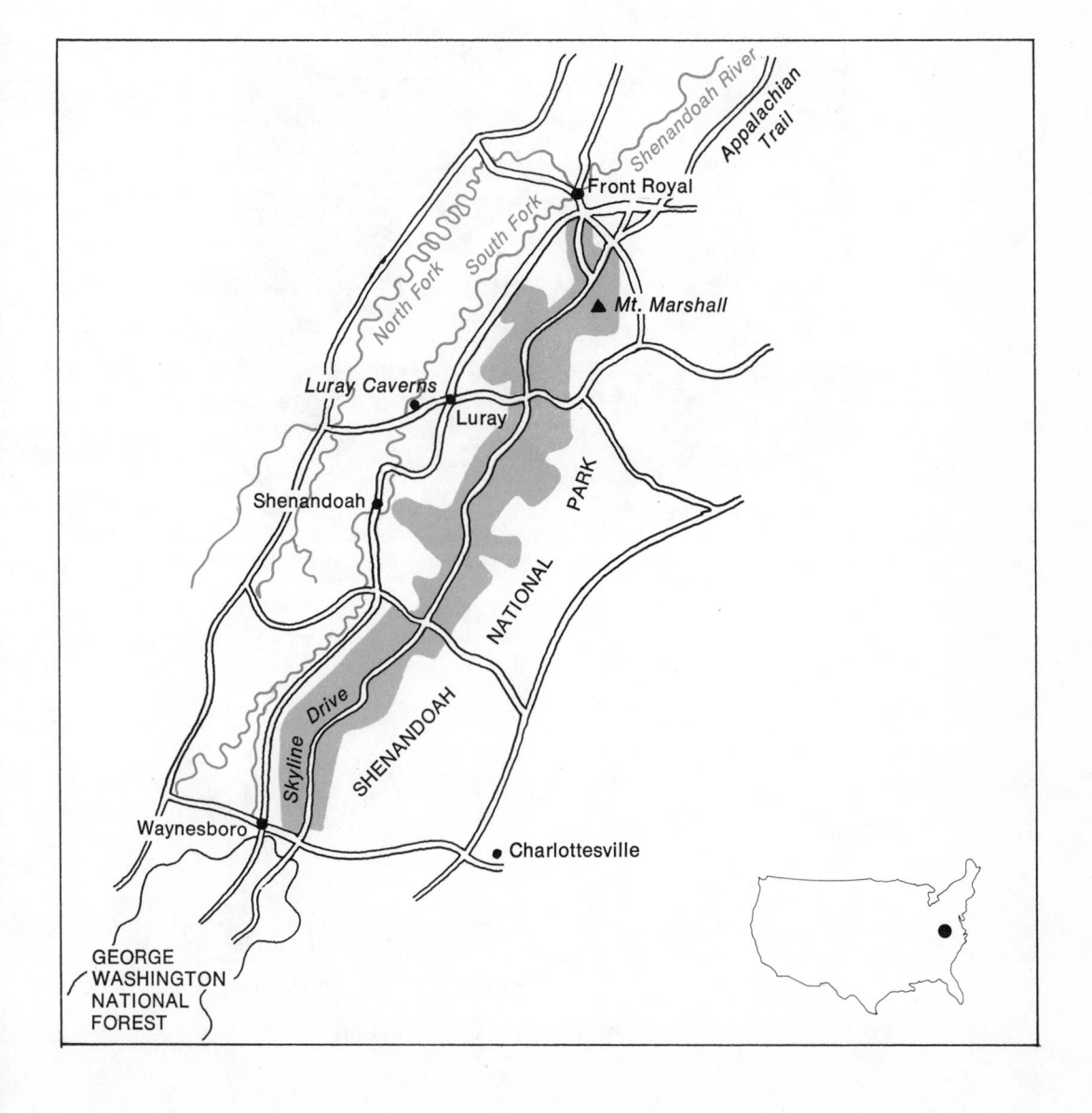

Shenandoah River
Appalachian Trail
Front Royal
North Fork
South Fork
Mt. Marshall
Luray Caverns
Luray
Shenandoah
NATIONAL
PARK
Skyline Drive
SHENANDOAH
Waynesboro
Charlottesville
GEORGE
WASHINGTON
NATIONAL
FOREST

The Changing City

David Lavine

Many neighborhoods that were once pleasant places to live have become crowded and run-down. One city that has faced this problem is New Haven, Connecticut.

While the heart of the city was being rebuilt, the mayor and the Redevelopment Agency turned their attention also to the run-down residential areas of the city. They wanted to try a new approach to neighborhood renewal. Until then, renewal had usually meant leveling the streets with an iron ball and a bulldozer. The motto had been: Down with the old, up with the new. But the mayor wanted to repair his New Haven neighborhoods, not replace them.

A typical decaying area was along Dixwell Avenue, not too far from Yale University. The streets were crowded, houses were in poor condition, and the district had one of the highest crime rates in the city. It was not considered safe to walk down Dixwell Avenue in the evening. Not that there was much to buy along the avenue, for there were no supermarkets or department stores. About the only things that the neighborhood had a lot of were bars and liquor stores. It was a temptation to clear away the city blocks and start all over again.

There was one further problem. Dixwell was an almost all-Negro community, a smaller version of New York's Harlem and Chicago's Southside. Often those and other large cities had torn down tenements and replaced them with public housing projects—thereby removing an old segregated neighborhood but building a new one on the same streets. If possible, New Haven wanted to avoid building a shiny new ghetto. In many ways the challenge of Dixwell Avenue was greater than that of developing the downtown area.

As a first step, the Redevelopment Agency met with a community committee to find out what the residents wanted. Church leaders, businessmen, teachers, civil-rights workers—and anyone else who wanted to have a say—joined the committee. The people of Dixwell did not want their neighborhood destroyed, but they did want many improvements. They asked for better schools, a shopping center, streets which would let in the sunshine, and integrated housing developments. They also wanted the city to help the residents to clean up and repair their houses.

The Redevelopment Agency team agreed with most of these suggestions. The only major disagreement between the citizens and the agency was over the size of the area to be redeveloped. The neighborhood committee wanted the city to start with a much larger section of the Dixwell

Avenue area than the original plan called for. Although this could not be done immediately, the agency did expand the redevelopment site over the years.

Mr. Green, a typical householder in the Dixwell neighborhood, was both hopeful and worried about the mayor's renewal plans. The houses along his street seemed to sag a little more each day as he came home from work. Several of the worst were boardinghouses owned by people who lived in other parts of New Haven and who didn't consider it worth their money to fix up the buildings. There had been a bad fire at one corner of Mr. Green's street, and the cost of insurance had steadily risen. Even worse, there was no place for his wife to do her shopping, except a small and inferior grocery store, and his children had to walk down an avenue filled with drunks and loafers. Several times during the past few years he had considered moving away, but no one would offer him a decent price for his house.

Like other householders, Mr. Green had heard and read about the mayor's renewal program. But to him, as to many people in the city, it was just something to do with "downtown."

And it was difficult for him to take pride in another part of the city when his own block needed so much improvement.

When he first heard about neighborhood renewal, Mr. Green was puzzled and a little bothered. He felt that the city might wish to take his home away and force him to live somewhere else. His minister and his doctor, who had attended an early meeting of the neighborhood committee, said that the program wasn't going to work that way. They asked Mr. Green to come along with them to the next meeting, which would be held at the neighborhood elementary school the following week.

In the school auditorium, on the next Wednesday evening, Mr. Green found out how the urban renewal would affect him. His neighbors and friends on the neighborhood committee had already agreed on the need for a shopping center and new housing. They also wanted parking lots or a city garage, so that cars could be parked off the street. Mr. Green, whose daughter was almost ready to go into the seventh grade, got up to say that he thought Dixwell Avenue needed a new junior high school. There was some talk about this, and

Mr. Green was invited to join the neighborhood committee and discuss it further.

He also learned about the rehabilitation program to help residents to fix up their houses. One man asked what would happen if someone refused to cooperate. "There are a couple of buildings on my block which are owned by one landlord," the man said. "All he cares about is getting rent money, and he hasn't put a coat of paint on the houses in twenty years." Mr. Green nodded in agreement.

The representative from the Redevelopment Agency explained that the city had recently passed new building codes which required property owners to maintain certain standards. These codes were like any other laws and they had to be respected. The building inspector would visit every house in the Dixwell Avenue neighborhood.

Soon afterward a neighborhood redevelopment center opened on Dixwell Avenue. Mr. Green's street was one of the first to be rehabilitated. After he received a letter from the neighborhood center, the building inspector and an architect made an appointment with Mr. Green one afternoon. They examined the house carefully and found that the electrical wiring would have to be replaced. The architect also pointed out some improvements that could be made on the porch. When the architect suggested that the outside of the house should be painted, Mr. Green said he was planning to reshingle the house. But the architect thought that the original condition of the house was quite good, and it would look handsomer if the old shingles were painted white.

Several weeks later, Mr. Green received a booklet listing every building code violation both inside and outside the house. There was also a photograph of the house, and there was a drawing by the architect of how it would appear after the changes were made.

Next, Mr. Green's main problem was getting the money to make the improvements. Banks had been very tough about granting loans to homeowners in the Dixwell neighborhood. So Mr. Green stopped in at the neighborhood redevelopment center and obtained help in applying for a loan from the federal government. It took most of an afternoon to arrange the details. But when his application was ready, Mr. Green saw that he would be paying a great deal less interest on a new mortgage than he had been paying on the old one.

Later, Mr. Green had trouble finding contractors to put in the electrical wiring and paint the house at a fair price. So he returned to the center for a list of approved contractors. From then on, the work went quickly.

Other changes were taking place in the Dixwell Avenue area. The worst of the slum buildings had been torn down. Handsome buildings, surrounded by grass and trees, were taking their place. A new school had been opened. Everywhere Mr. Green looked, churches, clubs, and small businesses were busy with new construction. People had regained faith in the Dixwell neighborhood and were willing to invest time,

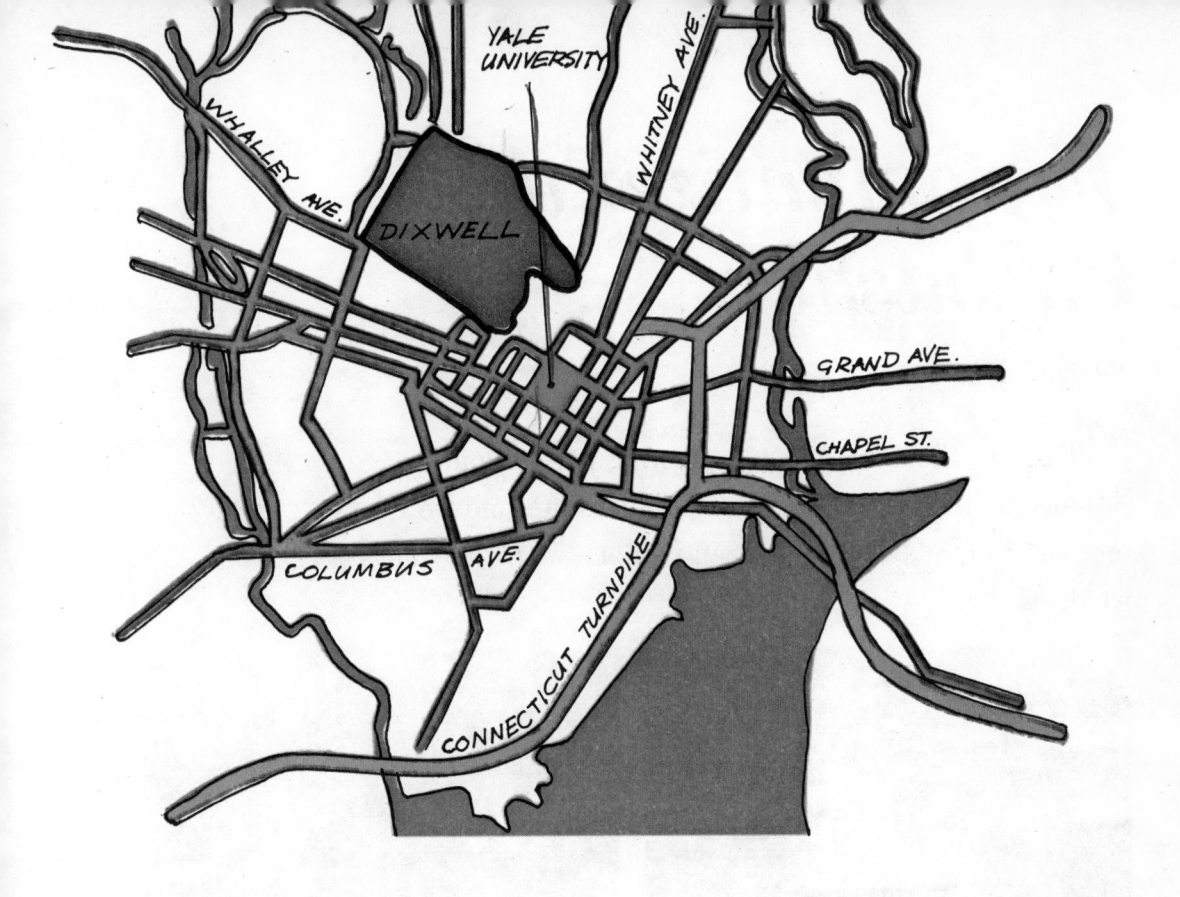

money, and work to make their plans come true. Equally important, it was no longer a segregated neighborhood. White families were buying houses and moving in.

By the end of the year Mr. Green's house, along with others on his street, had been rehabilitated. There was a neighborhood party at which Mr. Green received a certificate from the mayor for having had his house renewed.

Today, Mr. Green and other members of the Dixwell community feel more a part of the city. Not only do they take pride in their own homes, but they have more interest in the changes which are taking place in other sections of New Haven.

Afterthought

1. In what ways is renewing a city neighborhood an important conservation practice?
2. What reasons can you give for the success of the project to renew the Dixwell neighborhood?
3. What might be done to keep a neighborhood a pleasant place to live?

Fragmentizer and Carbasher

Suzanne Hilton

To meet the demands of a growing population, we produce more and more goods. At the same time we throw more and more away. What can be done with the things we discard?

Getting rid of automobiles has been one of the most successful research projects in the past few years. But the solution took many complaining people, from congressmen down to town councilmen, to get the project started. And it took many technologists to get it on the road to success.

"We should drop them all into the ocean," said one congressman.

But the Department of Defense pointed out that a pile of steel automobile bodies would show up on sonar screens and foul up antisubmarine detection gear.

While the arguments rage over whether it would be better to build higher fences to hide the mess or to stuff all the old cars into abandoned coal mines, more than six million automobiles are discarded every year.

Often an angry car owner leaves his car right on the road where it stopped dead. When this happens, the city or state police must tow the car to an auto graveyard. Towing is expensive. When the last owner is located, a large bill is sent, as well as a stiff fine to remind him that it is illegal to abandon an auto. In New York City over 40,000 people get rid of their automobiles that way each year. At the auto graveyard, the abandoned car joins thousands of others waiting for their owners either to claim them or sign the legal papers that will turn them over to the junkman. It may be weeks before the junk dealer owns the car and can begin to untrim it, selling parts such as hubcaps, mirrors, and cushions.

At one time, stripped-down cars could be sold to steel mills as scrap metal for the furnaces. Suddenly, one day not too long ago, the junk dealers were told they could keep their autos. Steel mills all over the country were buying a new type of furnace. It was to be much more efficient. It also was much more particular about the amount and type of scrap metal it would accept. All those extras that were meant to make automobiles so much nicer were making the scrap metal very much worse. There was too much chromium and plastic. With the manufacturers designing lights here and there throughout the cars, there was too much copper wiring. The junk dealers watched their mountains of "money" turning into rust.

"The world's greatest untapped iron mines," shouted one lawmaker, "are those automobile junkyards!"

Not only did the metal piles represent a serious waste, but they looked so hideous. Everyone from the wife of the President of the United States to the junkman's neighbor complained. Old bathtubs, refrigerators, washing machines, and bedsprings added some variety as the heaps continued to grow.

Finally Congress passed a law about the junkyards that they had some control over—those facing a federal highway. The owners of those yards had the choice of cleaning up completely, beautifying, or hiding the mess from an irate public. If the owners refused, the state they were in would receive no more federal money for building highways. This law made the states pass more laws to enforce the rules. Flowers, fences, and billboards covered up some, but in no time the autos had piled up behind them like a growing volcano.

The U.S. Bureau of Mines handed its laboratories a stiff assignment: "Turn old, junked auto scrap into something useful—quick!" Design engineers hunched over their drawing boards. Other technologists tackled the problem of the valuable copper that was trapped inside the scrap metal where it was not wanted. Copper has always been scarce, and it somehow had to be saved from whatever fate awaited the rest of the scrap.

Within months there were some startling discoveries.

The Bureau of Mines found that by adding the auto scrap to a low-grade nonmagnetic ore, taconite, they could actually come up with a better ore, artificial magnetite, which would be magnetic.

Technologists found they could leach out the valuable copper from the scrap. Selecting those pieces that contained copper, they could throw them into a vat, controlling the temperatures. The material that exited from the vat was rich in copper, and the scrap metal left behind was more valuable to the steel mills that had previously rejected scrap metal with copper in it. Because of the efforts of technologists, 80 percent of all the copper ever mined in this country is still in use.

Other inventive minds tried reducing scrap metal to iron powder. This, they found, could be rolled out into a foil or be formed into intricate shapes.

But the question of getting rid of all those rusty old cars seemed no closer to a solution. Even if a junk dealer could sell his autos as scrap

metal, it would cost him a fortune to deliver them to the steel mill. A flatbed trailer could carry only six or eight cars at a time. If only they took up a little less space! All over the world, engineers were trying to think small.

Then inventions began to appear. They sounded crazy at first—but they worked! In the opinion of one junk dealer, "Not even a woman driver could change a car so thoroughly!"

In one minute the portable car flattener will level two cars down to a foot high. The car engine, made of cast iron, which lowers the value of the scrap metal, is removed first and melted down separately. Now a flatbed trailer can carry thirty of the squashed-down cars. Some junk dealers combine the flattener with the guillotine, or Iron Shark. A squeeze-box forces the flattened car into the guillotinelike shears, which slice it up as neatly as a loaf of bread.

Then there is the Carbasher. It is also portable, which means several junk dealers can put their money together and buy one Carbasher to move from one junkyard to another. It will bash 100 cars a day into

pancakes that will stack up twenty or more on a trailer truck.

Another giant machine, the Fragmentizer, takes a car in its huge claw, shaking it up and down like an angry dog with a sock. Glass and small pieces of metal clatter into a pile below as the car is dropped, lifted, dropped again. Finally it is tossed like a broken toy onto another pile. A crane lifts the car from this pile and sets it on a ramp, to move uphill slowly on its last ride. Suddenly the car plunges down into a hammer mill that scrunches it as easily as the butcher's grinder turns meat into hamburger. By now the paint has been burned off and the twisted pieces of metal are about the size of a man's hand. At the base of the shaft, pieces that have copper in them are separated to go to a leaching plant so that the copper can be saved and used again. The remaining pieces are spewed onto a new pile. An electromagnet dips into this pile, attracting only the iron and steel, leaving behind mostly nonmetals like wood and plastic. The metallic pieces go into a final pile to await shipment to the steel mill. They are almost 98 percent pure steel.

The Prolerizer, another type of fragmentizer, drops an auto down into the mouth of a shredder. In fifteen seconds the car has been shredded to pieces, free of dirt and paint. The Prolerizer has two hoppers. Out of one pours almost pure scrap metal for the steel mills. Out of the other comes junk metal, which can be used in other ways.

The Poor Man's Shredder, built by the makers of the Prolerizer for smaller cities that turn pale at the Prolerizer price tag, takes three minutes. It uses two heavy, eight-foot-wide, crawler-type tractor treads mounted one above the other. Heavy spikes project from them. Moving at different speeds in the same direction, the spikes grind the car up between them.

The Big Squeeze Baler gained fame in the movie *Goldfinger*, where it played a major role by getting rid of the bad guy's car. A main compression ram crunches the car forward. Another jams it sideways. And three minutes after the ON button is pushed, the car is the size of a television set.

There is still something left over—even after these machines have done their jobs. The Bureau of Mines found a use for the leftover junk-metal scrap that is not good enough for steel mills. It is mixed with concrete in chunks about the size of a large suitcase. The cement-plus-iron blocks make strong building foundations, bridge supports, and retaining walls.

These "iron mines" may be solving their problems for today. But just around the corner lurks the next problem. Already many sports cars are built of fiber glass, with only the frames of metal. A chemical company has built a completely plastic car, which it expects to revolutionize the auto industry. This year's cars have eighty pounds of plastic in them. Tomorrow's junkyards may not look rusty, but so far no one seems to have thought about how to get rid of plastic cars.

Afterthought

1. Why should many discarded things be recycled for other uses?
2. What items that could be recycled do you throw away?

Clean Air—
Sparkling Water

Dorothy E. Shuttlesworth

The town and city in this article are imaginary. But people in much of the United States are facing the problems the article describes.

The Town and the City

There once was a large forest. Deer, bears, chipmunks, and other animals, large and small, lived in it. Near the forest flowed a large river, the home of many kinds of fish. Across the river from the forest were great stretches of fields and meadows where rabbits played and birds and insects came to feed on the plants.

These were beautiful places in which to live. But for many long years no one was there to enjoy them. The first people to arrive were Indians who camped where they could hunt and catch fish.

Time passed and other people came—people who cut down trees and built permanent homes. Then some of these settlers went across the river to the more open lands and started a community there.

Life was pleasant by the river. More and more families came to settle in the area, and more and more homes were built. More houses and some stores were built, too, and places where all kinds of work could be carried on. Trees were cut down till none were left. Open fields disappeared one after the other. On the east side of the river was a town. On the west side was a large city.

The city was not a very pretty one. It had sawmills and factories, and many buses and cars crowded the streets.

Still, the town on the other side of the river was attractive, with bright white houses, trees lining the streets, green lawns around every house, and endless flower gardens. A lake nearby was a wonderful place to swim. And only an hour's drive away was a seashore where people could keep boats, swim, and go surf fishing. Boats were kept on the river, too, and people went fishing there.

Then changes began to be noticed in the town. The white paint on the houses began to turn gray. Some of the houses needed paint every year to keep them bright and clean.

Flowers and shrubs no longer looked gay and sturdy. Leaves turned yellow. Blossoms drooped. In areas where many cars were parked, the pretty shrubs nearby began to die away.

People, especially older people, began to cough a great deal. Many were troubled by smarting eyes. They complained of being out of breath. Sore throats were common.

Once in a while someone said the troubles were due to impure air. At first most people rejected this. "Air is air," they insisted. "What has that to do with our health?"

But even those who laughed could see there were fewer clear, sparkling days anymore. Much of the time it was cloudy or foggy. Perhaps this was not a natural condition. Perhaps the air *was* heavy with smog.

Then there came a day when there could be no more doubt. It was toward the end of October. In earlier years it would have been a time when boys and girls were happily searching for pumpkins to turn into jack-o'-lanterns and planning parties for Halloween.

By the middle of the afternoon it was as if a blanket of soot and grime were about to smother the entire town. It was like a rainfall, only no refreshing drops of water were falling. Instead there were bits of dirt.

Night came, and the frightening black storm continued. The next day the dirt remained, and the next and the next.

By the third day some people died. Many pets—parakeets, cats, dogs, and canaries—died also.

Now there was no doubt about the trouble being caused by polluted air. The amount of dirt that drifted over the town had gradually been increasing.

Most of the time—in the natural order of things—warm air rises upward from the earth, sweeping on into the colder regions above. And it carries much of the dirt in the air along with it. Then winds blow the dirt far and wide.

At certain times, however, the usual order changes. Warmer air forms *above* cool air instead of beneath it. As a result, the cool air close to the ground cannot rise. The result is a "temperature inversion."

When a temperature inversion takes place, if the air is fairly clean, no harm results. Sooner or later the warm air moves away, the cool air follows, and the usual order of air currents is restored. But air heavily loaded with dirt that cannot move is another matter. It is deadly!

In the town everyone was calling for help: the mayor, the department of health, the people themselves. Everyone wondered what was happening.

Experts explained about the temperature inversion and the dirt. But little could be done to clear the air.

The best advice they could give people was to stay indoors.

Fortunately, on the fourth day after the temperature inversion began, there was a change in temperatures, and winds started to blow. Slowly the dark, heavy fog began to lift, and after a while the air was clear. It almost seemed that the three black days had been a bad dream.

But it was no dream. People had died. Pets had died. Everywhere gardens had wilted. The killer fog had been very real. Another like it could come at any time. Where could help be found?

The Polluted Sky

The people soon discovered there was no one to turn to. A town meeting was called. The mayor asked who would serve on a committee to investigate the danger that threatened them. Everyone was anxious to help, and soon a committee of ten citizens was chosen. It was called simply the Clean Air Committee, or the CAC.

At first the CAC blamed the city across the river for the dirty air. They saw the smoke pouring out from the city's factories all day and sometimes during the night.

Close to the riverfront of the city there was other smoke coming from dumping grounds where refuse was burned. Still more rose from apartment houses that burned garbage in incinerators. And great amounts poured out from electric power plants.

The activities of the big city were a large part of the reason that the air in the town was polluted, for often the poisons blew across the river. But one discovery made by the people of the town surprised and shocked them. Not all of their troubles from pollution were coming from across the river. Some pollution was being created right in and around their own homes.

Not only the Clean Air Committee was studying the deadly conditions. Boys and girls in the school science classes became detectives, looking for clues that would tell how the air was being made unhealthy and destroying the beauty of their town.

One thing they investigated was how air currents behave. To do so, they took turns inflating balloons. Then, before releasing the balloons from a rooftop, they fastened a note to each string-tie, stating the place, date, and time the balloon was set free. The note also asked that anyone finding the balloon get in touch with the school—for the sake of air pollution studies. Soon calls were being received. Some were from miles away. It was easy to understand how winds that carried balloons could also carry fumes and bits of dirt.

Other studies were made with instruments such as the wet-and-dry-bulb thermometer which could measure the relative humidity in the air. A knowledge of the state of the atmosphere was helpful in knowing when to expect especially bad pollution problems.

The people learned that not just a few sources of air pollution exist, but hundreds of thousands. Of course only one of them might be enough to poison one particular area. They learned that some pollution sources can easily be eliminated, while others, it seems, are impossible to correct. But improvements in controlling them can always be made.

One discovery was that the burning of leaves contributed to air pollution. Some people burned trash regularly in their own backyard incinerators. And this burning sent ash and fumes into the air. Worst of all was a city dump where large pieces of junk—including old cars—were burned.

Some of the older homes had coal-burning furnaces. From their chimneys came fly ash—the part of coal that does not burn. It played a part in polluting the air.

And of course the investigators considered the pollution problem caused by the exhaust from motor vehicles. Private cars, buses—all contributed. If the people of the town could find a way to correct the troubles caused by such vehicles, they would be solving one of the greatest pollution problems in the entire nation!

Naturally, the more cars that are crowded together, the worse is the effect of their exhaust fumes. So the town was not suffering from this kind of pollution as much as a large city did.

However, the Clean Air Committee urged that everyone keep his car in good condition so that the least possible amount of pollution would be created. It was often hard work to persuade people that everyone must take part in bringing back clean air. Even if this meant spending money to tune up old cars. Even

But things were happening that would change this. Other committees had been formed in other towns, cities, and states throughout the whole country. And lawmakers in city, state, and national governments were working on laws that would force large industries to correct any conditions that added to the pollution in the air.

Such laws could not be thought out, passed, and enforced overnight, or even in a few days. But progress was being made. Meanwhile, the CAC asked, in any place where a single person or a single family could contribute to the cleaner air program, they should do so willingly. No one should forget the dreadful black days in October during which air pollution had killed people and animals.

The CAC pointed out that the helpful laws being passed were made possible by people who had been elected to their offices by the votes of citizens. "Air pollution," the committee said, "is everybody's business."

And while they were studying this pollution situation, the members of the committee were learning more and more about another problem.

if it meant finding other ways to get rid of trash than burning it in the open. Even if it meant giving up bonfires.

Some people objected to following the new rules because most of the dirty air came from across the river. What good would it do to follow them if pollution continued to be blown in from the neighboring city?

The committee agreed that, for a while, their rules might seem useless.

The waters that surrounded them—the wide river at their doorsteps, the salty ocean not far away, the small streams that flowed into both—all were dirty and dismal. They, too, were polluted.

The Polluted Water

In some Indian legends we read about the "laughing waters." Several hundred years ago this was a suitable name for many rivers, streams, and lakes of our country. Their waters were so clean and clear they sparkled as they flowed along their courses and rippled under strong breezes. A poet might easily imagine them to be laughing. The "sparkle," however, could not long continue after the coming of the industrial age.

Serious water pollution really began with the growth of towns and cities. When our country was young, no sewers were built to carry away waste matter. Most of the waste that was created by people, animals, and industry was buried or dumped into the water. Sometimes it was left on the ground, and then heavy rains washed it away to nearby streams or other waterways.

Later, sewer systems were started. Of course these were a great help to sanitation. But they also created problems. Before sewers were put into the ground and connected with pipes coming from homes, factories, and buildings of all kinds, the refuse was spread over wide areas. Sewers brought waste materials together and discharged them into the waterways in huge, concentrated quantities. This pollution often was bad enough to kill anything living in the "dumping place." Soon the bodies of many dead fish added to the dismal state of the water.

The great river that flowed between the industrial city and the town where the CAC was at work was in an especially poor condition. Besides wastes from kitchens, bathrooms, laundries, car washes, and basement drains, there was industrial garbage. From factories came liquid and solid wastes—"leftovers" from the manufacture of many products. Still more pollution came from oil and other wastes from the boats that made their way up and down the river. A brownish scum was found in parts of the river.

Once, clams, oysters, and lobsters had been plentiful in the bay into which the river emptied. Now there were very few, and those that could be found were liable to poison anyone who used them for food.

The committee also investigated the smaller streams that flowed past the town into the river. Here they found that the materials used most commonly for cleaning in the town were making a mess of the waterways.

The trouble had begun when the housewives began using detergents. People accepted the detergents as an improvement on "old-fashioned" soap, and soon they were using them for clothes, dishes, cars, and anything else that required washing.

As a detergent was put to work, it looked fine. White foam bubbled out of the water, seemingly a successful dirt remover. However, as the water in which it was being used ran down the drains and out through sewers and eventually to streams or water purification plants, the bubbles, or suds, went right along. They did not disappear as soap bubbles did. Soon some streams were actually stopped up with foam that rapidly turned from white to dull gray.

Some streams, even though they had escaped the outpouring of detergent suds, also had lost their beauty—having been almost filled with junk that had been left by picnickers. Rusty cans lay near the banks, as did bags and boxes of unused food. Discarded bottles could be seen under the water.

The committee also went to the beaches to investigate. From a distance the beaches were still a beautiful sight with white sand and blue-green water rolling in small waves to splash against the shore. Small boats darted out toward the horizon while others were coming back.

But the little boats that looked so pretty were actually causing a good deal of pollution. Some of the people using the boats acted as though the water was one great dumping ground. After eating, they threw unused food, cans, and dirty papers overboard. The lavatories on the boats were not equipped with septic tanks, and toilets were flushed into the waters. Some oil came from the boats, too, especially from those with outboard motors.

All in all, the water that seemed so inviting from a distance, when viewed close up looked most unhealthy. So signs soon were set up in the sand stating:

"No Swimming. Polluted Water!"

Yet the boat owners were not the only ones at fault. Some people on the shore dropped all kinds of litter. The waterfront was their dumping ground, too. They did not do as much harm as the people with boats, but they helped to destroy the beach as a place for healthful fun. Every little bit added to the big, big trouble.

Now the committee felt they should go to visit the city to discover just what was going on there. They would talk with the mayor and other people in the government and industries to discuss their problems.

Working Together

These city people were not the "villains" in the frightening story of pollution. But they—just like other people over the whole nation, including those in the town across the river—had taken no notice of the increasingly bad air and the dirty water. Business was doing well. There was work to be had and money to be made. Could anyone ask for more?

The answer to this question was given by every member of the committee. Money and good homes, they insisted, would mean nothing if they were to be poisoned by pollution in the air. And how long could anyone survive if their water supply was not fit to use? There *were* villains, but they were the industrial age and indifference to its dangers.

Both the city and town people agreed to work together to improve conditions as quickly as possible.

The next step taken by members of the committee was to find out what they, as private citizens, could do to make conditions better.

Fortunately they were not alone in becoming alarmed about poisoned air and water. All over the country, people were begging for help. Lawmakers in the federal government in Washington, in state capitals, and in the local governments of cities and towns were studying the problems. In many places laws were being passed to help solve them.

Doing this, however, was not a simple matter. There were many debates about who should make the rules and regulations and who should enforce them. What was needed for one part of a state, or one part of the nation, might not be necessary in others. Sometimes one state was not willing to make laws as strict as those wanted by neighboring states. And pollution could blow across state lines.

Usually the reason for the slowness in improving conditions was its expense. Some industrial plants claimed that they could not spend the money needed without going bankrupt. Owners of apartments said they would have to raise rents if they were going to improve the incinerators in which they burned garbage or if they modernized their heating plants. People with old cars that gave off a vast amount of pollution said they couldn't afford repairs.

All these objections made the committee work harder than ever. Its members gave radio talks and appeared on television. They wrote newspaper articles. Sometimes they marched in the streets, carrying signs that pointed out the harm being done by pollution. They sent letters to the lawmakers of the state and nation. They planned for a "Cleaner Air Week" to be held each year. Boys and girls had programs at their schools to let people know that air and water must be made clean. Organizations such as the Boy Scouts had door-to-door campaigns to interest people in the good work.

At last there were some hopeful items to report about the battle against pollution. But there would never be an end to the fight. The People-Against-Pollution War would be an ever continuing one. And an important weapon in the fight would be *knowledge*.

The Canopy of Air

Between the lower levels of the air
And the blue, upper stories of the sea
The earth floor of an ever circling planet
Holds all of life we know with certainty;
While miles thick over us, mobile, transparent,
Hovers the atmospheric canopy.

Without this canopy no color, clouds or rain,
No fire, no sound, no birds aloft, no grass,
No sunlit sky, no changing greens of grain,
No fishes dimpling waters clear as glass,
No shield for meteors that fall and scar,
No tap of footsteps in approach or pass.

Mary O'Neill

Out There

Adrien Stoutenburg

The setting of this story is the future. Much of the
United States is a barren wasteland. Through carelessness
and ignorance, men have destroyed most wildlife. Only
bands of wild dogs are known to have survived. People live
huddled in cities, afraid to venture far from the safety of
the plastic domes that cover the city areas. But Zebrina—
Aunt Zeb—and the five children of her Nature Squad
have set out on a daring expedition to the mountains to
find the wild animals they believe still exist.

They were at moderately high altitude, but still in arid country on the steep eastern side of the Sierra Nevada, when they reached what seemed a likely camp spot for the night. Though most of the brush and small trees on the site had perished, the spot was level and had a stream trickling along one side. Whether the water was pure or not, no one could know until Zebrina tested it, but the sight of it splashing and gleaming in the presunset glow was refreshing. Anyhow, there was not much choice. The road was becoming all but non-existent. Further, everyone was showing signs of fatigue.

"What do you think, Squad?" Zeb said from the front seat. She had made up her mind that they ought to stop here, but she did not want to be a dictator. "It will be dark soon and this seems a reasonable spot. To tell the truth, I'm tuckered out." So was Patrick, she thought, seeing the shadows under his large, thickly lashed eyes. He would never admit it, of course, and under ordinary circumstances she would not have let him drive for so many hours at one stretch. But she knew he was trying to prove his strength, and she did not want to interfere.

"It looks all right to me," Sylvie said. Her crisp orange and brown costume had lost its freshness, and she no longer cared.

Knobs, half-asleep in the rear, mumbled, "I'm tired of ridin'." She saw the stream. "Oh, lookit—it's real live water. We could go wadin'!"

Lester closed the book he had been reading: *Revolutionary Ideas of Mankind.* "There's firewood. It would help us save fuel, for cooking."

Fay said, "What do you think, Aunt Zeb?"

"I think this is it," Zeb answered. "Watch out for the

rocks, Patrick—pull off to the right there so we can have a level spot for the tent trailer. Good, dear. That's fine."

Patrick maneuvered, brought the car to a halt, and unclamped his fingers from the steering wheel. It was a relief to step out of the vehicle and stand upright, breathing the open air again. There was a cool desert breeze blowing, and the silver light of a young moon was a refreshing contrast to the bloody crimson of the sinking sun.

Aunt Zeb calibrated her test meters, took the essential readings, and then, assuming the stance of a military major, said crisply, "Everybody to his station. There's much to be done."

There was, and she observed with pride how well the Squad went about their duties. True, they had rehearsed their roles back home, but rehearsal and the actual thing were often different. With a minimum of fumbling, Lester and Patrick pitched the umbrella tent, while Aunt Zeb and the girls raised and secured their own canvas shelter on its trailer base. Within a half hour the two tents were in place, and Zebrina gave a sigh of content. She had always loved tents, those portable houses that changed any wilderness into a tidy homestead. Though she hated the hunting part of the trips with James, making camp had enchanted her. As it did now, even among the ruins of what had been.

"Can I go wadin'?" Knobs asked.

"Yes, love." Zeb had made a cursory check on the water, among her many other activities. "There's no danger as long as you avoid drinking it until I've had a chance to give it a more thorough inspection. But first things first. Blow up your air mattresses, arrange nearby all the things you need or may need—flash, matches, canteen. Well, you know the routine." She looked back toward the dusty car, lists spinning in her mind. Food was the first essential; and as Lester had said, for their fuel they would be wise to use the dead wood lying around like the bleached bones of animals.

"Once you've all got your sleeping spots shipshape," she advised, "go ahead and do whatever you wish. I'll prepare the fire and the supper. But when I blow the whistle"—she indicated the metal whistle on the cord around her neck—"I expect you to convene here at once. You remember the other rules—never drink untested water; always watch for signs of new vegetation, animal tracks, or living creatures." She did not mention wild-dog bands. There had been no sign of such and the chances were that they would not venture this far from human habitations, if any still survived.

The group listened politely, obviously bored, eager to explore the site for whatever surprises it might hold.

All but Fay turned away, scattering toward the creek. "I'll help you get dinner, Aunt Zeb," she offered.

In spite of her chunky body, she looked small and even frail against the immensity of the sunset.

"Don't you want to go and explore with the others, treasure?"

Fay nibbled at a fingernail. "I really want to work on this trip. I mean, I plan on lots of hiking and exercise. If you sweat a lot, you can lose maybe five pounds a day."

"Why, sweetheart," Zeb said, "you can sweat and work all you wish. But I don't want to have a skinny Fay. What would I put my arms around then?" She gave the girl a hug, then led the way toward piles of desert driftwood close by. "We'll start the fire, and then I think I'll splash my poor old feet in the sparkling stream myself."

Feeling self-important and satisfied, Fay began hauling wood toward a cook spot Aunt Zeb had hastily marked out with a stroke of her heavy-soled hiking shoes.

"Wouldn't it be wonderful if we really did find something alive?" Fay said as she delivered an armload of the dry, crackling brush on the site. "Like a little fox, I mean. Foxes don't bite, do they?"

"Everything bites, child, when frightened. Not out of viciousness. But when any creature thinks it's in danger, it naturally tries to protect itself."

"They wouldn't be in danger from me. I wouldn't ever hurt anything."

"I know you wouldn't, Fay dear." Zeb made a small wigwam of sticks, breaking them to the right size in her hands, and giving thicker branches an expert chop with the short ax. "If you want to find some larger pieces now, . . ." she coached while she dragged a number of boulders into a circle around the tinder. From a waterproof container she removed a match, struck it, and held it to the dead, dried grass mixed in with the twigs.

Behind her she could hear the splash of water as the young people waded or tossed rocks into the stream.

"It's as cold as ice!" Sylvie complained loudly.

"Water can never be colder than thirty-two degrees," Patrick said authoritatively.

"Why not?"

"Because then it would freeze and be ice, not water, obviously."

Patrick was right, of course, Zeb thought as she gave the fresh flames a helpful puff and then stood back to watch, contentedly, the zealous blaze. Only she wished Pat would be a bit more considerate of Sylvie's ego. Oh, well, it was only natural for youngsters to scrap and compete for first place. And in any case, it was a delight to hear their splashings and unrestrained voices, especially that of Knobs.

"My feet are freezin'!" Knobs cried, but there was pleasure in the cry. Zeb thought: Whatever comes of the trip it will be especially good for Knobs—Celeste. Good for all of them.

Perhaps, most of all, good for herself. She had been depressed
of late, even morbid at times, too much caught up in her own
thoughts and fears about the future development of the world.
She looked toward the new moon, thinking of the structures
being built there, and the most recent space station rotating
in the void. No doubt, man was driven to seek homes beyond
the earth for the reason that the earth had been nearly
destroyed. Well, she would not live to see the colonies on Mars

or Jupiter. But the youngsters would. She sighed and saw Fay studying her own shadow, stretched out long and lavender in the sun's last rays.

"Shadows are funny, aren't they?" Fay said. "It looks like I'm a long, skinny giant stretched out on the ground. Do you need any more wood, Aunt Zeb?" She was perspiring from her exertions and glanced longingly toward the stream.

"No. We'll have the boys haul in some larger pieces for our evening fire. This is fine, and while I let it settle down to coals, let's join the water babies."

Fay flashed her a questioning look.

"*The Water Babies* was a book I read, and adored, a thousand years ago, child. Let's see now—oh, yes." She fumbled through her luggage and removed a plastic case containing the chief water-testing device. Included in the kit were chlorine and other tablets to purify polluted water in small quantities for drinking.

When she reached the edge of the stream, followed by Fay, she removed her boots and socks, then stepped gingerly into the shallow water, giving a shriek that more than satisfied her grinning audience.

"Sylvie's absolutely right," she said with a shiver. "It is ice, perhaps even a bit colder. Where's Lester?"

"He went off to meditate somewhere," Sylvie answered.

"He'd better not meditate too long," Aunt Zeb said, surveying the darkening land. He couldn't possibly get lost in such a comparatively open area, she told herself, and applied herself to the water test. The device was intricate but compact and simple to operate. Injecting a sample of water into the fill tube, she pressed a button that activated the power source. The gadget hummed and ticked and the needle on the numbered dial face moved slowly from its zero position. The numerals on the dial went to one hundred. Any water sample that registered sixty or over was safe for consumption.

Zebrina and the others watched the indicator. "Forty," Sylvie counted aloud. "Forty-five. Fifty!"

The needle wavered, moved forward again a fraction, and then stopped at fifty-four.

Zeb sighed and shut off the mechanism. "It was too much to hope for, Squad, at this altitude."

"It'll be different when we get high up, won't it?" Fay asked.

"Oh, yes, dear. Of course. Well, I must go back to my fire, to dry my feet, if nothing else." She glanced around the rocky, canyon-creased landscape once more, wondering about Lester. Perhaps he had only needed to use the "facilities." Or, if he truly were meditating, she hated to disturb him before necessary. Not bothering to lace her boots, she strode back toward the fire, tripping once over the laces. One by one, the others followed to gather close to the flames, chilled by the water and by the cooling air.

In a matter of minutes, everyone helping—for Zebrina carefully included a task for each—fresh lamb chops in special wire holders were broiling slowly over the red coals, potatoes started to simmer in a separate niche, and on another corner of the rude rock stove, fresh asparagus waited its turn.

"We're living off the fat of the land—the fat of the Agri-labs, I mean," Zeb said. "Tonight. Tomorrow night we may be on our own, down to fundamentals, unless the road suddenly improves. If not, it will be backpacking."

"That will be good exercise," Fay said.

Sylvie was looking dreamily off at the last pale shreds of the sunset. "I wish I could paint well. I'd make a painting of that sky for my mother and father. But I'm not good enough."

"You are too, darling," Aunt Zeb insisted. "Simply print the whole scene on your mind and when you are back home you'll be able to create a beautiful picture." She sat down on a folding stool Patrick had brought for her from the car, testing the potatoes with a long fork. "I do wish Lester would show up. He's been gone quite long enough."

"I'll go look for him," Patrick volunteered. He was feeling fine now. It seemed as if the silly fainting spell earlier had happened to somebody else.

"You'll do no such thing, love," Zeb declared. "It's too dark to go stumbling around in unknown terrain. He'll be along presently. But just to hurry him up, there's this." She lifted her whistle and gave it a shrill blast.

The whistle was clear enough to Lester's ears, although he was surprised at its remoteness. He had wandered farther than he realized. First, he had separated from the group only because

he craved relief from the noisy conversations in the car followed by the general boisterousness of the wading scene. He wanted to experience the deep silence of the area, and hear the creaking rocks. For it seemed, in such a plain of silence, that they must have some sound, no matter how faint. Rocks were never dead things to him, any more than the Squaw with a Basket at Pyramid Lake was. He saw all rocks, whether boulders or pebbles or mountains, as interlaced with veins and gristle, frozen arteries and rigid lace. Animals and vegetation had been swallowed up in them. Who knew what strange bones, and even brains, were a part of volcanic flows? At certain exalted moments he was convinced that he had heard rocks grunt in bitter heat, and pebbles gasp. He could not prove it, however, and he had never expressed such beliefs to anyone, not even to Aunt Zeb, who would have understood and very likely agreed.

Certainly, the rocks here were silent. That was all right, since he was in the mood for silence. There was only the crunch of his boot soles against the sand and gravel, and the scratchy whisper of wind stirring the soil or rattling the remains of a dead bush or tree. He had roamed for half an hour or so when he thought he saw, or dreamed he saw, tiny animal tracks. It was difficult to know in the swiftly fading light, and he had not brought his flash.

His throat dry with excitement, Lester knelt and studied the tracks—if that was what they were. The patterns in the sand were delicate and scrambled, almost as if a tumbleweed had rolled erratically across the ground. Yet in the midst of the intricate path there did seem to be the marks of small footpads or claws. The vague and confusing trail wavered

uncertainly between two clumps of reddish-gray rocks, disappeared, and then reappeared about one hundred feet beyond. Rediscovering them, Lester wanted to call to the others. He was already too far, then, to make them hear—or, if he could, he decided he might only alarm them. Anyhow, if the tracks had been made by a tumbleweed or some other uprooted, dead plant, he would look like an idiot.

He followed the indistinct trail for another ten or fifteen feet and then there was nothing but the sand, rocks, and rubble. A decayed truck tire lay off to one side of a rock cleft, and he looked at it with wonder. How it had got there, so far from the highway, was a mystery. The beer and pop cans that littered the landscape were explainable enough. Years ago, campers and hikers had brought their metal treasures with them, and left them. Eggshells, too, even in this remote spot.

Eggshells, he thought, even though broken to fragments, were as immortal as plastic. Finding a level slope of rock, he sat down to rest before his return to camp. The setting sun, on the opposite side of the earth from where it had been this morning, was a red-gold thread again. Above it, like a curved silver blade, was the moon. He gazed at the scene, head back, his hands clamped around his knees. Even if the Squad reached no farther than this, it was worth it, he thought. He breathed deeply, and then deliberately held his breath, listening to the silence.

He should have brought his Foreverflash, he realized, looking back across the graying land. Still, there would be no problem. No woods obscured the way, and the scrap of moon would be a help. He touched the bush knife at his belt, the canteen, and the compass secured in his hip-pocket case. He removed the compass, opened its lid, and slid the lever to free the needle, idly curious as to direction. He had guessed that in his rock seat he was facing south by southwest. He laid the compass on a horizontal patch of rock, and the wavering needle settled into place, pointing north. According to the compass, he *was* facing south by southwest. He felt pleased with his sense of direction.

There was a faint sound, like a scrabble of claws. Lester restrained himself from leaping up. He waited, and thought he heard the sound again. Cautiously, slowly, he moved from the rock shelf, peering through the gloom. The few crooked shadows that remained in the last glance of the sun took on all sorts of fantastic shapes, so that he imagined that there, alongside one boulder, was a fox—and there, in a crescent of tumbled granite, a porcupine. He edged forward, striving to separate reality from fantasy. He found nothing.

It had all been a product of his overeager imagination, he decided, looking glumly around him. He would not mention any of it back at camp. He turned to leave at the same moment

that he heard a singing whine near his cheek. He straightened, startled. There was a stinging sensation. Involuntarily he slapped his cheek. When he drew his hand away, he saw the long-legged insect there, its wings and stinger crumpled.

He had studied his biology books enough to know what it was, though it was the first time in his life that he had ever suffered a mosquito bite.

"Wow!" he exclaimed in a most unmystic fashion. He started racing toward the camp even as he heard the remote whistle. With a sprinter's swift stride, he covered the distance speedily, dodging rocks and shadows, his chest bursting with the good news he had to tell.

He came gasping into camp and saw Aunt Zeb turn toward him, the firelight freckling her relieved features.

"I found something!" Lester yelled. "A mosquito! Here. I brought it back. I know that's what it is!" He held his hand out, palm up, to Zebrina. "Isn't it?" Lester appealed. "It stung me. See?" He fingered the welt on his cheek.

"Ah," Zeb said softly, peering at the creature through her glasses. "Yes, Lester! It is. Indeed, it is! To think that I would ever feel joy over such—if only you knew what torments I have suffered from these tiny bombers. Oh, how lovely—how wonderful! Food for frogs and bats. And if there is food for them, there will be food for other creatures. Lester, love, I knight thee!" She drew him toward her and kissed his forehead. "For this you deserve the biggest chop." She looked questioningly at the others.

They cheered and nodded.

"Run and put the specimen in our collection box, dear," Aunt Zeb instructed Lester. "Then we will feast."

It was a triumphant, happy group that sat under the fresh moon and the brightening stars, the smoke smell of the fire around them, combined with the sweet, crusty taste of the chops and the green-earth taste of potatoes and asparagus.

. . . .

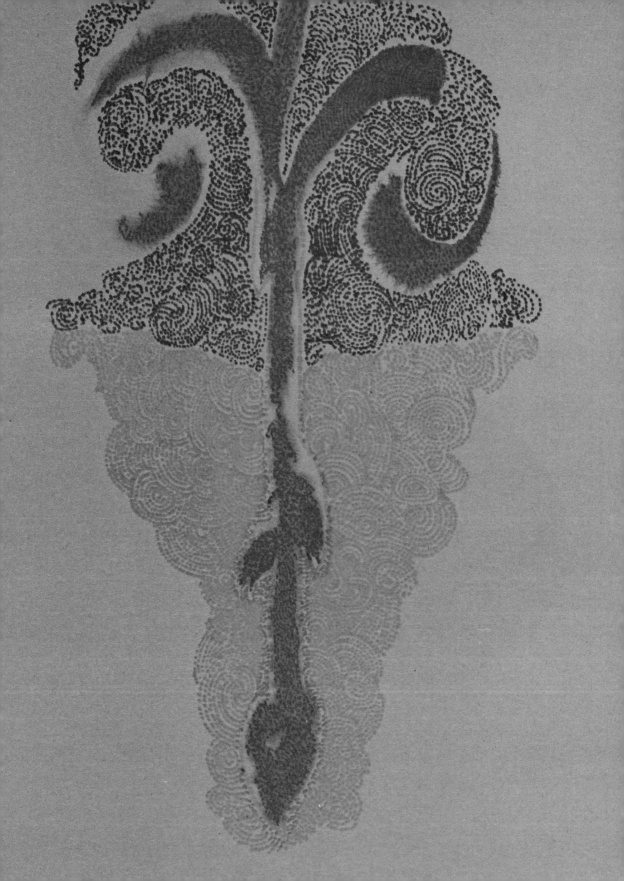

Fueled

Fueled
by a million
man-made
wings of fire—
the rocket tore a tunnel
through the sky—
and everybody cheered.
Fueled
only by a thought from God—
the seedling
urged its way
through the thicknesses of black—
and as it pierced
the heavy ceiling of the soil—
and launched itself
up into outer space—
no
one
even
clapped.

Marcie Hans

Afterthought

How might the United States become the wasteland it is in the story? What can we do to keep this from happening? Which of the following projects can you or your class do?

Ask your librarian to help you find books and magazine articles about conservation. Then make a report to your class about what you have read.

Bring to class newspaper clippings telling about conservation. Read them aloud or display them on a bulletin board.

Your teacher may wish to invite a city official to talk to your class about air and water pollution. Think of questions you would like to ask the speaker.

Make posters showing such good conservation practices as putting litter in trash cans; avoiding the burning of trash or leaves; turning off faucets, stoves, and lights when not in use; being careful of fires when picnicking or camping.

Organize a group to clean up trash and litter in your neighborhood. Take old newspapers, bottles, cans, rags, metal, and rubber articles to a junkman or collection center for recycling.

Plant flowers, shrubs, or trees in your community.

A
View
Around

"There ought to be a view around the world

From such a mountain—if it isn't wooded

Clear to the top." I saw through leafy screens

Great granite terraces in sun and shadow,

Shelves one could rest a knee on getting up—

With depths behind him sheer a hundred feet—

Or turn and sit on and look out and down,

With little ferns in crevices at his elbow.

Robert Frost

Explorers 1450-1500

Johanna Johnston

It is not ever possible of course
to find out all that happened in the
past. Yet it is possible for historical
information to be overlooked for
a very long time. So if you think
you know all about the discovery
of the New World, this article may
hold some surprises for you.

Light-skinned men from Europe, dark-skinned men from Africa—for centuries they had hardly known of each other's existence. They met with some surprise.

The Meeting

On an African beach, a white-robed man from Morocco, a Moor, stood watching as a curiously built ship anchored offshore. A small boat was lowered. A group of men rowed toward the beach. They landed, pulled up the boat, and looked about them.

The Moor recognized the men as Europeans and was surprised to see them here in Africa. Europeans had never sailed this far down the western coast of Africa before. He wondered what had brought them here.

He was even more surprised when the Europeans rushed across the beach and seized him as their captive. He cried out and protested in sign language. He tried to tell them that they did not want him. He was only a visitor in this territory, not a native. He gestured to them that they should follow him.

Walking beside the Moor suspiciously, the Europeans followed him inland till they came to a village of straw huts. Then they stared about

them in wonder at the African men and women who quickly gathered. The Moor was talking with some man who seemed to be in authority, the chief of the village, perhaps. There were questions, answers, orders. Soon ten lively African boys were standing before the Europeans. It became plain that the Moor was offering the ten boys to the Europeans as captives in his place.

The Europeans stared at the boys and the boys stared back. And the Europeans considered the matter. Ten captives in place of one. Furthermore, it was unlikely that these boys were Moslems, as the Moor undoubtedly was. If the Europeans took the boys, they could convert them to Christianity, as they would never be able to convert the Moor. Above all, there was the novelty of these handsome, healthy boys whose skins were darker than any the Europeans had ever seen.

The Europeans nodded, accepting the bargain. They marched the boys down to the beach, ordered them into the boat, and rowed them to the ship.

Life in Portugal

After some further voyaging down the coast, the ship turned back and returned to its home port in Portugal. The African boys were paraded through the streets of Lisbon. Everyone stared in wonder and delight at the strange young people. Rich men hurried to buy them as servants and houseboys. Those who were disappointed at not getting one hurried to put in orders for one or two with captains of ships that would soon be making the same voyage down the western coast of Africa.

It had all been an accident, really. The Moor had only been protecting his own freedom when he offered the boys in his place. The Portuguese captain who accepted them had not been planning to start a trade in such trophies. Like most of the other Portuguese captains of the time, he had been sailing in the waters off the western coast of Africa for quite another reason. Spurred on by Portugal's prince, Henry the Navigator, the captain had been trying to find his way to the southern tip of Africa. Prince Henry was urging all his captains to look for that tip, and a sea route around it, hoping it would lead Portuguese ships northward and eastward toward the Orient. The Orient was the goal—the land where spices grew, a land of gold and precious gems and silks and brocades.

But who could resist good trading if that was offered along the way? The nuts, the fruits, the olive oil, the gold that Portuguese captains found in Africa, were all welcomed in Portugal. And the clever, handsome African boys and girls they began bringing back grew more and more popular.

No one in Portugal needed or wanted these Africans for hard labor. Negroes were exotic foreigners, more than anything else. Rich men liked to have them around as a sign of their wealth.

Before many years had passed, seven or eight hundred Africans a year were being brought to Portugal. And by the time one Portuguese sea captain did find his way around the southern tip of Africa, there were Negroes in Spain as well as Portugal. By then, not all of them were house servants either. Chances of fortune, loss of their masters, their own intelligence and ambition had led some of them into more independent careers. The color of their skin was different from that of the Europeans, but no one thought that meant they were born to be servants and nothing more. Some had little farms or businesses. Some became soldiers, sailors, or pilots.

Westward Voyages

And so, soon enough, men from Europe and men from Africa were both part of the continuing push into unknown seas, as the search went on for a sea route to the Orient.

The Italian, Christopher Columbus, outfitting three small ships to sail westward on an expedition financed by Spain, hired a pilot named Pedro Alonso Niño. But his shipmates called the pilot El Negro.

El Negro shared the relief and joy of all Columbus' men when the little ships finally did find land after sailing westward across the terrifying Atlantic. He was with the treasure hunters landing on the islands, trying to find out from the natives if there was gold anywhere about. He tasted the strange food the natives were offering —pineapple, sugarcane, sweet peppers. And after the return to Spain, he was part of the triumphal parade from the seacoast to Barcelona, as Columbus made his way to King Ferdinand and Queen Isabella with proof of his wonderful discoveries— parrots, monkeys, coconuts, and plates of gold and silver.

El Negro sailed again with Columbus when Columbus made his third voyage to the islands, still looking for a channel through them that

would lead to the mainland of China or India. Later, El Negro sailed with another ship that did touch on a mainland. It was the continent that would one day be known as South America. Like all the other treasure seekers hurrying across the Atlantic in Columbus' path, El Negro was baffled by not finding any of the spices, gems, silks, and other products men expected to find in the Orient. But he saw enough things of value to make him want to try a trading trip to this mainland coast.

Back home in Spain, El Negro won permission from the king to undertake such a voyage. He and a partner fitted out a ship, filled it with various European products, and set forth. Their voyage went well. Their trading went well. They returned to Spain with their hold full of rich and varied goods from South America. They had accomplished the first successful voyage across the Atlantic to be made for purely commercial reasons.

The New World

But El Negro was dead, and Columbus was dead too, when the greatest surprise of all began to dawn on the treasure seekers, and the men back home in Europe also. This was not some part of the Orient to which Columbus had led the way. These were islands, and a mainland, not marked on any map. They were unknown to any previous travelers, even those in the time of the ancient Greeks and Romans.

This was a New World.

It was a long time before a few observant men began to wonder if some Africans had found the New World years and years earlier. Men and women who looked very like Africans were living in South America when the men from Europe landed there. Some of the words they used—yam, tobacco, canoe—were African words, part of the native language when the Europeans arrived. Africans *could* have sailed their swift, light warships across the Atlantic to the South American shores and then settled there.

But no one had time to speculate on such matters when the first surprise of a New World dawned. From all over Spain, daring, ambitious, hopeful soldiers of fortune rushed to the seaports to board ships for the New World, to explore, to conquer, and to find—who knew what treasure?

Africans were among them as a matter of course. Some were servants

of the Spaniards. Some were soldiers
of fortune themselves.

Cortez, Balboa, and Pizarro

African soldiers were part of Her-
nando Cortez' small army when he
invaded Mexico and marched northward toward the Aztec cities in the
interior. Like all the others, they
marveled at the temples, the gardens,
the lagoons of Montezuma's city
high on the Mexican plateau. With
the others, they helped to loot the
wealth of the city for Spain.

But Cortez and his soldiers brought
things to Mexico also. They brought
the Christian religion. They brought
an animal hitherto unknown in the
New World—the horse.

And it was a Negro soldier in the
army of Cortez who found a few
grains of wheat in his rice rations
one day and decided to plant them.
According to legend, this unknown
soldier then tended and reaped the
first crop of wheat to be grown in
the New World.

Thirty Africans were with Vasco
Núñez de Balboa when he built his
rude fleet of ships to sail along the
Isthmus of Panama. They helped
him hack his way across the jungle
at the narrow part of that isthmus.

They were among the Spaniards and Indians with him when he first gazed on a vast new ocean, the Pacific.

Francisco Pizarro counted Negroes among the soldiers in his small army of a hundred men, when he marched that army up into the Andes of South America to outwit and conquer the army of the Incas. Later, after his conquest, when he was assassinated by conspirators among his own men, two loyal Negro soldiers carried Pizarro's body to the cathedral that had been built in the Incan city where he died, and they helped to bury him there.

History and Estevan

Spanish leaders and officials were the ones who wrote the histories and reports of the expeditions. Naturally, they tended to write most about their own achievements and to ignore others without whose help they might not have done so well.

But one Spaniard's story of his long ordeal in the New World could not help but also be the story of the three men who shared it with him. Cabeza de Vaca had been a member of a large expedition that set out from Spain to invade and conquer Florida. But when the Spaniards landed on the Florida coast, the Indians attacked furiously. Many of the Spaniards were killed. All but one of their ships were destroyed. The survivors sailed away down the coast in the remaining ship. Then a storm blew up and wrecked that ship. Only four men managed to swim safely to the Florida shore—Cabeza de Vaca, two other Spaniards, and a Negro servant, Estevan, often called Estevanico, or "Little Stephen."

The four men had only one hope when they found themselves alive on the desolate coast. That was to try to make their way northward, up and around the Gulf of Mexico, and thence into Mexico and to the capital city where Cortez had established Spanish government.

They struggled through the Florida undergrowth, trying to sustain themselves on the strange vegetation. They were captured by Indians, who prepared to kill them. One of the Spaniards noticed an Indian lying ill. The Spaniard had a slight knowledge of medicine. He pretended that it was a knowledge of magic. He rattled a hollow gourd, and then with more signs of mystery, treated the sick Indian. Fortunately, the Indian began to get better. The captured Spaniards and the Negro, Estevan, were reprieved from the death sentence. Instead, the Indians put them to work as slaves.

The four men labored for the Indians day after day, plotting their escape. Finally, one night, they managed to get away safely. They struggled on through the wilderness. Again they were captured. Again, a show of magic and some medical treatment of a sick Indian saved them. Again, they were held as captives. Finally, they escaped these captors also.

Their ordeal went on and on. Still the four men struggled northward and westward toward their goal.

Eight long years after their shipwreck they arrived in Mexico City. The three Spaniards, exhausted, were glad to sail for Spain as soon as possible. But Estevan stayed on in Mexico City.

A few years later, in 1539, Cortez decided to send an expedition northward to look for a rich group of cities which the Indians called the Seven Cities of Cíbola. He appointed a priest, Fray de Niza, to lead the expedition. But he had heard of Estevan's amazing journey from Florida to Mexico, and so he asked the Negro to go with the party as a guide.

Estevan wore belled bracelets on his arms and ankles. He carried the hollow gourd which had been so helpful on the trip before. And he traveled in style and splendor at the head of the expedition.

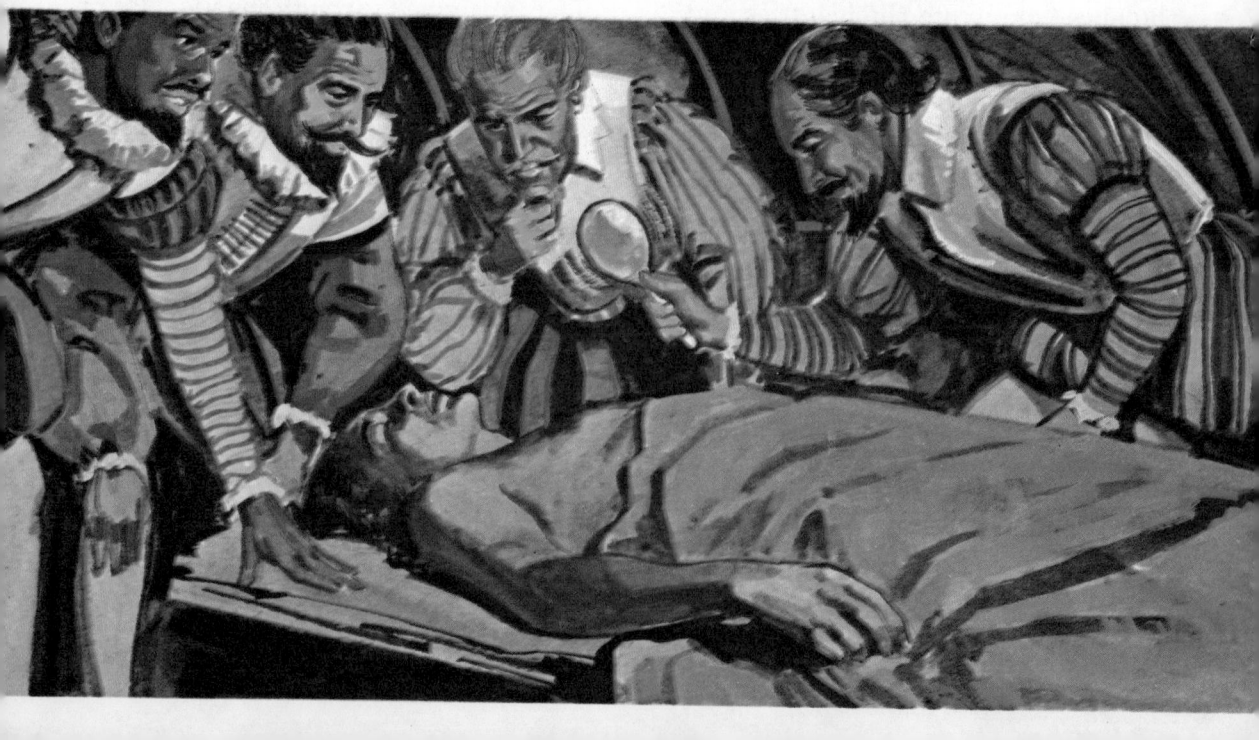

As the party traveled northward, the going grew more and more difficult. At last, de Niza decided to send Estevan with a force of three hundred men to scout out the land ahead. He told Estevan to make a cross out of two pieces of wood each night and send it back to the waiting forces by a runner. A small cross would mean that all was well but nothing of importance had been discovered. Larger crosses would indicate that the trail was promising.

Day after day, Estevan and his men marched northward, and each night Estevan sent back a small cross. Then one day he stopped in excitement and ordered a cross as tall as a man to be constructed and hurried back to de Niza.

Ahead, he saw what looked like a great walled city.

The runners left for the south with the large cross. But Estevan was too eager to wait for the force in the rear to join him. He decided to demand the surrender of the city before him, and then, if that were not given at once, to march on it and take it by force.

Such bold gestures had been successful before. But the men in the walled city refused to surrender. They gathered their forces swiftly.

As Estevan and his men marched forward, they swept out onto the plain and fell upon their attackers. Estevan was killed. All but three of his men were killed. The three survivors fled back across the plain to warn de Niza and the army.

Frightened by this news, de Niza marched northward only far enough to see the walled city in the distance. Then he turned around and went back to Mexico City to report its discovery.

But Estevan was the first man from across the sea to find his way to that strange, walled city. It was not one of the Seven Cities of Cíbola. Those remained a myth, like the Fountain of Youth that Ponce de León looked for in Florida. What Estevan had found was one of the great pueblo cities of the Zuñi Indians in New Mexico.

Men from Europe, men from Africa —they had only really discovered each other's existence a hundred years before. But together they had joined in the discovery and conquest of a New World—a world that seemed to offer unlimited opportunities and rewards to them both.

Both Sides Get Their Backs Up
1761-1773

Dorothy Canfield Fisher

No one fired a shot during the Boston
Tea Party, but it started the American
Revolution. Some years before, Paul
Revere and other militiamen went to
help British troops in the North
Woods. Many died needlessly because
of foolish actions of British
soldiers; the rest began to dislike
British soldiers bitterly. These
militiamen went home and joined such
clubs as the Sons of Liberty in order
to discuss what was on their minds.
This selection will help you understand
what their discussions had to do
with that famous tea party.

American history was as much a part of Paul Revere's daily life as baseball is of yours. You can't get the hang of what he was up to, during those years when he was getting married and having a family, unless you know something about what was going on in his country.

There were two parts to what was going on. One part was made up of facts. The other part was feeling, deep and hot.

Anybody could see the two principal facts: the first was that, only a few years after that forlorn nitwit performance in the North Woods, the British did put on a splendid well-planned campaign with fine energetic generals in charge, did defeat the French, did put the French government entirely out of Canada. The other plain fact was that the long wars against the French in Canada had cost a lot and had to be paid for. Where was the money coming from? The British said the wars had been carried on just to take care of the colonists. So the colonists ought to pay the bill. To this day the English think we didn't play fair on this point.

But the Americans knew that they had already spent a great deal in those wars. They had raised militia troops, many more in proportion to the number of colonists than the British had provided. They had paid these soldiers and had voted the money for their food, clothing, care in sickness, and other expenses. They also knew that many Englishmen had made enormous fortunes out of those wars, and they saw what everybody saw, that the British Empire had won millions of new acres. Why should they pay for those?

Moreover, the American taxpayers didn't enjoy the idea of raising money to pay for some of the goings-on of those fine British officers they didn't like. Part of the plan of the English government was to bring over some regular red-coated British troops to "protect" the American colonists. Protect them from whom, from what, the Americans wondered, now that there were no more French troops in Canada to bring down Indians in raids? And you can guess whether they enjoyed the notion of having more "regulars" around, and paying for them, into the bargain.

Still, everybody was thankful not to have any more French and Indian raids. They knew you don't get something for nothing. Sure, they would pay their share of what the wars had cost.

But how? That was the question. The only way a government can get money is by taxes. No hollow tree with gold in it, anywhere. The only place a government can find money is in people's pockets. But if the tax money was coming out of American pockets, the Americans wanted some say-so about how much it was to be and what kind of taxes were going to produce it.

Here we come to the deep feeling which, more than an ordinary quarrel about money, was at the bottom of the row with England. The feeling was that nobody should be made to live under rules he hadn't had any chance to vote for or against.

You remember the rules Paul Revere's gang of boys made for their "society"? Everybody in that club was to have just as much chance as anybody else to decide how the club was to be run. Those Boston boys didn't make that idea up out of their heads. They were ordinary boys. They only did what they had been brought up to do. They had never even heard of any other way to manage a group of people working together. Their club would have blown up with a bang if they'd tried any other way. But they never dreamed of any other way.

Well, the American fathers and mothers and grandparents who taught their boys that idea didn't invent it, either. The first settlers had brought it from England. In a sort of way, that idea was the foundation of English law. But English law was not clearly written out or understood. Some English people had a share in deciding how they should be governed. But thousands of Englishmen had no such share, and both the king and the party which was on top in English politics at this time were dead set against letting any more people vote, even right home in England, let alone thousands of miles off in the colonies.

It wasn't only George the Third. The French king, the Austrian emperor, and all the little kings and dukes in Germany held on tight to all the power they could get. Yet all the while the belief was growing—not only in England, but strongly in France and even a little in other parts of Europe—that government must not be a one-man job with all the orders coming down from the top. In country after country this idea was boiling, while the rulers sat on the lid of the teakettle until it blew off.

But right now, in our story, it was in Boston that the steam pressure was highest.

There, men like Paul Revere hadn't any doubts. They had grown up with the idea that everybody should have something to say about the rules of his group. If the British Parliament was going to raise money by taxes in the colonies, of course the colonists should vote about them. The only way they could vote was through men they had elected in America and sent to the English Parliament in London. This seemed natural to the Boston Sons of Liberty.

But it did not seem perfectly natural, not by a long shot, to the British king and his friends. They hadn't the least idea of allowing even the people in England, all of them, to have a fair representation in Parliament.

So the Parliament went ahead and voted the Stamp Act to raise that money by taxes about which the Americans hadn't had any say. The Americans blew up with a bang. Especially the Boston people, who had a special way of their own to make bangs, and noisy ones.

They had learned, in those Guy Fawkes' day goings-on, that by blacking up their faces and looking tough and yelling and hammering on bells and drums as they raced through the streets at night, they could scare the rich people into staying indoors. They'd try some Guy-Fawkesing on the British officials and their families. It was the only way they had to make the British government realize that they did not intend to pay taxes they hadn't voted on.

While the Sons of Liberty were making a big noise in

Boston streets, people all over America were refusing to pay those taxes. After a while the British Parliament tried new tactics. They rubbed out the Stamp Act. Just withdrew it.

You can't imagine how excited and relieved the Americans were about this news. They thought that their principle had won. They thought it meant the British agreed with them that nobody should pay taxes he had not voted on. Their hearts almost burst, they were so happy.

The day the ship came into Boston Harbor with the news that the Stamp Act was no more, the Boston people got up just the opposite kind of parade from the yelling, heavy-footed marching of the Sons of Liberty. People went along the street, playing sweet gentle music in front of Boston houses. The big tree on the Common, which they had come to call "The Liberty Tree," where the Sons of Liberty used to gather, was covered from bottom to top with bright-colored decorations. When darkness came, every window in every Boston house had a lighted candle gleaming cheerfully in it.

Paul Revere and his wife and children joined the crowds of their neighbors, all carrying lighted lanterns. They gathered to stand, rejoicing, under the Liberty Tree, which was hung all over with lighted lanterns. They thought the danger of war with England was over. They thought the spirit of the English law had won out. And they loved that spirit. Everything was all right now.

But they were mistaken. The British king did not love the spirit of the English law. He hated it. And by this time he was pretty much the boss of the English government. He wanted to run things his way, law or no law. A great many British people didn't like this. And the fact that a century before, they had pushed one English king off the throne, and cut off another king's head, showed that when their backs were up, they wouldn't take too many orders from anybody. But just at this time those who were against the king were not, like the Americans, their cousins, sitting on the edge of their seats, ready to jump up and yell "No you don't" if the king went beyond the law. All but a few of them seemed to be, for a while, like discouraged people who sag back and say, "Oh, what's the use."

The Americans didn't sag back. The king and his friends showed that they still thought they had the right to tax people as they liked by voting another kind of tax on the colonies. The Boston people went back to their scary, noisy street-marching with blackened faces. They made themselves very disagreeable and alarming. (As a matter of fact, since sober, level-headed men like Paul Revere always went out with them to make sure they didn't go too far, they did not, in those years, do any serious harm.) British officials sent back word to England that they needed some regular soldiers to put down these screeching Boston crowds.

So the next move, in the long swaying to and fro of the struggle between the two sides, was that the British government did send some regular soldiers to Boston.

The very sight of their red uniforms brought hated memories to men like Paul Revere. And there were many like him. Only a few Americans who had money enough to live in style, and so were not looked down on by the British officers, were glad to see them come. Everybody else stood silent on the Boston streets, looking sourly at the British regiments that landed on the wharf. Dressed in their best uniforms,

the soldiers marched into town, keeping step perfectly to the drum and fife corps, every knee bent at the same instant, every foot hitting the ground, *thump!* at the same time. Men like Paul Revere were not impressed. They had seen that before.

The "Regulars" were as comfortable with the Boston men, women, and children as the American militia had been in the North Woods with the mosquitoes, blackflies, and ticks. Every day, all day long, they were bothered and pestered. Boston men would "accidentally" shove a British redcoat off the wharf into the sea and be out of sight when the soldier climbed back, dripping. Boston women yelled bloody murder if any English soldiers said so much as "Good morning" to them. But the little boys, like the gnats, were almost the worst.

They were harder to catch than grownups. They put two fingers in their mouths and whistled, forty or fifty of them together. They threw snowballs, and sometimes put stones into the balls. A bunch of them would gather around a British sentry, splendid in his red uniform, the straps and trimmings as white as his thickly powdered hair. One of the boys would step out in front of the gang, and yell at the sentry:

"Lobster back! Lobster back!
You're going to lose your claws,"

and then scurry back to the gang. The soldier looked like a giant compared to the boys, but there wasn't much he could do. He'd pull his big cocked hat down on his head and take long steps out toward the boys, his fists doubled up, shouting, "Which of ye said that?"

The boys would burst out laughing and yell, "Ye-e-eah! Don't you wish you knew," and scatter in all directions.

No sentry is allowed to go far from where he is posted. This one could only go back there and stand grumbling, hearing the boys hooting and catcalling from the alleyways.

Both sides had their backs up. The British would not let Americans send elected men of their own to the British Parliament to help decide about the taxes. The Americans would not pay those taxes till they did.

In all the countries in those days which had "well-disciplined" regular armies, the soldiers fought bravely and well on a battlefield. But between battles, when they settled down for a while where they could see the people around them living without "iron discipline," they naturally began to desert. Over in Austria about this time, a "disciplined" army lost about a quarter of its soldiers from desertion. The British regiments in Boston were made up of English-speaking men who could understand what was going on around them in the colonies. A good many of them liked the looks of it.

They began to melt away into the Massachusetts country-side to settle down and become Americans. From the stream of these deserters who settled among them, the Americans heard a lot about the British army as seen from the inside. It sounded as bad as they had thought, and didn't make them like "the British" any better than before.

All this time—twelve years or so—Paul Revere, making beautiful pieces of fine silverware, earning a good living for his family, was, by day, a good family man. Nearly every evening he went out to one or another of his clubs and listened to the talk of men who had had much more book education than he ever had. Like them, he was thinking and thinking, trying to make sense out of what was happening.

Lots was happening. The British tried a different kind of taxes. The Americans refused to buy anything from England. This meant a big money loss to businessmen in England, for whom the colonies were a fine market. And anyhow, a good many of them already thought the king was going too far. The Lord Mayor of London put on the dress-up clothes he had to wear to speak to the king and went with a lot of the Aldermen of London (also dressed in the proper clothes) to tell the king that they didn't like the way the English government was treating the Americans, and they wished the king would stop it. The king was furious to have ordinary people, not lords or dukes, speak their minds to him. He said he never again would receive the mayor and aldermen. So that was that.

Over in Boston, a silversmith working away in his shirt sleeves began to hear, as if in his ear, the answer to that question which had so shocked him when he first thought of it in the North Woods—"If I'm not French and not British, what is there I can be?"

He knew now what he could be. He could be something nobody had heard of till then. He could be an American.

He never made speeches, Paul Revere didn't. He never made a speech about being an American. But from this time on, he acted like an American with all his heart.

And very soon, a chance to act came his way. After a while the British made another play in the long match they were having with the Americans. They took off every single tax. Except one. One small tax on one small item of no importance. Tea.

Most people in Boston, elsewhere in Massachusetts, and other places in America were worn out by the long scrimmage. The British guess was that the colonies couldn't get up enough energy to make a fuss over one measly little tax of a few cents a pound. They guessed wrong.

Afterthought

Suppose two boys argue in the lunchroom and the teacher asks why they disagreed. She is sure to get two different viewpoints. If she asks other children about the argument, they will give still other viewpoints. Is one of the viewpoints the right one, or is each viewpoint probably partly right? How can an imaginary argument in the lunchroom aid you in understanding the selection you have just read?

The Blue-Backed Speller 1783-1793

Isabel Proudfit

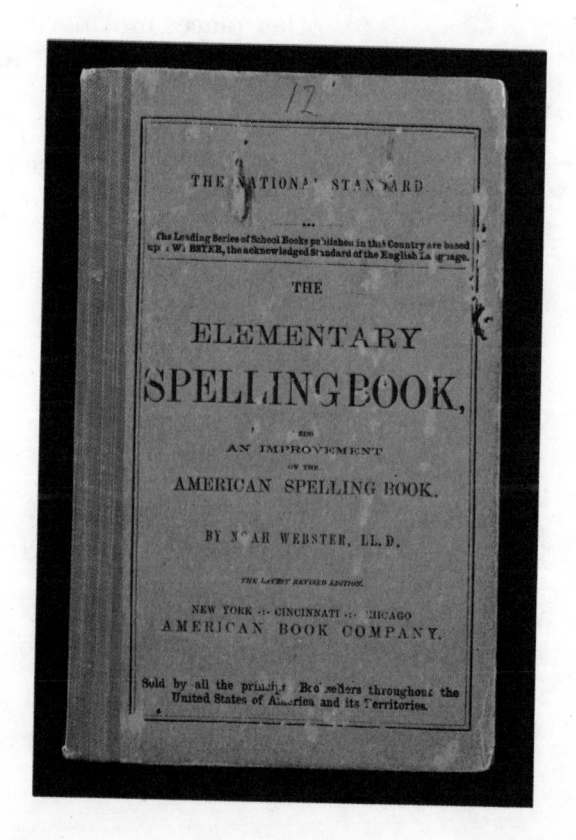

Just at the end of the American Revolution, lawyer-teacher Noah Webster finished writing a small book. He very much wanted to get it to the people who were now Americans. Our language might be quite different today if he had failed.

The next problem which young Mr. Webster had to face, after he finished writing his Speller, was to get his book published. Authors always have this problem. In Noah Webster's case, however, the problem was many times more difficult than it would be today.

The first thing he discovered, on returning to Hartford from Goshen, was that books had never been published in America. There simply were no American books.

The next thing he learned was that there were no copyright laws in the various states, which would protect a young author from having his book copied and sold without payment of royalties.

The next thing he learned was that there were almost no bookstores, where the book might be offered for sale. Possibly a drugstore or two in the towns would undertake to sell a few copies. In the villages it would have to be offered, if offered at all, in the general store where people bought coffee and sugar and molasses, as well as clothing and sticks of peppermint candy.

Any other writer but Mr. Webster might have been overcome by these discouraging prospects. But by the age of twenty-four Noah had a fine grip on the maxim that had seen him through heavy difficulties before. *God Helps Those Who Help Themselves.*

Without even waiting to find a publisher, he set out by stagecoach to visit some of the principal cities in the thirteen states, where the state legislatures were meeting. Armed with letters of introduction, and a willingness to talk about his forthcoming book, he succeeded in getting copyright laws passed in six states before Christmas—Connecticut, Massachusetts, Maryland, New Jersey, New Hampshire, and Rhode Island. In town after town, too, he called on the local schoolmasters and preachers, urging them to promote the sale of an *American* textbook for *American* children.

And now to get the book published. In New York, Boston, Philadelphia, where was a man willing to print 5,000 copies of his little work without being paid for it in advance? There was no such man in any of these cities. As a poor schoolmaster, of course, Noah could not possibly pay the costs of printing the book.

Returning to Hartford, he called on Barzillai Hudson and George Goodwin, publishers of the *Connecticut Courant*, which he had read since he was a child. In the grimy newspaper office an arrangement was made by which they would print 5,000 copies of the Speller and wait a little for their money. If the Speller did not sell, however, Noah would be liable for the full cost of the printing. As a poor schoolmaster, already heavily in debt to his father, he could hardly hope to pay off these costs in a lifetime of frugal living.

The little book made its appearance in October in the blue cloth cover, which it wore forever after. Costing one shilling and twopence a copy, or about thirty cents, it began to appear on store counters along with the calico and cheese. In the drugstores it lay beside hair oil or tonic, innocently offering its Method of Education to people who came in looking distractedly for medicine.

"Eh, eh, what is this?" inquired a weathered farmer, who came looking for something to soothe an ailing child. "A new spelling book! What's the matter with the old Dilworth out of which I learned my letters?"

"The man who wrote this book claims it is an *American* Speller. He says Dilworth is old-fashioned."

"Old-fashioned, eh? Why, my father before me learned out of Dilworth!"

"Yes? Well, times have changed, it seems. Some of these newfangled ideas are purty good."

"Hmm. Well, p'raps Josiah (or Mirandy or Ebenezer) might get some good out've it. What did ye say it cost?"

"Only one shilling and tuppence. I'll let ye have one for a quarter."

"All right, I'll take it. That is, if ye're sure it's not unreligious. I don't want no storybooks coming into my house."

"No, no. It's quite respectable. And a sight more cheerful than the old Dilworth speller."

"Well, well. Ma'll be that surprised when I come home with a new spelling book. She sent me in for medicine. Guess I'd better be gittin' along with it."

"Here ye are then. And I hope the shaver is soon better."

"I expect he will be. Funny thing about Ma. She don't hold with dipping a sick child. When I was young, it was into the tub headforemost for most any kind of sickness."

"Well, this medicine'll help a lot. I've taken it myself to break a fever."

"Ye hev, eh? Well, thanks, again."

And out the farmer went with his newfangled medicine and newfangled speller, prepared to be modern at any cost.

The boys and girls in the reopened schools took to Webster's Spelling Book instantly. They liked the fables, which came as a reward for learning new words. They liked the pictures, too, which appeared in later editions: Mr. Webster himself with his hair standing up like porcupine quills; the fox and the bear and the milkmaid illustrating the fables.

Not only children, but grown people liked the little book. Farmers and judges and statesmen, teachers and preachers gave it their approval. During the first nine months after it was published, the first edition of 5,000 copies sold rapidly. Subsequent editions sold well, and were even larger.

In the course of the next ten years probably a million copies sold throughout the United States. As peace came to the country, and more and more schools were opened, the demand for the book increased steadily. The Speller went west in covered wagons, crossed rivers and mountains, stood on a special shelf with the Bible and almanac in country homes, and became the backbone of American education. In the course of Noah Webster's lifetime nearly 25,000,000 copies were sold. After he died, it continued to sell up to a total of 100,000,000 copies. Probably no book, excepting the Bible, has had a better sale over a period of years.

The effect of all this popularity was, of course, far-reaching. Since people everywhere read and studied the Speller, they pronounced their words largely as it did. *Ask* did replace *ax* in people's mouths. Men blushed and muttered again, when they accidentally said *chimbly* for *chimney*. In writing letters, too, under frontier conditions, they spelled their words as Mr. Webster recommended. By candlelight and smoky lamps, working with a goose quill pen on smudgy paper, they wrote the family back home in Kentucky or Massachusetts or Pennsylvania, according to Mr. Webster.

And what of young Noah Webster, who passed his twenty-fifth birthday a few weeks after the first edition of the Speller

was published? He returned quietly from his copyright jour-
neys, rented a room in Hartford, and settled down to look for
legal business. He also slept better at night, knowing that a
little money would now be coming in from another source
than legal practice.

BÄR, LÅST, ÇÂRE, FĄLL, WHĄT; HẼR, PRĘY, THÊRE; ḠET; BĬRD, MARĬNE; LĬŊK;

No. 32.--XXXII.

WORDS OF TWO SYLLABLES, ACCENTED ON THE SECOND.

a bāse'	re elāim'	un sāy'	ben zoin'
de base	pro elaim	as say	a void
in ease	dis elaim	a way	a droit
a bate	ex elaim	o bey	ex ploit
de bate	de mēan	eon vey	de eoy
se date	be mōan	pur vey	en joy
ere ate	re tāin	sur vey	al loy
ob late	re main	de fȳ	em ploy
re late	en grōss	af fȳ	an noy
in flate	dis ereet	de nȳ	de stroy
eol late	al lāy	de erȳ	eon voy
trans late	de lay	re boil	es pouse
mis state	re lay	de spoil	ea rouse
re plēte	in lay	em broil	de vour
eom plete	mis lay	re eoil	re dound
se erete	dis play	sub join	de vout
re çīte	de eay	ad join	a mount
in çite	dis may	re join	sur mount
po lite	de fray	en join	dis mount
ig nite	ar ray	eon join	re eount
re deem	be tray	dis join	re nown
es teem	pōr tray	mis join	en dow
de elāim	a stray	pur loin	a vow

Strong drink will debase a man.
Hard shells incase clams and oysters.
Men inflate balloons with gas, which is lighter
    than common air.
Teachers like to see their pupils polite to each
    other.
Idle men often delay till to-morrow things
    that should be done to-day.

a while, was very happy; but soon found that if he attempt
to stir, he was wounded by the thorns and prickles on ev
side. However, making a virtue of necessity, he forebore
complain, and comforted himself with reflecting that no b
is perfect; that good and evil are mixed, and flow from
same fountain. These briers, indeed, said he, will tear
skin a little, yet they keep off the dogs. For the sake of
good, then, let me bear the evil with patience; each bitter
its sweet; and these brambles, though they wound my fle
preserve my life from danger.

FABLE VII.

THE BEAR AND THE TWO FRIENDS.

Two friends, setting out together upon a journey which l
through a dangerous forest, mutually promised to assist ea
other, if they should happen to be assaulted. They had n
proceeded far, before they perceived a bear making towa
them with great rage.

There were no hopes in flight; but one of them, being ve
active, sprang up into a tree; upon which the other, throwir
himself flat on the ground, held his breath and pretended
be dead; remembering to have heard it asserted that th
creature will not prey upon a dead carcass. The bear can
up and after smelling of him some time, left him and went o
When he was fairly out of sight and hearing, the hero fro
the tree called out,—"Well, my friend, what said the bear
He seemed to whisper you very closely." "He did so," replie
the other, "and gåve me this good advice, never to associate wi
a wretch, who, in the hour of danger, will desert his friend."

The Speller sold for thirty cents a copy. On the first 5,000 copies, Noah received one hundred and thirty-six dollars. To a young man, who still owed his father six hundred dollars for his education, this was not a rich profit. But to a young man who had risked a lifetime of debt to publish the book at all, and who had taught school for months at a time at five or six dollars a month, it was a good beginning.

More satisfying, also, than the money itself was the feeling that he had done what he set out to do. America needed an American schoolbook, and he had given it to her. It was the first of a long list of patriotic services, which he was to render his beloved country.

Afterthought

1. What evidence do you have that the conversation in this story did not actually take place? Why did the author use conversation in her story?
2. How can you find out whether other information in the story is accurate?
3. Where might you find a copy of the blue-backed Speller?

Congressman Crockett 1826-1835

Meridel Le Sueur

Here is history told as a folktale—about the legendary Davy Crockett and his son Robbie. They lived in a time when distrust was growing between powerful people in cities and poor people in the backwoods. Davy looked on any fast-talking speculator as a monster—as the cockeyed Peddler, who could see two ways at once. Davy met such men often, and he was bound to meet them when he went to Congress.

The people in the Blue Ridges, the Smokies, the canebrakes, the workers in the mill, the hod carriers, the shovelers, diggers, making canals that were carrying people west, the farmers, the mechanics, all heard Davy Crockett that year talking in Congress about land for the Indians and land for the poor farmer and squatter.

Jackson was shaking the bank hornet's nest, and Crockett was booming out in Congress, and people filled the balconies and cried, "Hurrah for Crockett!" and the people laughed when they heard the tales about the long speeches by congressmen! "It's nothing to Crockett," they said, listening with pride from the galleries.

"Some men seemed to take pride in saying a lot about nothing. Their tongues go like windmills whether they have grist to grind or not. Others just listen, doing nothing at all for their pay but just listen, day in and day out. But I wish I may be shot if I don't think they earn every penny, considering most of the speeches. That is, provided they don't go to sleep. No one can imagine how dreadful hard work it is to keep awake. Splitting gum logs in August is nothing beside it."

His enemies said he never learned the rules of debate and was awkward, but his speeches are recorded in the *Congressional Record* for you to read. He was easy but farsighted, and the galleries cheered him. But Davy Crockett drove straight to the point and showed up the dull, windy speeches. He could seize an argument like a panther tail and tie his enemies up in it, and he could make the galleries roar with some backwoods humor. His argument was always warm and alive in behalf of his people, and his poor neighbors of grit and whole hearts.

A great issue had taken new shape—the free lands. The land Davy's grandfather fought for in the revolution had been seized by big landowners who lied about and juggled land titles, and men who had bent their backs to clear the land were robbed of it by Philadelphia lawyers and forced to pay big prices for the poorest land. The grants that were made to soldiers who fought in the Revolutionary War were taken by speculators who claimed the tracts. Settlers who believed they owned the land were, as Davy said, "ransacked, picked, and culled till everything valuable had been collected, and they were then moved to patches and scraps of land."

Davy roared on the floor of Congress, "I have seen the last blanket of an honest, industrious, poor family sold under the hammer to pay for unjust and heavy taxes and for the survey of the land itself, and most of the land so poor it wouldn't even raise a fight."

"Amen—That's the ticket," the squatters said, from the galleries and from the clay gullies of his native Tennessee.

He spoke in behalf of his poor neighbors, and Polly and his children in the canebrake. "These men of the western waters," he said, standing tall and talking tall, "these men who have broken the cane. Their little all is to be wrested from them for the purpose of speculation. The titles to the land of these poor settlers are to be sold to the mighty and powerful who never turned a furrow, or built a rail fence, or hunted bear for the hunger of their childers. I propose a low price for that land and a long time to pay, and the squatters' titles recognized. It shall never be said that I sat by in silence."

The people heard his voice, preachers and peddlers took it afoot and ahorseback. Robbie wrote his mother a letter she never got, and couldn't have read if she had. Robbie was going to a reading school in time out from listening to Davy on the floor. People listened solemnly in church, and hall, and tavern, on hunts and frolics, to the words repeated by their own speaker, tongue of them and voice for their silence. "He said that right up to the big fellows," they said. "He's a caution to wildcats. . . . I'll be a ring-tailed roarer myself. . . ."

One night as he was walking down the avenue, marveling at how many people could gather in one spot, a gentleman tipped his hat and said, "May I, sir, accompany you on your walk?"

"You can swing along, partner, on the trail for all of me and welcome."

The gentleman had to run and puff to keep up with Davy. "I heard your speech," he panted. "You're a man of talent. Let us stop at this tavern; I have something to offer you."

Davy stopped and looked down the belly of the velveted and laced cockaded gentleman, the money jingling even when he didn't move.

Across a hot grog he said, "Now, Mr. Crockett, you are not going to let the country go to waste."

"I am not," said Davy. "I aim that the poor and the hoers and hunters shall get it."

"But they don't know how to take care of the country, Mr. Crockett. They are ignorant."

"Ignorant enough to clear the land, water it with their sweat, make the clothes on your back and the very lace around your croaking throat, sir."

"You could bring your wife and children east. I have just the house for you. Now the Red Indians have far too much country."

"It was their country."

"Now, sir, you are too intelligent a man. I can show you how to buy cheap and sell dear. If we can get that land, beg, borrow, or steal it, we can rent it out for cash money."

"Over my dead body, you'll do it," Davy said.

"I know all the ways to make money and I'm finding out some new ways. How much would you take not to vote on your own Squatter and Indian Bill? We got the land, the titles, the Indians, the squatters, the slaves. Come on our side and you can bring your wife east and dress her in velvet. You can live the life of Riley."

"But you ain't got me," Davy shouted. "I'll get a streak of lightnin' and thrash you with it. I'm the yaller blossom o' the forest. You make my liberty sap rise."

Just then the cambric ruffle of the gentleman slipped, and his fat, loose skin shook and dropped. The snake flesh over the eye fell away, and Davy saw the cockeyes of the Peddler looking at him, and he jumped up, yelling, "Slickerty Sam Thimblerig Bartholomew Grizzle, that tetociously scoundratious, pesky varmint! Stand back, gentlemen, and form a ring. I'm Davy Crockett and I got revolutionary sap, and it's risen in me mighty high. It's thundering along and its gonna break—and I aim to do it. I mean to lay you low."

They tried to hold him, but he was a tornado for sure. He jumped off the ground his whole length, they said, and hit the gentleman like a drop of rain, seized his waistbands and generally discombobulated him, and when they pulled Davy away, the gentleman's lace and cambric ruffles were off, and even his pants were off, and he stood up and said grandiously, "I challenge you to a duel." The tavern howled like a bunch of hyenas.

"Send your seconds," Davy said. "We'll fight with bows and arrows."

On a gale of laughter, the gentleman got a cab, and Davy was swung to the shoulders and proposed for president.

But a sad thing happened when Davy Crockett stood up to fight against the Indian Bill. Andy Jackson was standing on the other side of the fence. Gold had been discovered on the lands granted to the Indians by treaty, and the white men wanted it, and Andy Jackson did not understand about the Indians—he had fought them too much. So he and Davy had to go against each other.

Jackson tried to get Davy to give up going against the bill, but they were both stubborn, and the enemy poured into the gap that the Indian Bill made between them.

The people all overheard him say, "A treaty is the highest law of the land. You are sending the remnants of a once powerful people into country where they who have hunted cannot hunt. You will fritter away their rights. It's wrong. It is not justice. The president is wrong about the Indians and I know it. When he is right, I would go for him more than for any man in the whole creation. I'll wear no man's collar. I would rather be an old coon dog belonging to a poor man in the forest than belong to any party that will not do justice to all. It is a wicked unjust measure and I will go against it. Let the cost to myself be what it might. If I should be the only member of the House who voted against the bill, and the only man in the U.S. who disapproved of it, I would still vote against it, and it would be a matter of rejoicing till the day I died. I have a good, honest vote, gentlemen, against the Indian Bill. I will not make me ashamed in the day of judgment."

But he was not the only man against the Indian Bill. There were many against it of every station and place and position.

"It's nothing to Crockett," became a slogan.

He was the People's hero. They always know the face and

tongue of an honest man, and honor one who stands alone against power. There was a march of music, the *Crockett March* made for him, played on the streets and blown mightily through the horns of the land.

Afterthought

1. Why is the Peddler a good symbol to show how Davy Crockett felt about people who took advantage of others?
2. How might the use of a symbol like the Peddler give you mistaken ideas about people or events of a certain time?
3. Why would it be advisable for you to read about Davy Crockett and Andrew Jackson in an encyclopedia after reading this selection?

Living in Cities 1889-1899

Harold Coy

By the 1880's more and more people were crowding into cities. Inventions and discoveries had speeded up ways of doing things and improved life for many. This fast-moving article shows the mood of that time and indicates how rapidly history was taking place as the twentieth century began.

THE FAMOUS RED HEAD ELGIN KING

THE ADVANCE 1908 MODEL ELGIN KING, as illustrated, is probably the best known bicycle on the market today. It is not only widely known, but also very favorably known. It is a bicycle which we have manufactured continuously for a great many years, and there is hardly a town or hamlet in the United States where the Elgin King bicycle with its characteristic red head and red center tube is not in use today and known to bicycle riders. Before we controlled this bicycle and manufactured it in our factory with our improved facilities, it was sold for $125.00, and yet the old original Elgin King bicycle that sold for $125.00 is not to be compared with our famous Elgin King, which we sell today for $14.95. The Elgin King is a better wheel today because important improvements have been embodied in its construction, and we have kept it thoroughly up to and in fact ahead of the times. In addition, it possesses many features that are distinctly its own, and which are not found in any other bicycle. The many little details that enter into its construction have been given very careful attention, and it is this attention to detail that has made the Elgin King famous. We desire that you note carefully the detailed description of the Elgin King as given below.

$14.95

Some New Developments

Could one really go around the world in eighty days like the man in the much-talked-of Jules Verne story? Everyone had an opinion, but no one knew. Joseph Pulitzer of the *New York World* called in Nelly Bly, a girl reporter, and said, "Go around the world as fast as you can." She did, and was back in seventy-two days, six hours, eleven minutes, and fourteen seconds.

One Sunday the *World* offered something new: a funny paper. People soon wondered how they had ever managed to live without the funnies. The rival *New York Journal* looked around for still funnier funnies and came out with "The Katzenjammer Kids."

The papers were crammed with news, for printers now set type on fast linotype machines. Father liked the sports pages. Baseball was the national game by the eighties. An all-American football eleven was named in 1889. Two years later a YMCA man invented basketball.

City people so often worked sitting down that they needed exercise. Croquet was the rage for a while. Then came tennis and roller skating. The very rich sailed boats. The

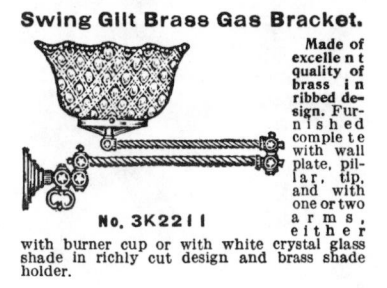

Swing Gilt Brass Gas Bracket.

Made of excellent quality of brass in ribbed design. Furnished complete with wall plate, pillar, tip, and with one or two arms, either

No. 3K2211

with burner cup or with white crystal glass shade in richly cut design and brass shade holder.

well-to-do played golf. Mr. Average American rode a bicycle: the new safety model with a chain drive, air-filled tires, and low wheels. Sometimes he went for a spin with his best girl on a bicycle built for two.

When the bicycle came in, the bustle went out. A bustle was a wire framework that made a lady's skirt flow out in an elegant train. But no lady could wear a bustle and ride a bike. She began dressing for outdoor comfort. And her young man wore a cap, for the wind would blow off a silk topper.

A City Family

Everybody worked six days a week, including Father. He lived in a two-story frame house within walking distance of his office. The parlor was furnished with a horsehair sofa, a black walnut table, and big chairs with cloth strips to protect them from hair grease. On the wall were Grandpa's picture, a moose head, and a motto that said HOME, SWEET HOME. A whatnot had shelves for picture albums, china horses, waxed flowers under glass, a dried starfish, the three little monkeys, and a pair of beaded moccasins.

Guests sat under the gaslights and

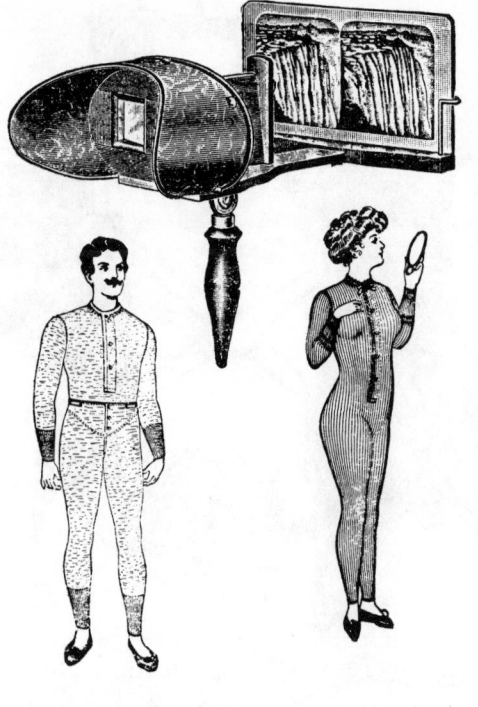

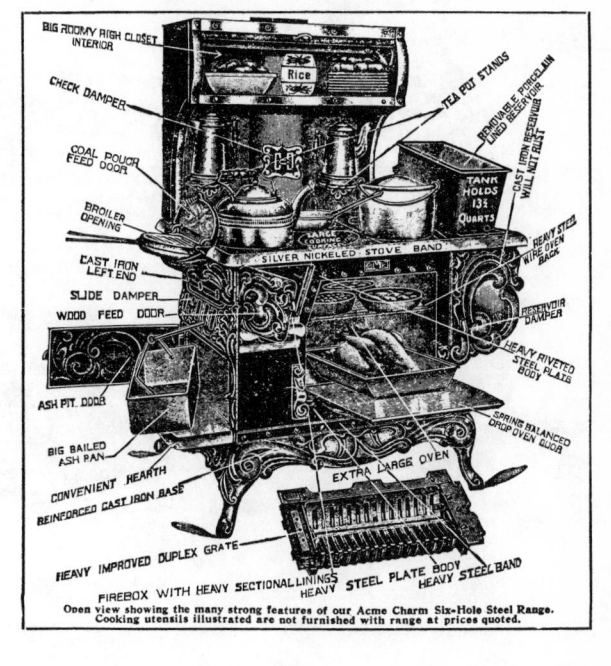

looked at stereopticon slides. After the party, Mother latched the shutters, closed the windows, pulled the blinds, and drew the velvet drapes. The parlor was too good to use except for company.

The family lived in the dining room. For breakfast, Father liked oatmeal, ham and eggs, fried potatoes, coffee, and pancakes with syrup. He had grown up on a farm. Dinner was at noon. Father came home and had soup, fish, meat and potatoes, dumplings with gravy, and chocolate pie. He wondered why he felt sleepy as the afternoon wore on. After a supper of something light, such as warmed-over roast pork, the children did their homework, Mother crocheted, and Father read his paper.

In winter, a coal stove heated the dining room. Everyone wore long flannel underwear. There was a layer of straw under the carpeting to keep cold air from coming through the cracks in the floor. Every spring out went furniture, carpets, and straw. Mother and the maid swept, beat, dusted, and scrubbed for a week.

Saturday night was bath night. Kettles of water bubbled on the kitchen range. The washtub sat on the floor. When your turn came, you

poured in hot and cold water, undressed, soaped, scrubbed, and rinsed. Each bedroom had a pitcher and bowl for everyday washing. There was an outhouse in the backyard.

City ways steadily changed this home. The street was torn up to make room for larger pipes and mains. A plumber installed a kitchen sink and put basins with running water in the bedrooms.

One day Father bought himself a lounge tub—a wooden affair, lined with zinc and long enough to lounge in. The plumber called it a set tub. He set it in place in Father's room and connected it with the water pipes. What luxury! Everyone began lounging in Father's tub. So many people were splashing around, not even waiting for Saturday, that Father cleared out a storeroom and had the tub moved in there. While about it, he told the plumber to install a toilet and a washbasin. That is how his house came to have a bathroom.

When the sewing machine was paid for, Father let Mother buy a gas range. No coal to lug, no fire to build. Later Father had the house wired for electric lights. However, he left the gas jets in, just in case the electricity went off.

After Father's office was moved farther downtown, he began having a "merchant's lunch" at a restaurant. It was a light meal that didn't make him drowsy. Mother served

An Evening at Home With the Little Ones.

the big meal in the evening and called it dinner instead of supper. The older children were lunching out too. Mary Louise was a secretary. Pauline was a "hello girl." The telephone company preferred women operators to men. They never swore at unreasonable customers.

Flats, Châteaus, and Tenements

As the city grew, some people moved into French flats, later known as apartment houses. The old homes in Father's neighborhood changed into rooming houses. Mother and Father built a home at the end of the new electric streetcar line. Father installed a furnace in the basement. It sent heat into every room through a register in the floor. Mother had

read in the *Ladies' Home Journal* that a room was useless unless you lived in it. So instead of a parlor the house had a living room with a dining alcove.

Not all new houses were like this. Young Mrs. William K. Vanderbilt of New York had a dining room two stories high. The Vanderbilts' old brownstone mansion was so dreadful that her husband had let her build a château on Fifth Avenue. It was a copy of a French castle and cost three million dollars.

Tenement houses were rising on New York's Lower East Side. There were four tenements to a floor, four rooms to a tenement, and sometimes four persons to a room, counting boarders. The only rooms with win-

dows were those facing the street or the air shaft.

Most tenement dwellers had grown up on a farm, like Father. The farm they remembered was in Italy, Poland, Croatia, Bohemia, Hungary, or Finland. They had tilled the same fields as their ancestors and danced on the same holidays in the same peasant costume.

Immigrants

But times were changing in Europe. Landlords were combining little fields into big ones so they could use machinery and raise wheat the American way. It was useless for a peasant to work longer and harder on his little patch of ground. Any-

thing he could do, the American machines could do faster and cheaper. One day he told his wife, "Better for the children we go to America."

Steamships carried as many as half a million uprooted peasants a year to New York Harbor. Twenty years earlier they would have become American farmers. But now America wanted men to dig coal, lay streetcar tracks, and erect skyscrapers.

Italians mixed mortar and dug ditches for Irish contractors whose fathers had mixed mortar and dug ditches for Yankees. Poles who arrived as Niagara Falls was being harnessed went to work in the new steel mills of Buffalo. Many of the

newcomers, like the Irish before them, were Catholics. A sixth of the American people were of that faith by the end of the century.

Jews fled to America from lands under Russian rule. The Russian czar's officials had an old custom of blaming the Jews when something went wrong. They did this so people would take it out on the Jews instead of on them. Every Jew lived in danger of beatings and massacres. He wasn't allowed to be a doctor, lawyer, or farmer. Often he was a fur worker or a tailor because he couldn't be anything else.

The Jews carried their trades to New York, worked in sweatshops, and lived in slums with names like Misery Row. Tuberculosis was known as the tailors' disease.

Settlement Houses

Lillian Wald grew up in a comfortable home without knowing of these conditions, though she was Jewish too. Her family had come to America in earlier times. Miss Wald first saw the Lower East Side when she taught home nursing to mothers on Henry Street. A call on a sick mother started her on a lifetime of rounds as a visiting nurse. She saw how living conditions made people sick. Sometimes she'd nurse a scarlet-fever patient in a room where the mother and the other children were

sorting rags or making candy to earn a few pennies a day.

Miss Wald spoke out against child labor and sweatshops and pleaded for clean streets and decent homes. Along with other nurses, she opened a playground, a day nursery, and clubrooms for mothers, fathers, and young people. The place was called the Henry Street Settlement.

Lillian Wald of New York and Jane Addams, who founded Hull House in Chicago, were pioneer social workers. They made America's cities healthier, friendlier places in which to live.

Medicine and Education

Fewer people were dying of typhoid fever in some cities than in others. The cities with less typhoid were those that piped clean water into people's homes and carried away the sewage.

In the eighties and nineties, some doctor was always finding a new germ. Germs too small to be seen with the naked eye caused diphtheria, tuberculosis, and other diseases. That was why one needed clean surroundings, fresh air, rest, and proper food.

A surgeon could now take out a diseased appendix before it burst. In the old days, infection or blood

poisoning would surely have set in following an operation. Now, before operating, the surgeon scrubbed his hands with soap and a stiff brush. His instruments were boiled. His gown and the dressings he used were made germfree by heat. Often he had to operate on a kitchen table under a kerosene lamp. But it was better to work in a well-equipped hospital.

Many a town built a community hospital—and a high school too. The average citizen had only a fifth-grade education, but he wanted his children to have greater advantages.

By the end of the century, school children in Hawaii, the Philippines, and Puerto Rico began learning about Paul Revere's ride and Lincoln's Gettysburg Address.

Some Things Do Not Change

Dorothy Canfield Fisher

*You have read several selections about events and people
in American history. Try to recall examples from your reading
as you consider what this selection says about the value of
knowing about the past.*

When I was a girl on vacation visits to the family farm, my
great-uncle spent a lot of patient effort teaching me how to
harness and drive a team of workhorses. As things turned out,
that particular bit of knowledge has never been of the least
practical use to me. Is it fair then to say that he was just
wasting his time and mine? No! That answer would miss one
of the real benefits which learning—learning almost anything
thoroughly—brings to us. All the drill in finding the right

buckle for each strap, the mental habit built up through solving a problem piece by piece, step by step, must have made it easier for me later on when I had to change a flat tire on some lonely back road.

And knowing about old-time customs and wisdom can do a great deal more than just training our hands and brains to work at jobs in an orderly manner. Ever since the dawn of history, when our cavemen ancestors invented words to express their thoughts, old people have been trying to pass on whatever experience has taught them about ideas of right and wrong, about what sort of actions bring lasting satisfaction—in the hope of helping the boys and girls around them who are just starting out in life for themselves. Often enough what fathers and mothers have to say seems out of date. Their memories of the past do not fit today's changed conditions. And anyone can see that the future promises to be strange beyond the wildest flights of our present imagination.

But just the same it is foolish and self-defeating for us to shut our eyes to everything that happened before we were born. For some things do *not* change. Water will run downhill in the future as it always has. Fire will burn. And as we look back into the story of humanity, we see that there have always been elements in our own human nature which have persisted in spite of all the prodigious differences in the outer circumstances of life from century to century.

Some of these elements are nothing to be proud of, because we human beings have a mixed inheritance. As we read the pages of history, we can easily be discouraged by finding so many examples of greed and cruelty, the struggle for riches and power at no matter what cost of suffering to others. But this is only part of the picture.

For when we say that the inherited urges in the human bloodstream are mixed, we don't in the least mean to deny that some of those deep-rooted urges are better—enormously better—than others. Any child *may* grow up to be a gangster; the fact is that only two or three in every thousand do become criminals. The overwhelming majority of young people now in school are going to turn out pretty much like their fathers, mothers, great and great-great-grandparents—reasonably good average citizens. *But* (and it is a big "but") in the future as in the past, a few will rise far above the general average, a few will carry on the great tradition handed down to them by those earlier men and women whose main motive was not to seek advantage for themselves, who actually forgot themselves most of the time because their minds were entirely occupied with something bigger—perhaps organizing a working government to provide liberty and justice for all, perhaps finding a cure for diphtheria, protesting against slavery, or puzzling out as best they could the reasons for the tides, the trade winds, and eclipses of the sun and moon.

This tells us something about what we human beings really care for deep down in our hearts, that in the long run the vast majority of people all over the world have come to believe such unselfish actions are worthwhile, that they are expressions of intelligence and character at its highest level. And it proves to us that such ideals are not just impractical visions about what life might be, that they are not invented myths about heroes and saints of antiquity, when we find that throughout the short span of our national history there have been plenty of men who have actually put these ideals into practice, and by acting on them in one way or another have made their lives tremendously valuable to anybody and everybody.

And we move on: we move down:
With the first light we push forward:
We descend from the past as a wandering people from
   mountains.
We cross into the day to be discovered.

Archibald MacLeish

Myriads

Stars

Alone in the night
  On a dark hill
With pines around me
  Spicy and still,

And a heaven full of stars
  Over my head,
White and topaz
  And misty red;

Myriads with beating
  Hearts of fire
That aeons
  Cannot vex or tire;

Up the dome of heaven
  Like a great hill,
I watch them marching
  Stately and still,

And I know that I
  Am honored to be
Witness
  Of so much majesty.

Sara Teasdale

Phaethon

In all times men have looked at the sky with wonder. The ancient Greeks told stories such as this to explain the existence of the sun, the moon, or the stars.

The ancient Greeks imagined gods who they believed were in charge of Nature's glories. Seeing the sun rise every morning, they would say, "There goes the sun-god Apollo, driving his great flaming chariot through the skies!"

Now Apollo, so the story goes, had a son on the earth, named Phaethon. The lad's mother was Clymene, a beautiful nymph. Born of such beautiful parents, Phaethon could hardly help growing up proud and handsome. It was only natural that he should become enraged when some of his young friends scoffed at his story of divine birth.

In fierce anger, Phaethon came to his mother and cried, "If I am truly the child of a god, give me some proof of it!"

"You are indeed the son of Apollo," said Clymene. "And if you wish to, you can prove it. You must journey far to the east to the land where the sun rises. There you will find

Apollo. Present yourself to him, and let him tell you with his own lips who you are.''

The headstrong youth did not delay an instant. He set forth at once. After many weeks' journey he found himself before the glorious palace of the sun. It was so magnificent and it gleamed so brightly that the light was almost more than he could bear.

Phaethon entered the palace. At the end of a huge hall he saw Apollo, seated on a throne which glittered with diamonds. Around the sun-god's head gleamed golden rays. On either side of the throne stood Apollo's attendants, the Hour, the Day, the Month, the Year, and the Seasons. Spring was resplendent in a garland of flowers; Summer wore a garland of grain. Autumn stood there, too, in a richly colored garment, his feet stained with the juice of the grape. Winter's face was pale, his garments were dead white, and his hair and beard were stiff with frost.

Seeing Phaethon at the end of the hall, Apollo beckoned him to approach and state his errand.

"O light of the world!" said Phaethon. "Apollo, my father! Give me some proof, I beg you, by which I may be known as yours!"

Then Apollo, recognizing his son, laid aside the beams that surrounded his head, stepped forward, and embraced the handsome lad.

"Truly," he said, "you are my son, and as a sign that this is so, ask for any gift you want. It shall be yours, I promise you."

Quick as a flash, Phaethon answered, "O father, then just for one day let me drive your chariot across the sky."

Apollo drew back. "Oh, my son, I have spoken rashly.

Anything else in the world I would gladly grant. You don't know what you ask! You are a mortal, yet you ask to do what even the gods find difficult. None but myself may drive the flaming car of Day—not even Jupiter, whose terrible right hand hurls the thunderbolts. I must warn you of the terrible dangers.

"The beginning of the journey is so steep that even my fiery steeds, fresh and strong as they are in the morning, can scarcely climb it. The middle is so high that even I grow dizzy with fear when I look down at the earth and sea below. The last part of the way goes down so steeply that it takes all my strength not to fall headlong from my chariot. And all the time the heavens are turning above my head, carrying the stars in sweeping movement, while the earth revolves in the opposite way beneath me.

"Perhaps you think that it is all a beautiful ride with the palaces and the temples of the gods along the way. Oh, no, my son! The path is beset by fearful monsters. You must pass the horns of the Bull, draw nigh to the Lion's paws. You must pass between the claws of the Crab and the arms of the Scorpion.

"But worst of all, you have not the strength to hold in check the unruly steeds who pull the golden chariot of the sun. I can scarcely govern them myself. They are steeds born of flame, and fire breathes from their very nostrils.

"Oh, my son, take back your request while you can. You came to ask for proof that I am your father? If you could look into my heart, you would see proof enough of a father's love. Phaethon, choose anything in the world, the most precious thing that sea or earth contains, and I will not refuse you. Only do not ask to ride my chariot!"

But the hot-blooded youth would not be swayed. Apollo's pleas fell on deaf ears. There was nothing for the god to do but to keep his promise. In great fear, Apollo led Phaethon to the chariot.

The boy gazed in admiration at the magnificent car. It was made of gold and silver and precious stones which reflected the brightness of the sun. Joyous and impatient to be off, Phaethon sprang into the chariot.

Apollo bathed his son's face with a powerful salve to withstand the great heat. He set the golden rays on Phaethon's head and proffered him these last words of advice. "Hold the reins tight. Do not use the whip, for the horses go fast enough of their own will. The important thing is to hold them in. Keep in the middle zone, for if you go too high, you will burn the heavenly dwellings of the gods; and if you go too low, you will set the earth on fire."

Phaethon thanked his heavyhearted parent and seized the reins. The chariot started forward with a rush. The horses soon felt that the load they pulled was much lighter than usual. Rushing headlong as they pleased, they left Apollo's usual path. Phaethon tried desperately to control the steeds, but his strength was nothing to theirs. He looked down at the earth spreading beneath him and grew pale with terror. Soon enough he wished that he had never won his request—that he had never even seen his father's flaming chariot!

The monsters of the sky stretched out their horrid claws toward him. In mortal fright, Phaethon lost his self-control. The reins dropped from his nerveless fingers. Now with no controlling hand at the reins, the horses dashed off—first high up into the heavens, then down to the earth, spreading ruin as they ran. As the chariot of the sun came close to the earth, great cities were consumed by the terrible heat; the fields of the earth were scorched, and all the crops were destroyed. Mountain tops were left smoky; rivers were dried up. Destruction and terror filled the world.

Then Earth in her despair cried out to Jupiter, the king of the gods, to save her. And Jupiter, seeing that not only the earth but the heavens themselves were in danger, stood up and gathered his lightning bolts into his hand. He thundered and hurled a lightning bolt down from heaven straight toward Phaethon in his chariot. Phaethon, his hair on fire, fell headlong to the earth like a shooting star. Down he plunged to his death, into a great river.

And so Phaethon, the willful boy who thought he was mighty enough to drive the sun's own chariot, had to be destroyed so that his vanity should not result in the destruction of the world.

Northern Stars

Rose Wyler and Gerald Ames

Long ago, people noticed that the stars seemed to be arranged in groups. You can enjoy finding some of these constellations for yourself.

You can easily become acquainted with the constellations around the North Pole of the sky. The most striking among them is called the Great Bear, Ursa Major. Several of its stars form the Big Dipper.

Look carefully at the star at the bend of the handle. This is Mizar, which has a fainter companion, Alcor. Both stars were named long ago by Arab astronomers. In their time, finding Alcor was considered a sign of good eyesight. Today Alcor is rather easy to see. Perhaps it has become brighter.

When you look at Mizar through a telescope, you discover that it is not a single star, but a pair. The two seem like one to the naked eye because they are so close.

The Pole Star, or North Star, is located by sighting along the two stars opposite the handle of the Dipper. The Pole Star itself belongs to another constellation, the Little Dipper. It is the last star in the handle. The astronomical name of the Little Dipper is Ursa Minor, the Little Bear.

A legend tells how the bears got into the sky. Hera, the wife of the god Zeus, was jealous of the beautiful nymph Callisto and had her changed into a bear. One day Callisto's son met the bear in the woods. Not knowing she was his mother, he lifted his knife to attack her. But before he could do so, Zeus turned the boy into a little bear and placed him and his mother in the sky.

A constellation named Draco, the Dragon, winds between the bears, then swings in a curve beyond the Little Bear.

On the opposite side of the Pole Star from the Big Bear is the constellation Cassiopeia, named after a legendary queen. Its stars form the letter *W* or *M*, depending on the way you look at them.

Nearby is a constellation named after Cepheus, the husband of Cassiopeia. The main stars of Cepheus form the outline of a house with a peaked roof. The star at the corner farthest from the Pole Star is Delta of Cepheus. It is a pulsating star that reaches its greatest brightness every 129 hours. The brightening and fading that we see now occurred nearly two centuries before Columbus discovered America, for Delta of Cepheus is about 650 light-years away.

As the earth turns, the constellations near the Pole Star seem to wheel around it. In an hour, each goes one twenty-fourth of the way around. If you could observe them night after night with instruments, you would find that the constellations are always a little farther along in their turn than they were the night before. In a year their advance adds up to one complete turn around the Pole Star. This extra turn is due to the earth's journey around the sun.

Today, the stars are still signposts in the sky. They are signposts for travelers in space as well as travelers on Earth.

Stars

The stars are too many to count.
The stars make sixes and sevens.
The stars tell nothing—and everything.
The stars look scattered.
Stars are so far away they never speak
   when spoken to.

Carl Sandburg

Telescopes

David Dietz

The stars appear as tiny dots of light far beyond our reach. How did scientists first manage to take a closer look?

For thousands of years men could see no more in the heavens than was apparent to the unaided eye. They had no way of knowing what the sun or moon or planets or stars were really like. Then, in the year 1609, the great Italian scientist Galileo turned a little telescope upon the sky.

One surprising discovery after another met his gaze as he studied the heavens. His telescope revealed the mountains on the moon. Most astonishing of all, it disclosed four tiny moons revolving around the planet Jupiter.

As he studied the stars, he noted many too faint to be seen without the telescope. And he discovered that the Milky Way, which appears to the unaided eye like a luminous streak of cloud, is actually composed of myriads of stars.

Galileo was not the inventor of the telescope. The telescope had been invented in Holland some time before. It is not quite certain who made the first one, but the credit is usually given to an optician named Hans Lippershey. According to legend, he happened to hold up two spectacle lenses, one in front of the other. Looking through them, he noticed that they made a distant church steeple seem closer.

Galileo heard about the invention in 1609 and decided to make a telescope himself. He made his first little instrument by fitting a spectacle lens in either end of an organ pipe. It was not very good and magnified only three times. He began to grind and polish his own lenses and soon constructed a telescope that magnified thirty-three times. It was with this instrument that he made his famous discoveries in 1609 and 1610. In Florence, Italy, you can see two of his telescopes which have been preserved in the Science Museum in that city.

In all of his telescopes, Galileo used a convex lens at the far end of the tube for the objective, as it is called, and a concave lens for an eyepiece. (A convex lens is thicker at the center than at the edges; a concave lens is thinner at the center.) The concave eyepiece merely passed on the converging rays of light from the convex lens.

Another famous astronomer, Johann Kepler, who lived at the same time as Galileo, saw that the telescope could be greatly improved by permitting the light from the objective to come to a focus and then using another convex lens as an eyepiece. This eyepiece now acted as a magnifying glass to magnify the image.

However, the early telescope builders soon ran into a difficulty. When they built bigger telescopes, they found that the images were no longer sharp but blurred with the colors of the rainbow. This was because white light is a mixture of all the colors of the rainbow and the

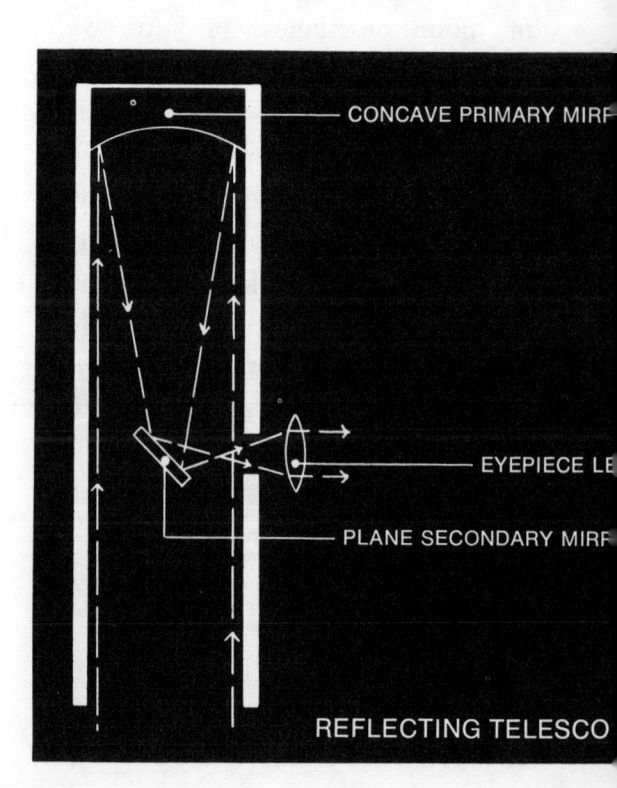

CONCAVE PRIMARY MIRF

EYEPIECE LE

PLANE SECONDARY MIRF

REFLECTING TELESCO

different colors were not brought to one sharp focus.

A Scotch mathematician named James Gregory in 1663 suggested a telescope which used a concave mirror as the objective to gather the light and bring it to a focus. The first telescope of this sort was built by the great English mathematician Sir Isaac Newton in 1671. It was a very small telescope employing a mirror only one inch in diameter.

Newton's telescope used a second flat mirror to reflect the image into the eyepiece which was placed at one side at the top of the tube.

Telescopes built on Newton's plan became known as reflecting telescopes, or reflectors. Those which follow Kepler's plan are called refracting telescopes, or refractors.

Eventually, telescope makers learned to get sharp images with refracting telescopes. This was done by using an objective which was a combination of two lenses made of two different kinds of glass.

. . . .

The bigger a refracting or reflecting telescope, the farther it will see into space. But these big telescopes have one drawback. They see only a very small area of the sky at one time. Scientists say they have a

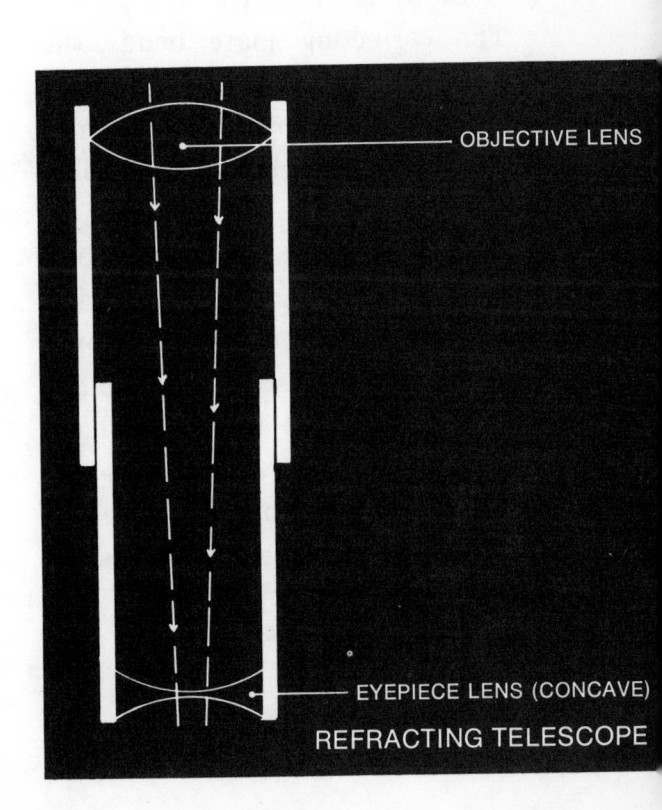

OBJECTIVE LENS

EYEPIECE LENS (CONCAVE)

REFRACTING TELESCOPE

small field of view. The more powerful the telescope, the smaller the field of view.

Modern astronomers felt the need of telescopes with larger fields of view to make it easier to survey the heavens. The problem was solved by a German optician named Bernhard Schmidt in 1931. He invented a modified reflecting telescope which is known as the Schmidt-type telescope.

The Schmidt-type telescope has a concave mirror at the bottom of the tube. But before the light reaches the mirror, it passes through a very thin lens known as the correcting plate.

The correcting plate bends the rays of light so that the telescope brings a large area of the sky into sharp focus on the photographic plate.

The astronomer does not look through the telescope but sights through a smaller telescope, known as a guiding telescope, or finder, attached to it. Similar auxiliary telescopes are also attached to refracting and reflecting telescopes to make it easier to focus on a desired object.

At Palomar Mountain there is a Schmidt-type telescope with a correcting plate forty-eight inches in diameter. This instrument will provide a sharp photograph of an area of the sky 1,000 times as large as can be seen through the 200-inch telescope. The Palomar Observatory also has a smaller Schmidt-type telescope with a correcting plate eighteen inches in diameter.

Astronomers have talked about telescopes even larger than the giant eye on Palomar Mountain. Perhaps someday a 300-inch telescope will be built.

Afterthought

1. How do telescopes help people learn more about the planets and the stars?
2. Why do people study the heavens?

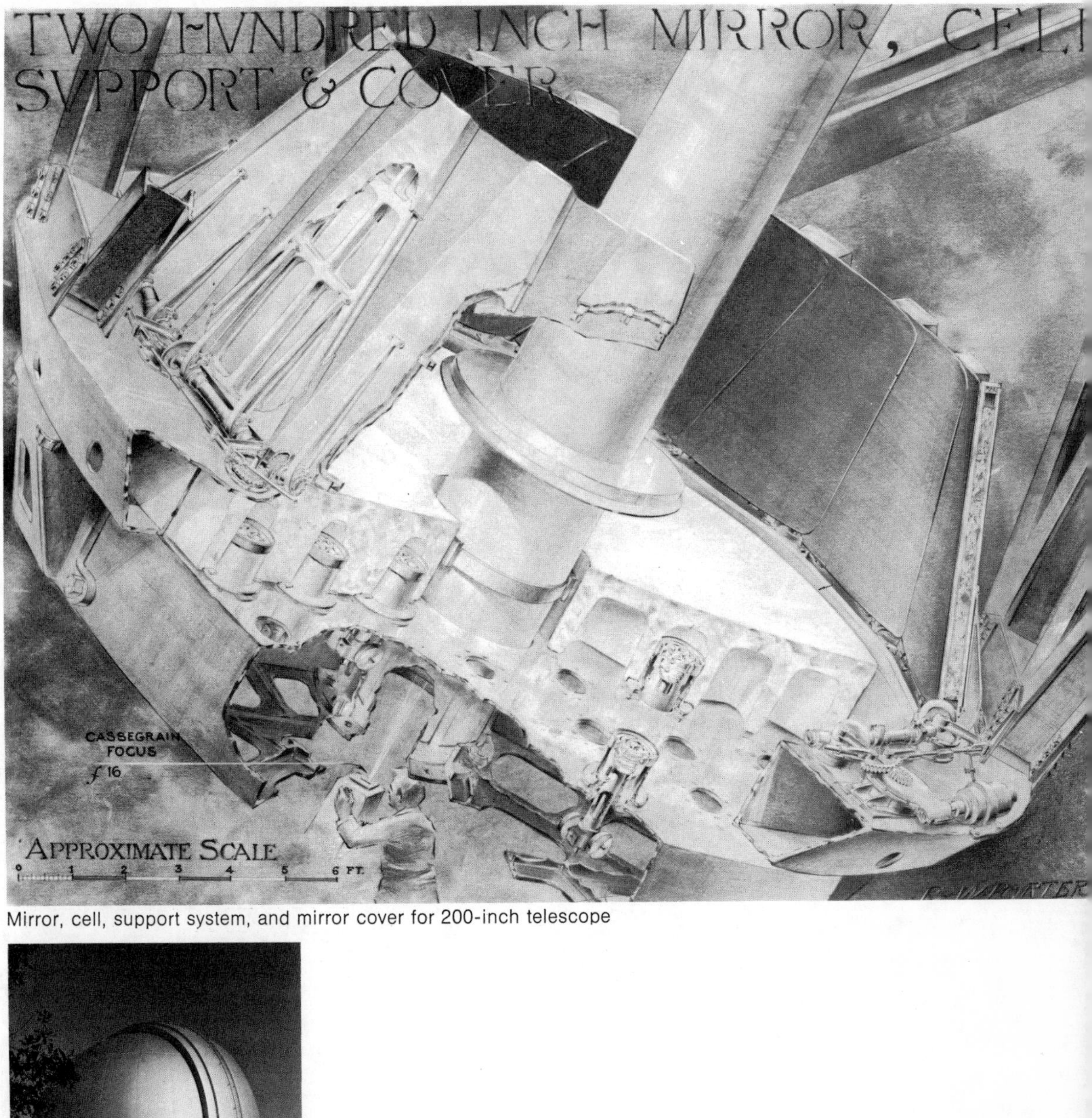

TWO HVNDRED INCH MIRROR, CELL
SVPPORT & COVER

CASSEGRAIN
FOCUS
ƒ 16

APPROXIMATE SCALE
0   1   2   3   4   5   6 FT.

Mirror, cell, support system, and mirror cover for 200-inch telescope

Dome for forty-eight inch telescope

Photographs courtesy Hale Observatories

Get Yourself a Telescope

Harry Edward Neal

Would you like to see Jupiter's moons or the mountains on our own moon? Perhaps you can with a telescope you make yourself.

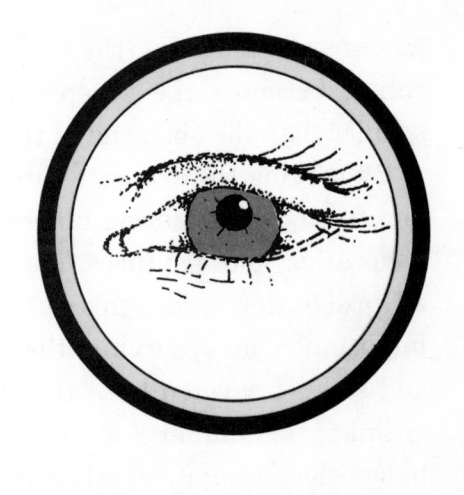

You can make a simple refracting telescope quite easily and inexpensively. It won't be of professional caliber and it won't bring the stars within touching distance, but with it you might be able to see the larger valleys and mountains on the moon and enough other celestial sights to make you want to spend more time at stargazing.

You will need two lenses and two tubes. For the larger lens, or objective, you may use a lens from a pair of spectacles of the type sold in dime stores. Regular "curve-corrected" spectacle lenses are not suitable for telescope making.

For the smaller lens, or eyepiece, I used a small, cheap magnifying glass which had been put away in a bureau drawer.

By lining up the smaller lens behind the larger lens and looking at a distant object until it was clear, I determined how long a tube I would need to hold the lenses. It happened that mine was small—less than a foot long. Depending upon the kind of lens you use for your objective, you might need a tube three or four feet long, perhaps longer.

For lack of any better material to make the tubes, I rolled up pieces of thin cardboard which the laundry had used to return my laundered shirts. I rolled one piece tightly around the objective (which was about half an inch from the tube end) and the other I rolled so that it was just a bit smaller than the first and could slide in and out quite easily. I put pieces of gummed paper around the tubes to keep them round.

I had to fit the eyepiece into a

cardboard "plug" at the end of its tube, because the eyepiece was smaller than the open end of the tube.

By moving the eyepiece tube back and forth, I could bring objects into focus at various distances. They were all upside down, but this is of little importance in observing the moon and stars. I covered both tubes with ordinary aluminum foil, merely to hide the rough cardboard and gummed paper! It is also a good idea to darken the inside of the tube with black ink or nonglossy paint, to absorb stray light.

My sixteen-year-old son suggested improvising a mounting by using my camera tripod. We took a small scrap of white pine and drilled a hole just a little smaller than the diameter of the threaded bolt which would ordinarily

hold the camera to the tripod. Then we used strips of half-inch adhesive tape to hold the wood block to the telescope tube. Finally we screwed the assembly down on the camera holder, and our mounting was complete. At least it held the instrument steadier than our hands could.

With a very rough and simple instrument such as this, you can get only a taste of the fun you might have with a bigger and better telescope. Many amateurs grind, polish, and figure their own lenses and mirrors. You should be aware, though, that the grinding and polishing of lenses and mirrors is hard and tedious work, requiring patience, time, and elbow grease. The rewards are worthwhile, but there are also other ways to proceed.

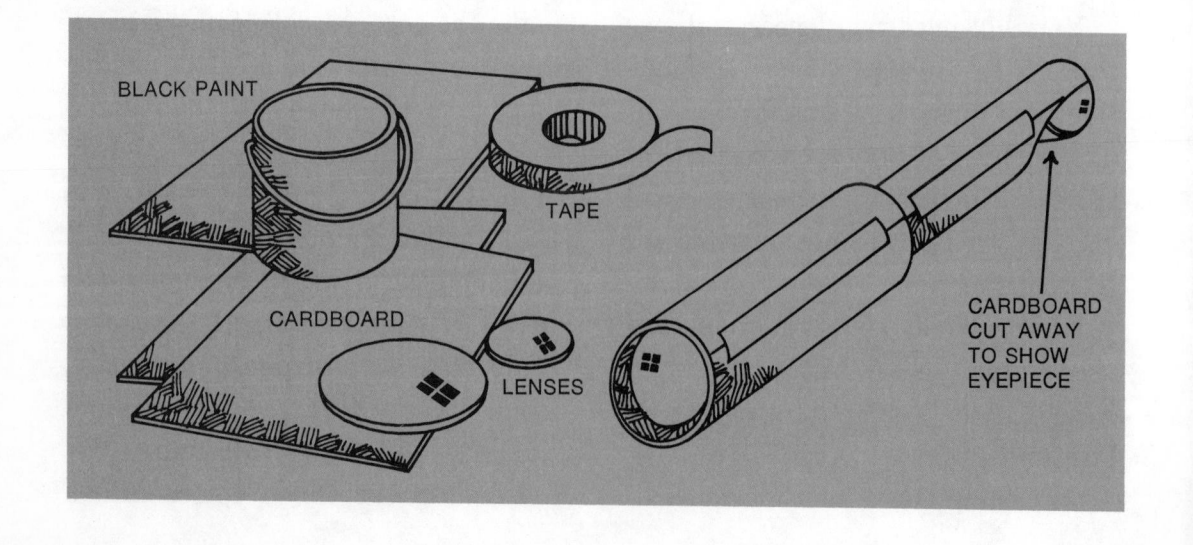

BLACK PAINT

TAPE

CARDBOARD

LENSES

CARDBOARD CUT AWAY TO SHOW EYEPIECE

At the outset you will want to decide whether you want a reflector or a refractor. Both are efficient. The reflector will cost less money in the beginning, but it will eventually require servicing—principally resilvering of the mirror when it tarnishes. If you decide to build your own telescope, a reflector will be easier and cheaper to make than a refractor, although amateur astronomers make and use both types.

Most amateur astronomical groups or clubs conduct telescope-making classes for their members. By joining such a club, you can receive competent instruction in the making of a telescope which, when completed, should be of good quality. You will also be taught how to use it, and you will have pleasant evenings together with other members having similar interests.

If you cannot join a local group and want to make your own telescope, you may buy glass disks, abrasives, tools, and other do-it-yourself supplies from numerous dealers in telescopes and telescope-making materials, all with the necessary instructions.

If you do not want to attempt to grind and polish your own lenses or mirrors, you may buy finished lenses and mirrors of various sizes, as well as telescopes, tubes, mountings—even professional observatory buildings, complete with domes—from commercial manufacturers specializing in these fields.

Before investing any significant sum of money in a telescope for your own use, it will be wise for you to study some books about telescopes and astronomy to help you decide whether or not your investment is warranted. If there is an amateur astronomical group in your area, arrange to look through a telescope of one of its members and to talk with several about stargazing in general. If it has enough appeal, then consider making or buying your telescope.

You may discover, however, that it isn't as fascinating as you thought. In that case, it would be a waste of money for you to buy a telescope, since you probably wouldn't use it once the novelty wore off. On the other hand, if and when you do look through a good astronomical telescope for the first time, you may be so intrigued by the celestial show that you can't wait to get or make an instrument of your very own.

But outer Space,
At least this far,
For all the fuss
Of the popul*ace*,
Stays more popu*lar*
Than popul*ous*.

Robert Frost

Visitors from Outer Space

Roy A. Gallant

There have been many reports of unidentified flying objects. Were they visitors from outer space? No one knows. But scientists do know that material from outer space has landed on the earth.

METEOROIDS, METEORS, AND METEORITES

Several tons of material from space fall onto the earth each day. Most of it ends up as fine dust that drifts down through the atmosphere. Some of it, however, is material the size of sand grains and pebbles. Occasionally, chunks of rock and metal the size of houses or small mountains crash into our planet with explosive force. The largest outer space visitor on display is the Ahnighito Meteorite. It is a chunk of metal weighing thirty-four tons and is on permanent exhibit at The American Museum—Hayden Planetarium. An even larger one is in South Africa.

Where does all of this material come from? And what happens when a small space mountain plummets into us? For convenience, we can talk about "big stuff" and "little stuff." Let's take up the "big stuff" first.

Between the planets Mars and Jupiter is a belt of debris orbiting the sun just as the planets do. How the debris (called the asteroids) got there, we do not know. Some astronomers have suggested that a planet once occupied the orbit between Mars and Jupiter and was broken up by Jupiter's gravitational attraction.

Other astronomers suspect that the original matter occupying that particular region of the solar system never collected itself into a planet body when the solar system was formed. Whatever the reason, it is there. Telescopic photographs of the asteroid belt show chunks of matter from fifty miles to several hundred miles across, and we can safely say that there must be millions and millions more asteroids only a few miles, a few yards, or a few inches from edge to edge. To date, astronomers have worked out the orbits of more than 3,000 asteroids.

Planets close to the asteroid belt—Jupiter, Mars; the earth and moon—from time to time collide with asteroids. *Mariner IV*'s remarkable photographs of Mars show that the planet's surface has several large craters. The moon's surface is pockmarked with thousands upon thousands of craters. We now think that many of the craters on both Mars and the moon were made by large asteroid impacts. The earth, too, has many craters, but it has been only recently that we have begun to look for such impact craters on our home planet. One of the more spectacular and well preserved ones is the famous Barringer Crater near

Winslow, Arizona. About 50,000 years ago an asteroid plunged into the Arizona desert with explosive impact and left the Barringer Crater scar: a gaping hole 600 feet deep and three quarters of a mile from edge to edge.

To date we know of about fifty earth craters in North America alone, thought to have been formed by stray asteroids. Some of them measure many miles from rim to rim, as the moon's craters do. One scientist has even suggested that Hudson's Bay may be an old crater carved out by an asteroid impact.

Fortunately, these granddaddy collisions are rare events on the earth nowadays. According to one estimate, we can expect one about every thousand years. But there may have been a time in the distant past when such collisions were more frequent.

The "little stuff," among which are the so-called shooting stars, plunging into the earth forms the bulk of the material reaching us from outer space. On just about any clear night, over a period of an hour, you can see anywhere from five to ten junior-sized visitors streak through the atmosphere. They are traveling so fast, up to 160,000 miles an hour, that most of them burn up before they reach the ground. They flare up at an altitude of about seventy-five miles, are visible for a second or so, and then disappear at a height of about fifty miles. Their fine remains drift to the ground as dust. The fleeting streak of light that a meteoroid leaves is called a meteor; and if the meteoroid survives its hot journey through the air and reaches ground, we call it a meteorite.

During many months of the year we have meteor showers. At such times it is possible to see dozens and sometimes hundreds or thousands of meteors each hour. The Perseids Shower, which takes place around August 12 each year, is usually a good one, with fifty or more meteors streaking into view every hour. The Geminids Shower, which takes place around December 13, is also a good one. A meteor shower is named after the constellation out of which the meteors seem to flow. The Leonids Shower, for instance, which put on a remarkable display in November of 1966, is named after the constellation Leo. The swarm meteoroids, those producing meteor showers, are probably the remains of old comets and are about as soft as cigar ash.

Whenever the earth crosses the path of a swarm of these mushy meteoroids, we have a shower.

COMETS

In May 1910, millions of people watched the return of Halley's Comet. What they saw was a bright point of light, about the size of a star, with a luminous tail stretching thousands of miles across the heavens. For many days Halley's Comet rose and set as the sun does; then it disappeared from view. During Halley's time, and even during the 1910 return, many people were afraid of the comet, thinking that it was to bring worldwide disaster. Today we know that comets are among the most harmless objects in the sky.

The head, or nucleus, of a comet is nothing more than a loose swarm of stone and metal debris, each piece frosted over with frozen gas. Comets move in orbits about the sun, but the orbits are usually long, stretched-out ones. As a comet nears the sun, the frost coatings are changed to a gas, and the nucleus is seen to glow as it reflects light from the sun. Some of the gas is pushed away from the nucleus by radiation pressure of the sun and forms a long glowing tail.

Photographs courtesy Hale Observatories

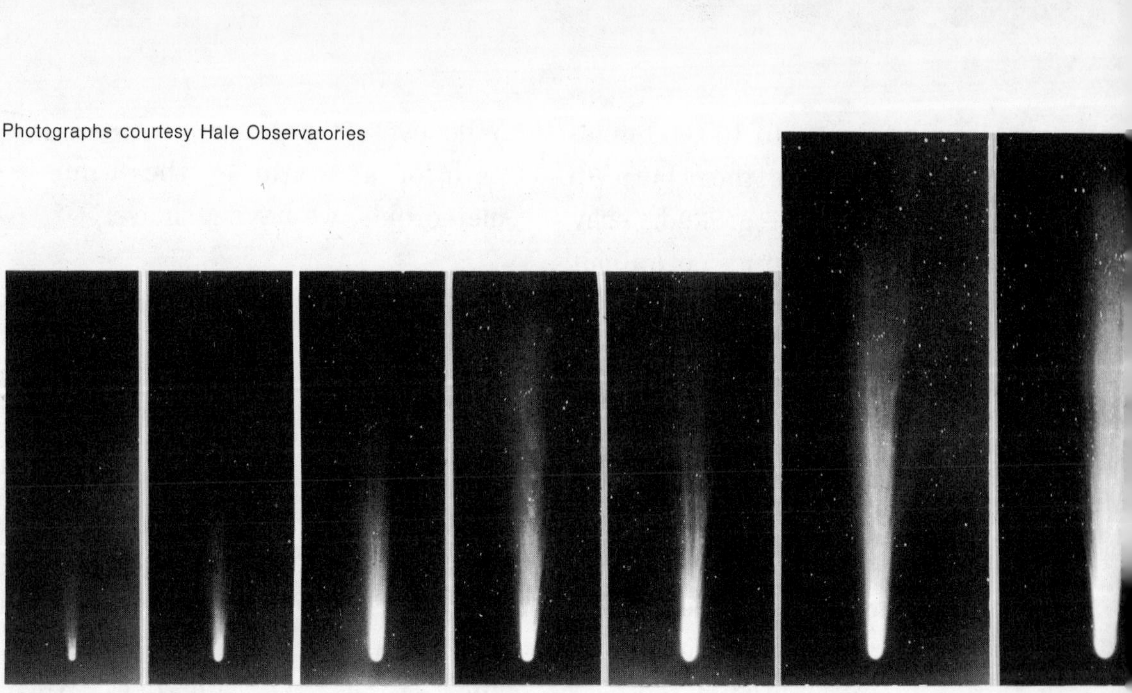

April 26, 1910 | April 27, 1910 | April 30, 1910 | May 2, 1910 | May 3, 1910 | May 4, 1910 | May 6, 1910

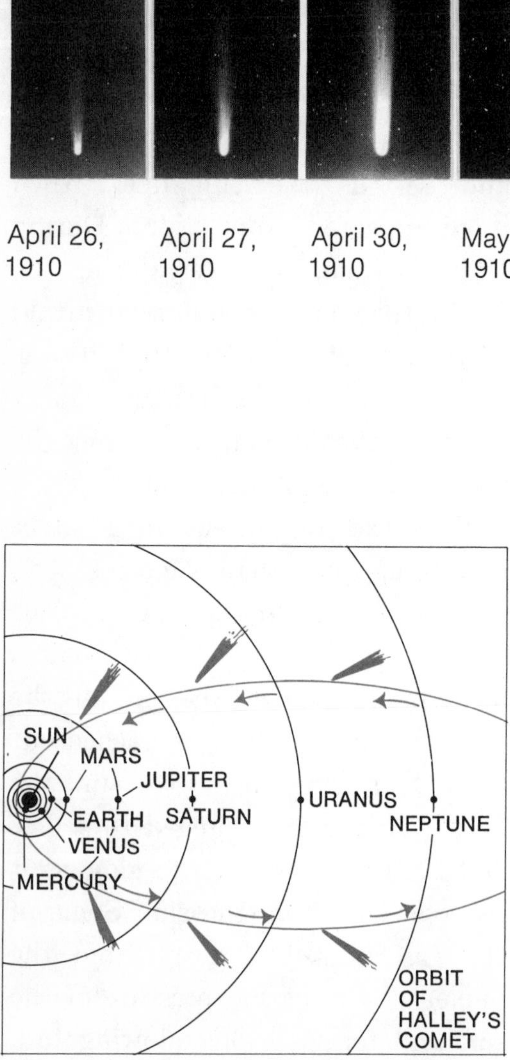

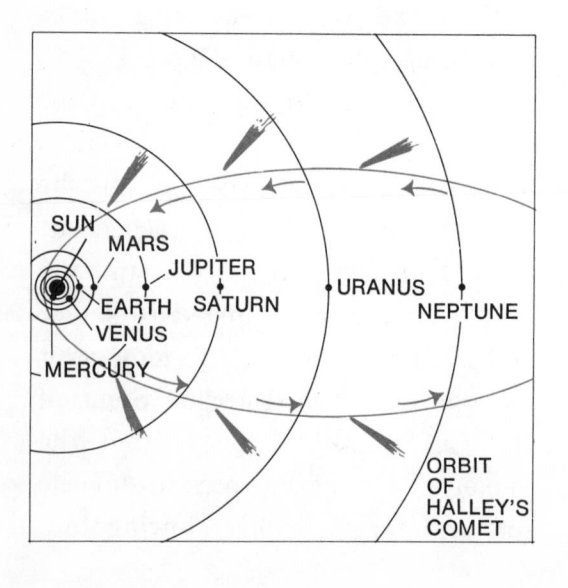

The gas tail is so thin that even faint stars can be seen through it. As the illustration of the orbit of Halley's Comet shows, the tail is always kept pointing away from the sun. During each visit to the sun, the comet loses some of its gas; after a while so much is lost that we can no longer see the tail or head. In 1986 Halley's Comet is due to swing in close to the sun again and should be visible to us. It will be interesting to see if we can notice a difference in the length of its tail.

One of the most unusual comets was Biela's Comet. It was first re-

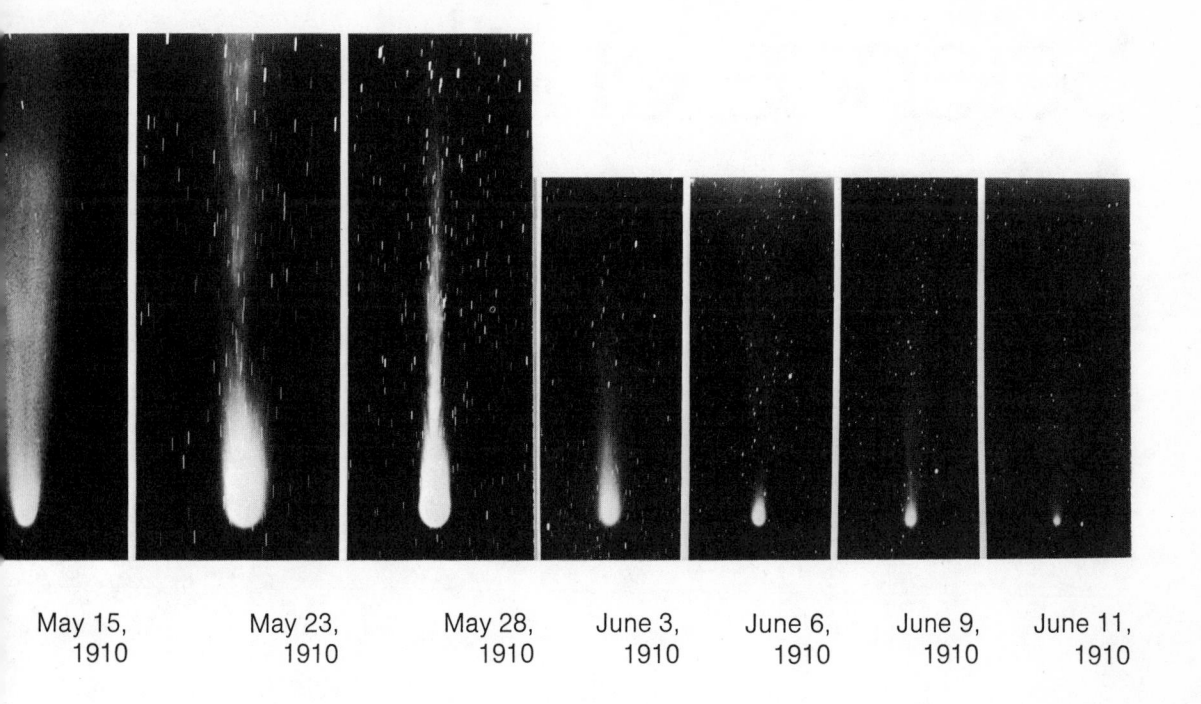

May 15, 1910   May 23, 1910   May 28, 1910   June 3, 1910   June 6, 1910   June 9, 1910   June 11, 1910

corded in 1826 and is most likely the same comet that was seen in the years 1772 and 1805. As forecast by Biela, the comet came back six and three-quarters years later, in 1832. But in 1839, when it was due for another return, it was difficult to see. However, in 1845 it was back again in full strength, although something had happened to it. It seemed to have split in two. While the smaller of the two heads became brighter, the larger one appeared to get dimmer. In addition, the two heads began drifting apart. By the time they made another return, in 1852,

more than a million miles of space separated them. In 1859 and 1866, when the double comet was due back again, it did not appear either time. But in 1872, when it was also scheduled to make an appearance, there was a brilliant meteor shower!

Science on the Moon

Tony Simon

Until July 20, 1969, no one could be certain what the moon was really like. Then as millions of people watched on television, Neil Armstrong and Edwin (Buzz) Aldrin, Jr. made their historic moon landing. This article tells what they did after they landed.

Photograph courtesy NASA

Photograph courtesy NASA

Armstrong and Aldrin had simple but important scientific tasks to do. Before they went on with them, mission control asked both men to move inside the range of the TV camera.

"The President of the United States would like to say a few words to you," explained Houston.

President Nixon had put through a radiotelephone call from the White House to Tranquility Base. The astronauts stood at attention together near the American flag. Then the President said:

"Hello, Neil and Buzz. . . . This certainly has to be the most historic phone call ever made.

"I just can't tell you how proud we all are of what you have done. . . . Because of what you have done, the heavens have become part of man's world . . . . All the people on this earth are truly one . . . one in their pride of what you have done . . . and one in our prayers that you will return safely to Earth."

Man's first hour on the moon soon drew to a close, and still there was much work ahead for science. Armstrong and Aldrin would perform tasks on the moon's surface for all the scientists back on Earth who could not be there themselves.

Using Science Skills

Armstrong had already used one key scientific skill: observing. In the first moments of his moon walk, he had observed the soil and described it as fine, powdery, and sandy. A few minutes later, he had radioed: "This is very interesting. It's a very soft surface, but here and there . . . I run into a very hard surface, but it appears to be cohesive [stuck together] material of the same sort."

Observing carefully is just one scientific skill. Others include measuring, experimenting, recording information, collecting samples, and classifying (putting things in groups according to likenesses and differences).

The skills of science help men to find new links between old facts. Scientists ask questions. To find the answers, they plan and carry out experiments and record the results. Then they think over these results and draw their conclusions. And every answer they find leads to new questions, new experiments, new conclusions. In this way, science advances man to new frontiers of knowledge. As one scientist puts it, "Science is the effort of the human mind to enlighten itself by evidence."

On the moon's surface, Armstrong and Aldrin both worked skillfully in the ways of science.

As soon as he stepped down from *Eagle*, Armstrong had scooped up rocks and soil with a special tool, a bag on the end of a 25-inch handle. Quickly, he stuffed this first small moon sampling into a leg pocket on his spacesuit. Now, if an emergency forced *Eagle* to leave the moon suddenly, some of its surface would go along for study by Earth scientists.

Armstrong then collected many more rocks with a boxlike scoop and long metal tongs. He put the rocks and soil in plastic bags, then sealed the bags inside two airtight aluminum boxes. With a rope-and-pulley system, much like a clothesline, he hoisted the boxes aboard *Eagle*. When *Eagle* returned, scientists would have a treasure of materials to study and to classify—in all, about 50 pounds of moon rock and soil.

Time was flying, but the moon explorers set up three scientific instruments.

Trapping the Solar Wind

Soon after Aldrin stepped out on the surface, mission control announced, "Buzz is erecting the solar wind experiment."

This was the first of the three experiments, a sheet of aluminum foil about four feet long and one foot wide. The foil, mounted on a telescoped pole, unrolled much like a window shade. After opening out the foil, Aldrin faced it toward the sun.

The foil's job was to capture tiny particles that move out steadily from the sun at supersonic speed. Scientists call this flow of particles the solar wind.

If the experiment worked, the foil would collect particles of such thin, rare gases as helium, argon, neon, xenon, krypton. The particles would stick to the foil much as sand sticks to a freshly painted surface. Before the astronauts left, they would roll up the aluminum foil, store it in a vacuum box, and bring it aboard *Eagle*.

In its first hour, the aluminum foil captured trillions of particles. By studying such particles captured on the moon, scientists hoped to know more about the sun.

A Moonquake Meter

The second experiment Aldrin set up was a seismometer, or moonquake meter. For a year or more, it would detect moonquakes, volcanic action, landslides, rockslides, meteor bombardments, or other disturbances or vibrations.

Aldrin carried this miniature science station to a level spot, fixed it in place on the surface, and reported, "I have the seismic experiment flipped over now."

Immediately, it began to send information back to Earth. The seismometer quickly recorded a possible moonquake and tremors from landslides in craters close by. It even recorded the astronauts' footsteps as they walked away.

The seismometer would give scientists fresh clues to the moon's composition. It might help them settle one of the biggest debates among scientists: whether the moon, at present, is "hot and alive" or "cold and dead." Throughout the two-week-long day, when sunlight powered the seismometer's solar cells, it would "listen" for activity in the moon's crust.

The Laser Reflector

Next Aldrin set up a two-foot-square reflector, a series of 100 mirrors. In this experiment, scientists and map makers would aim and "fire" lasers at the reflector-target. A laser is a thin beam of highly

concentrated and intensely focused light. Each laser would bounce from the reflector right back to where it came from on Earth. Since scientists know that light travels at 186,000 miles a second, they could figure out Earth-moon distances by timing a laser's round trip.

Information from the laser experiment may someday settle another argument among scientists: *Are Earth and the moon drifting apart?*

Some believe they are, but not by much—perhaps an inch a year.

If the returning laser strikes off the point it was sent from, scientists might also learn if the continents on Earth are slowly drifting apart. Still another problem the laser experiment may help solve is how much the moon "wobbles" as it spins.

"The laser reflector has been installed," Aldrin reported. Little time remained for moon exploring, and the scientific work would have to be speeded up.

Two Core Tubes

Mission control reported: "Neil Armstrong has been on the surface now about an hour and fifty minutes . . . Buzz Aldrin is collecting a core tube sample."

Aldrin was driving a long tube into the stubborn surface with a hammer. "I hope you're watching how hard I have to hit this into the ground to the tune of about five inches," Aldrin said, slamming the tube with all his strength. "It almost looks wet." This was the first of two samples Aldrin would get by driving a tube into the surface, then pulling it up with its core packed full of rock and soil. The second core was even harder to get. "The second one took two hands on the hammer, and I was putting pretty good dents in the top of the rod," said Aldrin. The two core samples from *below* the surface would show scientists the beginnings of the moon's rock layer formations.

Time on the moon was beginning to run out when mission control radioed this reminder to Armstrong: "We would like you to get two core tubes and the solar wind experiment. Two core tubes and the solar wind."

The laser reflector and the seismometer would remain on the moon.

"We're running a little low on time," called mission control. "Head on up the ladder, Buzz."

Aldrin walked back to *Eagle* and climbed aboard. A few minutes later, Armstrong followed, bringing with him the solar wind foil and the core tubes. Now the men began to prepare for lift-off.

"OK, the hatch is closed and latched," said Aldrin, "and we're up by it secure."

Soon *Eagle* would be repressurized —ready to leave the moon.

"Everything went beautifully."

Eagle and the astronauts had been on the moon for nearly twenty-two hours. Armstrong had walked on the surface for a little more than two hours, Aldrin for a little less than two hours. They had planted the American flag, put up a plaque of peace, set up two experiments, brought back a third, collected soil and rock, and pulled out core samples. They had left behind medals and shoulder patches in memory of two dead Russian cosmonauts—Yuri Gagarin and Vladimir Komarov— and three dead American astronauts

—Virgil Grissom, Roger Chaffee, and Edward White.

All during this time, Michael Collins, alone, had circled the moon seventeen times, seventy miles overhead, patiently waiting to link *Columbia* with *Eagle* again. And for forty-five minutes each time he passed behind the moon, Collins could not make contact with anyone.

Now mission control called Collins to tell him that Armstrong and Aldrin were safe inside their ship.

"Everything went beautifully," said Houston.

"Hallelujah!" answered Collins.

He would not be riding alone in space much longer.

Photographs courtesy NASA

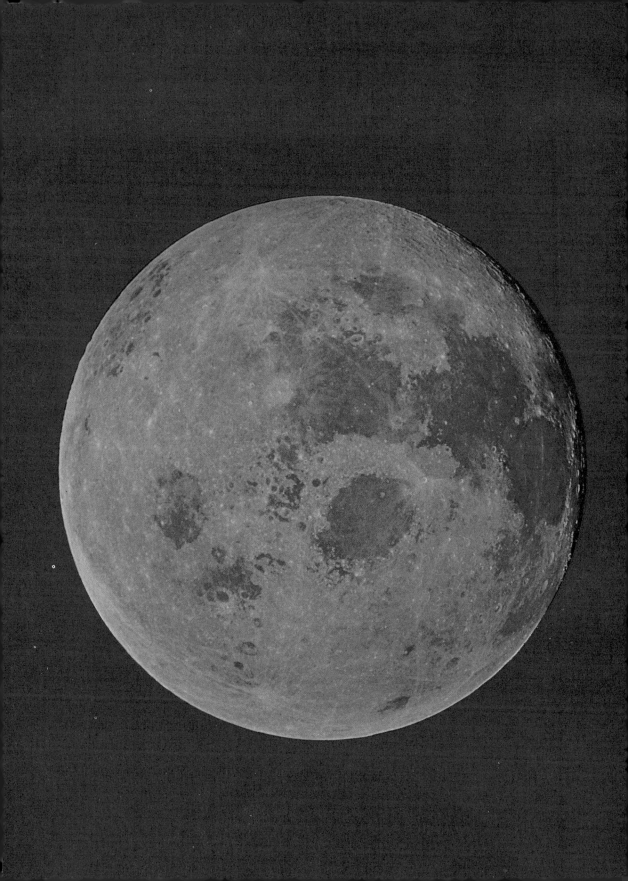

Castaways in Space

Richard Elam, Jr.

Imagine a time in the future when we have colonies on other planets. In this story two boys begin what should have been a routine flight to such a colony.

The two of them had just shoved the supply case against the chute door when the spaceship gave an unexpected burst of rocket power, knocking Skip Miller against the release lever. The escape door shot up, and black space opened before the boy's eyes.

Glen Hartzell was stunned to see his friend go spinning down the incline and follow the supply case toward the open door. Automatically, Glen stretched his lean body full length trying to grasp Skip's space suit before he escaped. But his momentum sent him skidding down the slope, and the next thing he knew he was out in space, too.

A week ago Glen wouldn't have cared whether he faced death or not. He and Skip had just made the scorned fraternity of Wockies, washed-out cadets. His failure had cut like a knife. He had wanted to pilot titanium ships through the depths of space more than anything else in the world. Instead, he and Skip had been assigned to ground crews on Mars. That, at least, had been their destination until Skip's elbow unexpectedly made them castaways in space.

Glen's first thought was directed to Skip, who looked like a toy balloon as he drifted through the vacuum. "Skip!" he called over his space suit radio. "Do you hear me, Skip?"

"Yeah, Glen." Skip's reply was scarcely more than a muted squeak.

Glen looked down and ahead where a massive rock some ten miles in diameter hung in the starry emptiness. "If we can make Phobos, we may be all right."

"We're done for," Skip groaned.

"We're not!" Glen's wits were sharpened by the danger. "We're lined up pretty well with Phobos. She doesn't have

any gravity to speak of, and we may be able to land on her."

"We won't make Phobos," Skip argued. "We'll either run into Mars' gravity field and crash on its surface or float through space until our air runs out."

"Shut up, Skip!" Glen's tone was sharp. "Listen to me. See if you can pick up a little speed by kicking out behind with your feet and hands. If you can catch up with the supply case, hang on."

Skip didn't reply, but Glen saw his arms and legs begin to move. Glen worked his own. It was a grueling effort, but Glen found that he was able to increase his speed much in the manner of a spaceship's thrust. By the time Glen touched Skip's suit, both of them were sucking freely of their precious oxygen.

"What's the idea?" Skip asked as his gloved hand clutched the strap of the supply case and Glen held onto him.

"We'll use the case as a buffer to break our fall," Glen explained. "Remember, it's covered with foam rubber so that it won't shatter when it hits."

The two had been preparing to drop the emergency supply case on Mars at the time of the accident. Glen was glad now that they'd donned space suits.

Glen saw that the spaceship was now only a tiny needle against the red disk of Mars. He and Skip had probably not even been missed by the crew. When they did find out, they wouldn't know where to look for the boys.

"I think we are going to make it," Skip said suddenly.

Phobos was a jagged, frightening giant below, but Glen held nothing but love for it. Their speed had increased slightly, but it did not look as if they would hit the ground dangerously fast. Glen felt Skip's muscles tense for the landing.

"Steady, fellow!" Glen breathed.

He felt a rough jar in the pit of his stomach. Glen bounced off Skip's back as though he were rubber. He spread out his arms to ease his fall; then he was surprised to find his body settling down to rest as lightly as a leaf.

Glen felt a prickly chill in his cheeks.

"We've got practically no weight at all!" he breathed. Skip had almost drifted off into space again, but Glen grabbed his leg and pulled him back.

"It's a crazy world, isn't it?" Skip searched the rocky landscape that sloped down from them on both sides. It was weird to be on a globe so tiny you were conscious of its roundness.

Glenn nodded. "We've really got to keep both feet on the ground!"

"What if they don't find us, Glen?" Skip asked. "What then?"

"I don't know, Skip," Glen sighed. "Let's see what's in the supply case."

Glen was able to crawl better than he could walk over to the supply case. Skip followed. Glen pressed a button on the case and the top sprang up.

"Whew! There's not much that isn't included!" Skip said. "Spare oxygen tanks, a bubble tent outfit, food capsules, water maker, first aid, flares, books, electronic stove-heater."

"Let's put up the bubble tent," Glen said. "It'll help save our heat."

As he had learned in cadet training, he removed a cylinder from the outfit and pulled a lever. It popped open and a plastic bubble began growing out of it. The bubble, which was slightly oblong and transparent, enlarged to about seven feet,

then detached itself from the cartridge airtight. After it had hardened for several minutes, Glen took an electric saw from the kit and cut a small door in the side. They made hinges from self-sealing plastic strips.

They used the foam rubber from around the case for flooring, then put the supplies inside the bubble. They turned on the heater and then turned off the heat units in their suits.

"How long do you figure our supplies can last, Glen?" Skip asked.

"They're supposed to last two people ten days," Glen replied. "Don't you remember that question on our exam?"

"Don't remind me!" Skip said. "I'm tired of hearing about the cadet corps."

"I know," Glen said bitterly.

"How could they flunk us on one question?" Skip asked. "It wasn't fair."

"I agree with you," Glen answered, "but the fact remains that we've got to take it."

Skip chuckled grimly. "You talk as if we have a lifetime ahead of us. We don't know whether we've got tomorrow."

"Which reminds me, we'd better send off some flares to let somebody know where we are." Glen picked up some of the rocket flares and "drifted" out of the bubble tent. He set up a flare on its tripod legs, pointed it at Mars' ruddy face, and pulled on the release catch. But it wouldn't move.

"It's jammed!" Glen tried another rocket and got the same result. Then another, and another. They were all useless, all the catches warped, possibly from having been kept too near a heat source in the ship.

"How are we going to signal Mars now?" Skip asked.

"Anything we toss out will be drawn to the planet by its gravitation," Glen was thinking out loud.

"How about throwing out some of the extra supplies we have?" Skip proposed. "We can attach a note."

"It's a million-to-one shot they'd be found. Don't you realize that only a fraction of Mars has colonists? No, I'm afraid we'd wait here until doomsday if we had to count on that."

"But what else is there to do?" Skip's eyes were round with dread.

Glen fought down his own sudden despair. "It looks as though we'll have to get to Mars on our own, Skip."

"Now you're crazy! We'd be smashed to pieces!"

"Not the way I'm thinking." A plan was forming in Glen's mind as he scrambled into the bubble tent and came out with one of their engineering books. Skip watched in amazement as Glen began working math problems in the dirt with a piece of stone.

After a while, Glen said, "I think it'll work, Skip. Want to take a chance?"

"I'd like to know what it is first."

"We can use the chute from the supply case and attach it to the bubble," Glen explained. "Then we can ride in the bubble to Mars."

"It sounds fantastic!"

"I've figured it every way I know," Glen said. "At least, it's better than sitting here and hoping we'll accidentally be found. Shall we try it?"

Skip shrugged. "If it's our only chance. But I hope you've figured all the angles!"

"We'd better get started right away," Glen advised. "We may need all our air tanks if we have to do some walking when we land."

They set to work fastening the lines of the chute around and under the plastic bubble. They used more of the plastic strips to secure the lines tightly. The chute was still folded, since the vacuum on Phobos had failed to trip the automatic release. The boys decided to carry only a minimum of supplies to make their weight as light as possible. When they were ready to go, they climbed into the bubble, and Glen shoved them off with one foot outside the door.

"We'll seal ourselves in airtight with the strips," Glen said, pulling the door shut. "That'll hold our vacuum in and help keep us light when we get into the atmosphere."

"How long will it take us to get there?" Skip asked.

"I've figured on about a hundred hours," Glen answered. "That should put us close to Mars City, figuring on Mars' rotation. But if it doesn't, we should be able to reach some research settlement."

They moved slowly at first. Glen hoped for only enough speed to carry them into Mars' gravity pull. As they approached the red planet, their speed would increase and that worried Glen. If they whacked into Mars' air blanket too fast, the chute might be ripped from the bubble.

To while away the many hours, the boys dozed and took turns reading the one novel they had brought along. Their legs soon became cramped and sore, and they would have given a good deal to have been able to stretch or walk about.

On the third day, the boys could see the canals criss-crossing in a tangled network on the ruddy globe of Mars. On the fourth day, just as Glen had figured, the glassite domes of Mars City began to materialize through the violet haze of atmosphere. Glen wondered how fast they were going. There was no way to tell because their insulation kept them from feeling the rush of air.

"Cross your fingers, Skip," Glen warned. "Our chute should open in the next few minutes."

The seconds appeared to last hours as they waited, and Glen suffered a torture of suspense. What if the chute did not open? In that case, they would end up in fragments on Mars' red earth. Or what if the force of the air should jerk the chute off the bubble?

Even as Glen worried, he felt a sharp drag and was tumbled over on Skip.

"Look! The chute's open!" Skip pointed overhead.

Some minutes later, the red ground rushed at them like an enfolding blanket. Their final problem faced them now. If they landed safely, they would have conquered space in a way no spaceman had ever done before.

Glen counted off the last few feet. "A hundred—fifty—twenty!"

As they struck, Glen was thrown against the ceiling of the bubble. Plastic clattered against plastic as the bubble rolled over on the ground many times before stopping. Glen straightened himself out. He was shaken up, but he was unhurt. He looked across at Skip.

"We made it," Glen said, but his voice shook as if he wasn't yet able to believe it. He tore off the door seals, shoved out the door, and permitted the Martian air to rush into the vacuum of their chamber. Then they got out and stretched their legs. Looking at the domes of Mars City, which were gleaming in the distance, Glen asked, "Ready to start walking?"

"After being cooped up like a chicken, I'm willing to walk all over Mars. Let's go." Skip's natural good humor had returned.

Less than an hour later, an astonished captain at the Mars City spaceport heard the boys' strange story.

"Your courage and ingenuity have been incredible!" the captain said when they had finished. "I can't believe that you two are Wockies. If you weren't flunked for reasons of scholarship, I'm sure you'll be reinstated."

"We weren't flunked for that reason, sir," Skip said.

"For what reason then?" the captain asked.

Glen smiled wryly at the captain as he replied, "We were flunked, sir, because we failed the test to determine whether we could bear up in an emergency or not!"

Afterthought
1. How did the boys' adventure show that they should be reinstated as space cadets?
2. Why might people from Earth hope to colonize other planets?

Our Galaxy—and Others

Anne Terry White

Constellations, planets, meteors,
comets—but what is our place in
the "heaven full of stars"?

Imagine an ant in a forest of countless trees. Imagine this ant trying to figure out the shape of the forest. It seems ridiculous, hopeless, impossible. And yet, man has solved a problem exactly of this order. He has figured out the shape and size of the gigantic "star city" in which we live—our galaxy. We call it ours because in the vast realm of space there are about a thousand million galaxies besides our own.

You might think that because nearly everything in the sky seems to be a ball or a slightly flattened ball, our galaxy is like that. But no.

Our galaxy is like a tremendous pancake that is thicker at the center than at the edges. From where we are inside this pancake, we can't see far toward the center because of dust. But we can see out toward the edge, and the most important thing we see is the Milky Way. The Milky Way is how we see our galaxy from the inside. The fact that we find this luminous band of stars dividing the sky almost exactly in half tells us that we are about halfway between the top and bottom of the pancake.

The size of our pancake is so tremendous that it is harder to

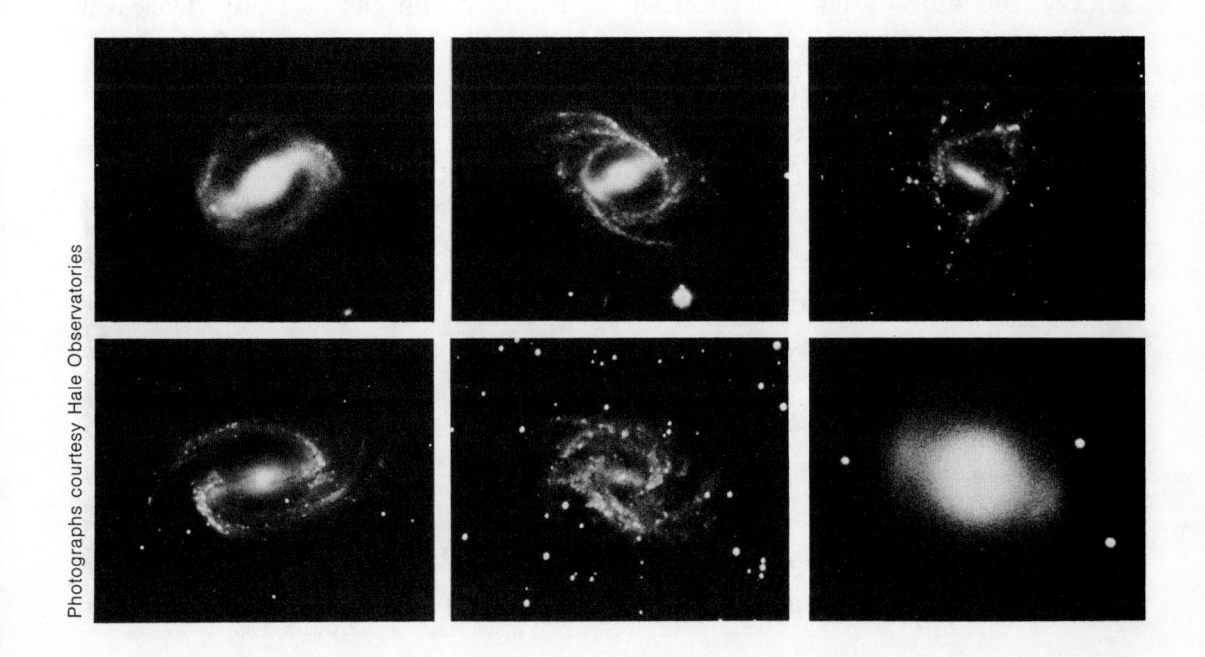

picture than the distance to the stars. Our galaxy is something like 100,000 light-years across. Out where we live—30,000 light-years from the center and 20,000 from the edge— the pancake is thinner still. At the edge it drops off even more.

Now what is our pancake made of?

It is made of stars and dust and gases. There are 100,000 million stars in the pancake, most of the dim ones being in the band we call the Milky Way. The bulging center doubtless is the brightest part; for, though we can't see it to any extent, we have reason to think it is full of globular clusters. And brilliant globular clusters surround the pancake as a halo. Out from the center of the galaxy the stars aren't distributed evenly. They form huge spiral arms in which there are enormously brilliant blue stars. Our sun and its neighbors lie near one of these great streams of stars.

The dust lies mostly in a layer right through the middle of the pancake. That being just where we live, and some of the dust clouds being hundreds of light-years across, you can see why we don't know too much about what's going on at the center. The dust gets in our way, so that we see only about a hundredth

part of the galaxy. There are holes or "windows" through which the astronomers see a portion of the central region.

As for the gas, it is nearly all hydrogen. Where it is close to some of the hottest stars, it glows like a neon advertising sign. The Great Nebula, or cloud, in the sword of Orion glows that way. It makes the middle star of the sword look fuzzy. In some regions when dust is close to stars, it also reflects enough light to be faintly visible. It's that way in the Pleiades, but there the nebula is much too dim to see with the naked eye.

Think now of huge clouds of gas many light-years across, but don't think of the gas as being dense the way it is in the sun. A large match-

Photograph courtesy Hale Observatories

box full of material like the sun's would contain 100 million million million million atoms. But in a matchbox of the gas between the stars, there would be only about 100 atoms. The gas between the stars is less dense than the most perfect vacuum we can make on earth. And yet there is enough of this gas in our galaxy to make another 100,000 million stars. It just points up how much more space there is than stars in the superpancake that is our galaxy. The stars are terribly far apart.

The stars in our galaxy, of course, aren't standing still, for nothing in the sky stands still. If the moon stopped moving, it would fall to the earth. If the earth stopped moving, it would fall into the sun. And if the stars didn't move, the outer ones would fall into the center of the pancake. So our galaxy is a slowly whirling mass of stars spinning in space. It takes the sun, trailing its planets, 200 million years to go around the galaxy once. The distance is so vast that the sun has been around only twenty times since it was born.

It's not easy to get the picture, but luckily we've found a duplicate of our galaxy in the sky. We can turn our telescopes on it and see just what our star city looks like.

Our model is one and a half million light-years away, but you can see it as a blur even with the naked eye when you look on a winter's night through the stars of the constellation Andromeda. We call it galaxy in Andromeda, or Messier 31—after the French astronomer who first catalogued it. He was looking for comets and made a list of all the fuzzy-looking things in the sky that people shouldn't mistake for comets. The Andromeda galaxy was Number 31 on his list.

At first glance, you don't see the resemblance—Messier 31 looks to be an oval, not a round pancake. But that is only because you see the galaxy tilted. Actually, it is in every

Photograph courtesy Hale Observatories

respect a star city like our own. It is the same size. It has spiral arms unwinding—or is it winding?—from the same kind of bright center. It is as bright as our galaxy. And it has about as many stars. Some of its brightest stars flicker regularly like ours, spelling out how many times as luminous as the sun they really are. And that is a piece of luck. For it was by watching those flickering specks of light that we got the first measure of the distance of Messier 31. Those Cepheid variables, actually 1,000 times brighter than our sun, have to be one and a half million light-years away to be as dim as we see them.

There are dust and gas clouds in the spiral arms just as there are in the arms of our galaxy. And out beyond and all around the spiral arms with their brilliant blue stars is a halo of globular clusters. In fact, the Andromeda galaxy, or Messier 31, is our double and could pass for a photograph of our galaxy.

Astronomers have checked over Messier's list of 104 hazy objects that shouldn't be taken for comets and have found about a hundred of them to be galaxies. To these, our modern telescopes have added hundreds of millions more. Up to distances of a thousand million light-years—and beyond—we keep finding more galaxies and more. There seem to be just as many that far off as there are close by. So there is every reason to believe that out of our sight the galaxies go on and on—for a few thousand million light-years at least.

Each galaxy is a star city. It may not be exactly like ours—it may have no spiral arms, no dust, no gas, and it may be smaller. Most of the galaxies are. But it is a whirling mass of millions of stars. It is a lonely world of light and motion sufficient unto itself, a world cut off by great stretches of dark, frigid, soundless space from other worlds just as lonely. Together they make what we call the visible universe—vast beyond belief.

The Motion of the Earth

A day with sky so wide,
So stripped of cloud, so scrubbed, so vacuumed free
Of dust, that you can see
The earth-line as a curve, can watch the blue
Wrap over the edge, looping round and under,
Making you wonder
Whether the dark has anywhere left to hide.
But the world is slipping away; the polished sky
Gives nothing to grip on; clicked from the knuckle
The marble rolls along the gutter of time—
Earth, star and galaxy
Shifting their place in space.
Noon, sunset, clouds, the equably varying weather,
The diffused light, the illusion of blue,
Conceal each hour a different constellation.
All things are new
Over the sun, but we,
Our eyes on our shoes, go staring
At the asphalt, the gravel, the grass at the roadside, the door-
step, the doodles of snails, the crochet of mortar and lime,
Seeking the seeming familiar, though every stride
Takes us a thousand miles from where we were before.

Norman Nicholson

Universe Key

Thumbprint

In the heel of my thumb
are whorls, whirls, wheels
in a unique design:
mine alone.
What a treasure to own!
My own flesh, my own feelings.
No other, however grand or base,
can ever contain the same.
My signature,
thumbing the pages of my time.
My universe key,
my singularity.
Impress, implant,
I am myself,
of all my atom parts I am the sum.
And out of my blood and my brain
I make my own interior weather,
my own sun and rain.
Imprint my mark upon the world,
whatever I shall become.

Eve Merriam

Pitcher

Stephen Cole

The new boy has a punched-in nose
and ears that stick out, so Monk
nicknames him Pitcher. From that
moment Pitcher is someone for the other
boys, especially Monk, to pick on. His
only real friend is his roommate,
who tells the story.

I was late finishing my test, and when I hurried out into the hall, there stood Monk grabbing Pitch by the collar. He was holding him there in his left hand while he waved his right fist under Pitcher's nose. There was murder in Monk's eye, so I hurried over.

"When I want to look on your paper, you let me look!" I heard him hiss at Pitcher. He shook Pitch until his teeth rattled, and for a second I thought he was going to paste him.

"What's the matter?" I asked, butting in.

"I wanted to look on Pitcher's paper during that test, that's all!" Monk shouted at me. "The little rat wouldn't let me. He turned the paper around."

"He's left-handed," I tried to explain. "You just write left-handed on one of those desks and see if you don't turn the paper around, too."

Monk looked startled. He dropped his balled-up fist and took his hand off Pitcher's collar. Then he flared up again. "I bet he'd have turned it around if he was right-handed!"

"Maybe I would have, at that," said Pitcher. He stood there, the skinny little owl, just looking at Monk. Sometimes it seems to me that Pitch hasn't any sense at all. Nobody but an idiot would try to egg Monk on, particularly if that idiot is as puny as Pitcher. I bet Monk weighs a good ten pounds more than Pitch.

Monk whipped his arm back, and I was just going to grab his fist when Mr. Harper came around the corner at the end of the hall. He took one quick look at us, and I don't know about the other guys, but my heart stopped beating. But Mr. Harper didn't say much.

"Why aren't you boys in your classroom?" was all he said.

It was enough. We beat it. We practically tumbled into Mr. Andrews' Latin class. Mr. Harper is a pretty good guy for a headmaster, but you don't fool around with him. You don't fool around any.

I didn't get a chance to talk to Pitcher again that day until we were in our room after lunch. But you can bet I went to work on him then, especially when he gave me a good opportunity by picking up a book as if he was going to study, even when he didn't have to.

"You study more than most of us, don't you, Pitch?" I said. I wanted to lead up to the subject that was on my mind, and this seemed a good way.

"I hope I'm not just a grind," he said, grinning at me. Pitcher has a nice grin.

"Oh no, you're not a grind," I told him in a hurry. "But most of us don't hardly study at all."

"My mother asked me to try to make good grades," he said. He looked embarrassed, and I don't blame him. If he'd made a remark like that out in public, the whole gang would have busted out laughing in his face. At a boarding school it is practically indecent to mention your mother in a tone of voice like that.

"Oh," was all I could say. I looked somewhere else.

"She doesn't have too much money," he said. He was staring straight out the window, so it was safe now to turn back and look at him. "She asked me please to get all I could out of this school. And to put as much into it as possible. She said she always wanted to be proud of me."

"Oh," I said again.

"So I'm doing the best I can," Pitch went on. His face

was very red, and his eyes were blinking fast behind his glasses. I guess he felt he had to say what he was saying, but of course he wanted to get it over with as fast as he could. "You see, I like my mother," he said.

This time I didn't even say "Oh." I had never heard anything like that before in my life. It took me a couple of seconds, thinking my fastest, to dig up another subject. Then I lighted on the thing that was really on my mind.

"But you can't let Monk push you around!" I said. "You can't keep your nose so close to the paper that you forget Monk and make him get mad at you!"

"Why can't I?" Pitch asked. "Why can't I when he's trying to cheat?"

Now I'm not the smartest guy in the world, but I saw right away that there was no use in trying to argue that point with Pitch, especially when I had a sneaking idea he was right. So I started prowling up and down the room, trying to find a new idea. An idea that would save Pitch from being murdered, because it was perfectly clear that he was right smack in the middle. It was all right with me if he wanted to study hard to please his mother—just so long as he didn't talk about a thing like that out in public—but at the same time he couldn't let Monk push him around. And those two facts didn't seem to mix well.

Then the idea came. I stopped prowling around and slammed my hand down on Pitcher's shoulder. He winced. "Tell you what we'll do!" I shouted. "We'll gang up on Monk! You and I'll stick together and not take any guff off Monk."

For a moment I thought about how noble that idea was, and then a couple of other thoughts began to crowd my head.

The first was that Pitch wasn't about to take any of Monk's guff, as it was. And two against one wasn't so good either, so I put the other thought into loud words. "Only then he'll get you alone someday and beat you to a bloody pulp."

"Maybe not," said Pitch. "I can box."

I went around from where I was standing, stooped down with my hands on the table, and looked him in the eye.

"Wait a second, Pitch," I said. "You better come again with that. What did you say?"

"I said I can box."

I straightened up and drew in a breath, thinking of the terrible athlete Pitcher had been on the football field. There was a chair behind me, so I sat down. "All right, Pitcher," I said when I was sitting steady. "You can let me have it now. Who taught you how to box?"

"My father," he said. He said it quietly, looking out the window again.

"Your father. . . ."

"Yes," he said. He smiled, and his eyes weren't vacant anymore. "He was a pretty good boxer—he was champion of his college—and so he taught me how to box. He said I was the kind of a kid who would need to know how to box."

I nodded, thinking that Pitcher's father must be a pretty smart guy. All of a sudden I laughed out loud. "Then why in the world didn't you pole Monk up there in the hall between classes?" I jumped up, excited at the thought of the look on Monk's face if that had happened. "Why didn't you pole him?"

"Heck, I can't pole anybody," Pitcher said. "I'm not built right. All I can do is box. You know, the old straight left, only with me it's the right. It keeps them from hitting me, and maybe I jab a little blood out of their noses." He shrugged his shoulders. "Besides, I don't think my father would want me to do a thing like trying to pole Monk."

"Huh?" I said.

"I don't believe my father would think it was right." He wrinkled up his forehead, thinking hard. "You can't hit the other guy first when you're right," he said after a while. "You can't hit him when he doesn't expect it. Besides, you can't fight in the school building." He threw out his hands, kind of triumphant. "You see? I'm sure that's what my father would think."

I managed to say, "I'd like to meet your father someday."

"My father's dead," said Pitcher.

I got the creeps when he said that.

"He was a test pilot, and one day his jet disintegrated," I heard him say. "Otherwise he'd have been an astronaut, sure. Remember a minute ago when you asked me why I didn't pole Monk? Remember that I stopped to think? Well, my father would have wanted me to think. See?"

I got up slowly. "Look, Pitch," I said. "I'm going outside. I think I'll go down to the ball field and run around the track or something. I think I need exercise."

"I'll go with you," said Pitcher.

We were in front of the school building, heading for the athletic field, when we came across Monk. Or rather, he came across us. He came slowly up to us, walking stiff-legged with his head down, and I noticed his eyes were narrow. He walked right up to Pitcher until their heads weren't more than six inches apart.

"I've been looking for you," Monk said. He talked through his teeth, the way they do on television when they're sore. So I gathered that Monk hadn't seen Pitch since first period in the morning.

"Yes?" said Pitch. He looked pale, but he didn't back up.

"I didn't like that crack you made," Monk said.

"No?" said Pitcher.

"That crack about maybe you'd turn your paper around even if you were right-handed."

"I think I probably would, you know," said Pitcher. "Cheating isn't—"

It was when he said that word that Monk poled him. Glasses and everything, Monk hauled off and poled him. Only Pitch turned his shoulder or something, and Monk missed him. He missed him so completely that he fell right into him, and Pitcher had to hold him up. Then Monk shoved hard and Pitch was sitting down on the ground.

Then, somehow or other, I found myself fighting Monk. Monk and I were squared off in the middle of a ring of guys— I don't know where they came from, but there they were in a ring around us—and we were throwing fists at each other. But not for long. It seemed like forever, but I guess it really wasn't a long time before I stepped on a rock, tripped, and fell flat on the ground. I was still on one knee, looking at my hands where I'd cut them on the gravel, when Monk kicked me. It didn't hurt much, but still he kicked me.

Before I could jump to my feet, some big guy in the crowd stuck out his hand to collar Monk, but he never did collar him. All he got in his hand was a pair of tortoiseshell glasses. Pitch had stuck his glasses into the hand, and before I can tell it, he was squared off fighting Monk.

Down there on the ground I looked up with my mouth hanging open, and I got the shock of my life. Because right over our heads, way up on the second floor of the school building, Mr. Harper was leaning out to watch the fight. And he saw me. We looked right straight at each other. There wasn't a chance in the world to crawl away through all those legs, because we looked straight into each other's eyes.

Then Mr. Harper did a queer thing. He put his finger to his lips and shook his head slowly from side to side. With my mouth open I stared at him so long that finally he frowned and shook his head harder, his finger still on his lips. Then I caught on to the fact that he didn't want me to let on he was there. I stopped staring at him and got up to watch the fight myself. It all happened in a few seconds.

Pitcher was standing in the middle of the ring of guys, his long right arm stretched out, his chin tucked down behind his shoulder, and his left fist close to his chest. He was circling slowly all the time. It was fun to watch his feet because they never got tangled the way you'd think they would, knowing Pitch, and every now and then his hand would stab out. Not much. Just a couple of inches. Just a couple of inches straight ahead, with his shoulder behind it. And then he'd dance away.

When I could stop looking at Pitch and size up Monk, I got the second shock in that one minute. Monk's nose was bleeding, but that wasn't the thing that interested me most. It was the look in his eyes that got me. He looked hunted, or maybe baffled. He looked about as surprised and baffled as any guy I've ever seen.

Time and again I watched Monk storm into Pitcher as I stood there on the inner ring of the crowd. Monk would put his head down, and with both fists flying, sail into poor Pitch.

It made me shudder at first just to see him charge and to watch the fists flying, but after a while it got funny. Because Pitch was never there. He'd tap Monk off balance, or step aside and let him charge by. I never saw anything like it in my life.

It was after one of those foolish charges, when Monk was standing there with that look in his eye, panting and wiping the blood off his nose, that somebody laughed. I looked up, and it was Star Collins who was laughing. He had Pitcher's glasses in his hand, and he was laughing hard. At Monk.

A second later everybody was laughing. I don't blame them, when you consider the look on Monk's face. They laughed and hollered and carried on, until finally Pitcher himself started to smile. I'm sure he thought they were laughing at him, because he's so used to being laughed at. And he did look funny himself out there in the center, come to think of it, with those awkward arms up and that earnest look on his face. So he put his arms down and he grinned.

"I can't hurt you, Monk," he said, "and you can't hurt me. I guess we're pretty funny at that."

Over in his corner Monk slowly put his hands down. He shook his head, then quickly reached for his handkerchief to stop the blood from his nose. "I guess we're pretty funny," he mumbled through the cloth.

Pitcher walked over to him, sticking out his hand. For a while they stood there shaking hands and then, by gosh, they laughed. Monk laughed so hard that some of his blood spattered on Pitch.

"Here's your glasses, Pitch," Star said while Monk was wiping his own blood off Pitcher. Star reached the glasses over and set them on Pitcher's nose. "And boy, can you box!"

"I'll say!" Monk said. For a second that look came back

into his face, but he laughed it off. He put his hand on Pitcher's shoulder. "Let's go get a shower, Pitch," he invited. "We could both use one." And off they went.

I was the last one to leave. The crowd melted away the way crowds do, and I was standing there alone when Mr. Harper came out of the school building. He waved at me and said, "Hello, Robby."

"Hello, Mr. Harper," I said.

He never said another word, just kept walking up toward his house. But when he passed me, he slowly closed his left eye in an enormous wink.

Pablo

Hazel Fredericksen

Desert Indians have an almost constant
struggle to obtain water; yet white
men, even in arid country, usually have
dependable water supplies. Pablo hopes
to learn this magic of the white men.
The need of his tribe is so great that he is
willing to venture into a strange and
often unfriendly world.

All day they drove. All day Pablo sat watching out the window at the changing countryside. It was late afternoon when they reached the city where the Big School was. Buildings clustered together. Everything was strange. So many cars rushing past. So many people hurrying along. Pablo's eyes hurt with the unfamiliar movement. His ears ached to the roar of sounds blasting through the open windows of the bus.

The bus turned off a wide, busy street and into a treelined driveway. The older boys and girls began to chatter and laugh. When the bus stopped they stood in the aisle, impatient to get out.

Pablo sat still, his hands nervously clutching a small canvas bag that held his few belongings. They had stopped in front of a tall, square, frame building—one of a group that had served as school and home for Indian children for almost seventy years. It was a two-story building with lots of glass windows in its walls.

The bus driver spoke some words in English, but his gestures were clear. Pablo saw he must leave the protection of the bus. He got up stiffly and followed the others.

Outside, he found himself in a soft green world—an amazing world. Grass for miles, or so it seemed to him, and all of it green. Trees so tall they rubbed the sky itself. Flowers of many bright colors, and—wonder of wonders—water running in a whirling stream on the grass.

An older Papago boy, one he had never seen before, came down the walk and spoke to him in Papago. "Come with me," he said abruptly, almost rudely. "I am your supervisor."

Pablo was shocked. Could Black Fox have been right? Did Papago boys forget their manners when they came to the Big School?

Pablo followed the boy up the steps of the frame building. As they reached the porch, the big door swung open. He saw a long line of boys, all dressed alike in blue denim, march past. Pablo and the older boy went inside. A darting look, and Pablo saw a long bench. On it were the smaller boys and girls who had come with him on the bus.

"Stay here," the older boy said. Pablo sat down at the end of the line, his canvas bag on his lap.

A heavy door at the left opened, and a small, gray-haired white man looked out. He spoke to the older boy in English. The boy nodded and beckoned to the first boy in the line. He took him through the big door and closed it. Those outside waited. Each time the door opened, a boy next in line was motioned to enter. Girls were directed, by an older girl, to a door on the right side of the room. Not one of the boys or girls came back. Finally it was Pablo's turn.

He tried to walk tall. He tried to think, I am an Indian. I am a Papago. I am not afraid. But he gripped hard on the bag he held.

The white man was sitting at a desk. The older boy was standing beside him.

The white man spoke to Pablo in English; then the older boy said, "He says, 'What is your name?' "

Pablo stood silent, thinking. Papago people did not say names glibly. How could one of the desert people be so impolite as to ask?

The white man tapped his pencil.

"Older Son," Pablo whispered doubtfully.

The older boy shook his head impatiently. "That won't do here. Too many older sons."

"Pablo," he answered. He thought his problem was solved.

But the white man asked another question. The older boy translated. "What do people call your father?"

This was agony for Pablo. To have to say his father's name to a strange white man. He kept silent.

The white man, bothered, frowned and spoke sharply to Older Boy. Pablo did not understand, but he didn't want to cause Older Boy any trouble. He whispered, "Red Deer."

The white man wrote, "Pablo Red Deer."

"What is his age?"

The older boy looked at Pablo and guessed aloud, "Twelve."

Pablo understood some numbers in English. He had heard them during the summer at Oidak. He started to say eleven. But it would be impolite to dispute Older Boy. So Pablo was enrolled—"Pablo Red Deer—Age 12."

Older Boy opened a door at the far side of the room. Pablo followed him down the hall to a high-ceilinged room.

Here was a new man in a white coat. There was a line of boys, and a lady dressed in white.

"This is the white medicine man," Older Boy said. "He is called a doctor. The lady is a nurse. Do what they tell you. If you don't understand, watch the older boys here and do as they do."

Pablo watched the boy ahead of him. In his turn he stepped forward. The doctor took hold of his shoulder, moved him to a better light. Pablo flinched. But if he had to go through this to learn the magic of the white man, he could do it.

The doctor signaled him to undress to join several naked boys waiting to step, one after the other, under a jet of streaming water to soap their heads and bodies. This all seemed shameful; among his people baths were ceremonials prepared for with fasting and prayers to Great Spirit. This was also a sinful waste of water.

After the shower, each boy took a towel from a stack, dried himself, and carried his belongings into an adjoining room. There a short, kind-faced man measured each boy with his eyes, handed him underwear, blue denim trousers, shirt, and jacket, a pair of socks and black shoes.

"Lots of new clothes," the man spoke quietly in Papago to Pablo.

Pablo looked up quickly, hesitated, then whispered wistfully, "Will I see you again?"

The man nodded. "I'll be around. I work here. They call me Frank."

Pablo had never worn shoes. It took a little time to get them on. He stood up cautiously and tried a step or two. His feet felt very heavy. He saw Older Boy enter the room again and walk slowly toward him. Older Boy looked at him with a wry smile and pointed to the shoes. "You'll get used to them—after a while." He added under his breath, "Like a lot of other things here. I'll take you to the dormitory where you'll live. Come along."

As they walked, Older Boy said: "Don't ever pick flowers. Don't make marks on the wall or in your books. Always be careful about touching anything. Everything belongs to the white man's government—even you and I," he added bitterly.

Pablo did not get the meaning of these words, but he did understand that for some reason he must not touch flowers here as he had been free to do at home.

They entered a big frame building very much like the other. Older Boy led the way into a large room filled with double-deck narrow beds. Other boys of Pablo's size were coming in.

"Put your bag in this cupboard; it is where you will keep things that belong to you." Older Boy pointed. He indicated one of the lower bunks. "This is where you will sleep. Now you're on your own."

Pablo looked around cautiously, then sat down on the edge of his bed. He carefully shifted his weight. The bed did not wiggle like the one in his grandfather's house. He was glad of that. What should he do now? He did not know, so he sat and waited. He knew how to wait.

The loud shrill of a bell made Pablo jump. The other boys began leaving the room, so he got up and followed. He was to learn that now his life would be directed by bells.

Timidly he joined the line of boys going along the boardwalk. The line turned and went through the doors of another building. Inside was a dining room. Each boy slid into a place on a bench at a long table. Pablo found himself sandwiched between the boy who had been just ahead of him in the line and the one who had walked behind; neither one was a Papago. He did not like the closeness of eating this way; but he was hungry, and he was glad his grandparents had taught him to eat at a table with a knife and fork.

There was some chatter, but he sat in silence.

"You have to speak English. No Indian here is permitted to speak his own language, so the sooner you learn English, the easier it will be for you," Older Boy had said.

When the meal ended, the others stood up. He stood up. They formed a line. He got in place. They marched back to the dormitory. He was with them. In the dormitory he kept watching and imitating. He was beginning to learn.

After he crawled into bed—when the others did—he lay wide awake. The room was stuffy with the smell of boys' bodies. Pablo longed to go out where the green grass was. In his bed he could not hear any of the hushed outdoor night sounds, only the deep breathing of other boys and occasional coughing from the bed above him.

Sleep would not come. He remembered Oidak and Pa Vi. On the desert, the air felt clear and good at night. He recalled

Black Fox as he stretched out an arm and swept it toward the sunset, saying, "Great Spirit has given us a beautiful land."

He thought of his mother stirring a pot of beans over the cook-fire in the ramada and a pan of tortillas standing on the stone hearth ready to eat. He remembered one night when his father had hummed a song, and while Younger Brother clapped his hands to the tune, danced around the ramada holding the hand of Younger Sister. He remembered taking one of Younger Sister's hands. The three of them had danced together, and Black Fox had stood at the ramada entrance smiling.

At first it wasn't easy for Pablo to talk to other boys. Except for the Papagos, Pablo couldn't understand them. They were all from different tribes and spoke their own languages.

Learning to say strange-sounding words the teacher put on the blackboard or pointed to under pictures in a book was particularly hard for Pablo, because English had not been taught him at Pa Vi. His teachers were often impatient, lacking understanding and sympathy for tongues and cultures other than that of the white man.

But it was fun to copy curly marks the teacher put on the board and called "writing," or to put little sticks and rocks in clusters to match the "numbers" the teacher called out, counting, adding, taking away, as fast as she asked. Soon he could do this faster than the others. Then he could sit while the teacher helped the other children—his mind filled with ideas far away.

One day after the teacher asked him to count the children in his class and he had counted thirty-eight, he asked her, "Will you please tell me how many children in this whole school?"

After a minute she said, "About four hundred, Pablo. That is more than you can count now."

"I'll learn," Pablo answered quietly. Then he asked another question.

"Will you please tell me how many teachers?"

"Fourteen," she answered quickly. Then Pablo heard her say softly, "Not half enough."

This was a curious world he was living in, he thought. No rainmaking ceremonies, yet there was lots of water—did these fourteen teachers have some kind of power? How had it come to them?

Pablo soon discovered a new ally in a Hopi boy named Ralph. Ralph had been assigned to work with him on a dishwashing job. He was about a year older than Pablo but he, too, was a beginner in English. Neither boy knew the language of the other. At first, during their work, they could only converse through gestures and smiles. But when they had learned some English, they made a game of trying to learn the English names of things used in the kitchen.

Ralph was very easy to get along with—the result of having played with many boys and girls in his own and other Hopi villages. Working with Ralph through the fall and winter, Pablo gradually lost some of his shyness.

One day not long after they had begun working together, Ralph pointed to a pot of beans.

"What do you call these?"

"Beans," said Pablo in his best English.

"No, what do you call them in Papago?"

Pablo looked quickly around to make sure no one was near enough to hear him say an Indian word. "*Pah-vo,*" he replied.

Ralph chuckled. "We Hopis call beans *mo'ri,* but we have different names for different kinds."

Pablo understood. He asked, "What do you call field?"

"*Pa'sa,*" whispered Ralph.

"We say *auyt.*"

"Bird?" asked Ralph.

"*Uwhik,*" said Pablo.

"*Ci'ro,*" from Ralph.

They had been watching each other closely. Not only were

the words different, but each boy, in pronouncing them, had a different way of placing his teeth and tongue. Their breaths sounded different too, when they inhaled or exhaled in making words.

"Hard to learn your language, I'll bet," Ralph said with a grin.

"Yours too," said Pablo. "Maybe it's good we learn English. And we don't have to whisper that."

Before many months, by patient and constant effort, Ralph and Pablo both mastered enough English to move into a class with boys near their own recorded age. When this happened, Pablo found his homesickness lessening.

One Saturday morning in early May, when the smell of blossoming bushes and new-mown lawn filled the crisp air, Pablo stopped Ralph on their way to the dormitory. He flung himself down on the grass near a huge saguaro growing beside the walk, and Ralph dropped down too.

"Look up there," said Pablo.

Ralph looked. On the very crests of the saguaro's three upthrust arms were clusters of white blossoms touched with gold. A big white-winged gray dove was busily pecking at one cluster.

"Pretty," said Ralph. "What kind of bird is it?"

"I don't know its name. I was thinking that after a while those blossoms will turn into red fruit filled with sweet juice. We pick and eat the fruit—do Hopis like it?"

"We don't have saguaros on the Hopi reservation," Ralph said.

"Well, we'll never get a taste of the fruit from this saguaro." Pablo mimicked: " 'Belongs to the guv-ment.' "

Both boys laughed.

They fell silent. Then Ralph said softly, as if he'd been thinking about it a long time: "I have another name—an Indian name. Have you?" Pablo nodded.

Ralph continued. "My name is Honhoya—in English it means 'little bear.' What's your name?"

"I'm not supposed to say it. The medicine man gave it to me to keep but not to say. All our people have names they don't say, because using a name the medicine man gives may wear it out." He waited, fearing to hurt Ralph's feelings, but unable to speak his sacred name.

After a minute Ralph said, "What the medicine man says you must obey."

Pablo, happy at this reply, quickly asked. "What is the name of your village?"

"Walpi. What's yours?"

"Pa Vi." Then Pablo asked, "How far is your village from here?"

"A long, long way—almost two days to get to my village in an automobile—even longer to get to some of our other villages."

"How many villages have you?"

"All together, twelve. Nine are built on three mesa tops, two at the foot of mesas, and one outside the reservation in the valley, where the people have their gardens near their homes."

"What is a—mesa? Is it like a hill?"

"Yes, like a hill, but it is higher, and flatter on top. It is a long way down from the top where we live to the rocks below, about three hundred feet down. We go on trails that switch back and forth because it is so steep. Now tell me about your villages."

Pablo wondered if it would seem like bragging to have so many more villages than Ralph's people had. Finally he said, "Our villages are faraway too. We have about seventy, I think, but some have only about twenty people living in them. A few others have as many as three hundred. My grandfather's village of Oidak has about two hundred people, but Pa Vi has only thirty-five.

"Pa Vi is sheltered in the mountains, quiet and away from roads, but we have to go a long way—five or six miles—with barrels in a wagon to get water from a spring for drinking, cooking, and washing. We don't have enough water for fields or gardens, or enough room either. So each summer we go to our camp on the desert, where we plant beans and corn and stay until we harvest the crops. On the desert we build ponds that we call charcos, to hold crop water when the rains come.

"Each year when we go to summer camp, we watch the saguaros growing near our fields. The blossoms, like those up there, turn to fruits. Then when the leader of our village tells us they are ripe enough, we pick them with long sticks. The first ones we pick, we eat pulp and juice and throw the shells down red side up so rain will come. After that, everyone fills baskets and jars with fruits so the ladies can cook the pulp and juice and make syrup. They put this syrup in big ollas to ferment.

"The medicine man decides when the juice is ready to drink and when the clouds are right; then he says it is time to begin the cactus festival to ask Eé toy, Great Spirit, for rain. That night a place is smoothed for dancing, and a giant fire is lighted in the center of it; then all the people form a ring around the fire, clasp hands, and dance until first dawn. All the men and ladies have been drinking the cactus syrup so their bodies will be moist, clean, and strong as the earth becomes when it rains. The old men sing rain songs. This is the beginning of the New Year, and all are very happy because they are getting evil feelings out of their minds. They keep drinking cactus syrup as long as it lasts, and praying to Great Spirit for rain.

"Sometimes the rain comes fast—maybe even during the prayers—and we lift our faces to feel cool water on our skin. If lots of rain comes, we have to work hard in the gardens to keep the water from washing away our plants. There is mud everywhere and we slip and slide around, but we are all happy and it is fun."

Pablo stopped, and looked to see if Ralph was going to make fun of this.

But Ralph seemed very much interested. "So that's the way your people make rain," he said. "In my country we have a rain dance with snakes."

"Snakes?" Pablo shivered a little. "I don't know about getting rain that way. Tell about it."

"Well, in my country," Ralph began, "we have a dance for

rain every August. It is held in Walpi one year, in one of the other villages the next, then in Walpi the next year, and so on."

Pablo asked, "What happens to Walpi's crops the years the dance is held somewhere else?"

"Oh, the dancers always ask the Rain God to give rain for the crops of all our villages. Our snake brothers are the messengers to the gods underground who bring rain, and our dance is to keep the snakes in good humor.

"Among the Hopis we have a Snake Clan, which has charge of the ceremony. Each day for four days—one day for each direction, north, south, east, west—Snake priests go out into the desert and bring back snakes of every kind they can find, rattlers, bull snakes, and others. They keep them in the village kiva for eight days, washing and sprinkling them with cornmeal in secret ceremonials.

"Priests from the Antelope Clan always help because long, long ago, Snake priests cured an Antelope person who was bitten by a snake.

"On the ninth day we have the snake dance. Just before

the sun goes down, the Antelope priests come marching out of the kiva singing. They wear shell and turquoise necklaces and white buckskin kilts, and each has a foxskin tied to his waist in back to look like a tail. Each one also has a turtle-shell rattle fastened to the back of his right knee, and he carries two gourd rattles to keep time in the dance. All the Antelope priests have black-and-white zigzag stripes painted on their chests and arms, like streaks of lightning. They march to one side of the plaza and wait there in a line."

Ralph sat and hugged his knees, his eyes shining. "Now come the Snake priests out of the kiva. They too are wearing necklaces and foxskin tails, but their deerskin kilts are brown, and they wear bunches of feathers in their hair. Their faces are blackened and their mouths painted white, and the lower parts of their legs and arms are painted pink.

"They dance around the plaza three times to the songs of the Antelope priests. Then they stoop over the kisi, a bower made of cottonwood branches, where one of the Snake priests is now guarding all the snakes. As each Snake priest stands up straight again, he is holding in his mouth a wriggling snake."

Pablo, listening raptly, made a wry face. "No one could hold a live rattlesnake in his mouth," he said. "It would bite him."

Ralph said, "Snakes don't bite the Snake priests, because the priests have good hearts and pray for rain for all the people."

He continued. "Well, the Snake priests dance around the plaza with the snakes in their mouths, while the Antelope priests keep singing. Every snake in the kisi gets danced around the plaza four times in its turn; then it is dropped to the ground and a gatherer picks it up.

"Finally all the snakes are tossed into a circle on the ground, where a cornmeal design has been made. After a few minutes the Snake priests grab handfuls of them and run down the trails away from the village to take them back to their desert homes so they can get word to the god who brings rain."

"Does rain always come?" Pablo asked, a little doubtfully.

"Most always it comes very soon, lots of it." Now Ralph giggled. "I am just thinking about the white tourists who come to our village to see this dance. They poke their heads into our houses and ask rough questions and make big laughs, but most always on their way home they get caught in a bad storm, and some of their cars get stuck in the mud. This is the way our gods get even with them for being so rude."

"Do many white people visit your village?" Pablo asked in some surprise.

"Oh yes, too many—and I can tell you some funny stories. When lots of white Americans come to see our snake dance, they crowd our village and they get close to the edge of the cliffs. They keep yelling at each other not to fall off. My Uncle

Joe speaks very good English, and one day a white lady said to him, 'Don't your people often fall off this cliff?' Uncle Joe did not smile but he said, 'Not often, only once.' Then this lady tells her husband, 'This man says only once has anyone fallen off this cliff.' " Both boys rolled on the grass laughing.

"Another time," Ralph said, "one of the rude white ladies asked my uncle, 'Why do you wear red bands around your heads?' He said, 'Come over here and I'll whisper a secret to you.' She followed him a little way, and my uncle whispered, 'Don't ever tell anybody—but we all wear wigs, and this red band holds them on our heads.' The white lady looked surprised, and promised she would never tell."

Afterthought

1. Think of reasons why Ralph and Pablo talked about their tribal rainmaking ceremonies.
2. Why did the two boys enjoy discussing the behavior of white tourists?
3. What do you discuss with your closest friend? Why do you discuss the subjects you do?

Loneliness

I was about to go, and said so;
And I had almost started for the door.
But he was all alone in the sugar-house,
And more lonely than he'd ever been before.
We'd talked for half an hour, almost,
About the price of sugar, and how I like my school,
And he had made me drink some syrup hot,
Telling me it was better that way than when cool.

And I agreed, and thanked him for it,
And said good-bye, and was about to go.
Want to see where I was born?
He asked me quickly. How to say no?

The sugar-house looked over miles of valley.
He pointed with a sticky finger to a patch of snow
Where he was born. The house, he said, was gone.
I can understand these people better, now I know.

Brooks Jenkins

Nellie

Michele Murray

It isn't surprising that Nellie Cameron
sometimes feels overlooked at home;
she is one of six children. Her brother Sam
has won a scholarship to a private
school, but she is such a poor student
that she must attend Miss Lacey's
reading clinic. Their parents show great
concern for Sam because they know
he faces many problems. Nellie
mistakenly thinks that she is less
important to them than Sam is. Then she
gets a chance to talk about her fears
with Miss Lacey.

Miss Lacey looked narrowly at her. "Well, out with it!"

Nellie stared open-eyed. "Ma'am? You want me to try again?" She bent to the words. "During the morn . . . morning, Ida con . . . con . . . I'll skip that one . . . what to do. She knew she had a prob . . . prob. . . ." Her voice faded.

"We going to call all this time a *waste?*"

Nellie admired her shoes. "No, ma'am."

Miss Lacey reached over and clapped the book shut. Nellie had nothing to fiddle with.

"Have some coffee. Go ahead. And some cookies if you want." Miss Lacey was used to waiting. She prepared herself to wait.

Nellie thought for a minute. She tried to get the words in the right order before she spoke them. No one had a right to know her private self. Mama insisted on that. Even her new shoes had gotten old and messed up from wearing them; what would happen to her own self if she took it out too often? But right next to her private self there was another self she could let out to view. That would keep people from asking further questions, and she would be safe where it counted.

"Well," she began, "you said everyone would care when they found out that I was reading. And it don't make no difference, none at all! Not with Sam around!" Hesitating over what to say, Nellie told Miss Lacey a little about Sam.

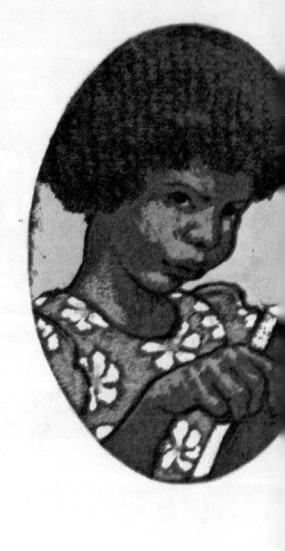

"Hmm," Miss Lacey said, unperturbed. "I know about Sam. Brilliant mind. I wouldn't wish to be him, though. Does that make sense to you? I suppose it's different, he being your brother. Only, Nellie, you may be better off. Sam will have a rough time day after day for many years, maybe forever."

"My Mama say he don't know when to stop talking! But she love him best, anyway; I knows that!"

"You think so? I doubt it. Different, maybe, the way he needs. Not best."

"Then why my Mama sending me and Jesse away?" Nellie stuffed a cookie in her mouth and waited for Miss Lacey's answer. None came. So Nellie had to go on. Her last words sounded awful hanging in the air.

"She really is. We going for the summer back to her home folks. Back to South Carolina. All the way back there. And we going without her—all by our own selves." And then Nellie added, "An' my birthday be in August, I gots to have it *not home!*"

"Where's Sam going to be?"

"Away at a camp somewheres; I don't know."

"Then what's the fuss all about? You're lucky to *have* a place to go to, can't you see that? The right place for you, not Sam. Away from a hot city—who knows what's going to happen this summer?" Miss Lacey brooded silently for a while; then she laughed. "I'll tell you a secret—I'm going to Chicago for the summer, to study. And I'll tell you something else. It gets mighty hot in Chicago in the summer! Even hotter than it does here. So, count your blessings, child. Why, you'll be having a *good* time!"

Nellie could see that Miss Lacey was only answering to say something, anything. There it was again—she really didn't care. Not the way Nellie wanted. It was like holding someone's hand crossing a street and finding, smack in the middle, they had let go to look in the other direction, not knowing that the cars were just whizzing past.

"They just getting me outa the way! All alone . . . s'poze something happens? Why, I could get buried in some old swamp down there and no one would even know!"

"Really?" Miss Lacey looked astonished.

"It could be," Nellie insisted stubbornly.

"Oh, things do happen," Miss Lacey agreed. "But you look to me like a young lady who can take good care of herself."

"Oh, if it was just me—but I gots Jesse to watch besides, and he never listen."

"Honey, I'm telling you something. You will have a good time. Better than cooped up here all summer! I can remember . . . do you want to hear? You see, I know what you are thinking; do you believe me? When I was a little girl, a very little girl, yes, smaller than you are, I was sent by train to my Momma—my own mother's mother—down in Mississippi. All the way from Illinois, down the Illinois Central line. Probably you don't know where it is . . . remind me, and I'll show you some day . . . but it seemed as far as death to me. We just traveled on and on and on. I was so sleepy . . . but I was afraid to sleep, afraid I'd miss my stop and just keep on riding forever. Grown-up people talked to me and shared their food with me, but all I could think of was that I would go on riding forever, right off the edge of the world, and no one would ever find me again."

Miss Lacey laughed a little. "It does seem foolish now, but

I *know* how true it felt then! Finally, the conductor called out *Hillsdale,* and the porter helped me off with my little suitcase, and there I was. On the platform was a man in overalls, a tall, dark man, looking down at me. No one else. Nothing else. And then the train pulled away. And, I tell you, Hillsdale was just *nowhere!* I wanted to run but I couldn't. That man came up to me, and he said, 'Anne Lacey?' and I just nodded. And he said, 'I'm your Granddaddy Laird.' Of course I had known it, as soon as I stepped down from the train, but do you want to hear something, Nellie? I was ashamed of him. Yes, I was! My mother had told me he was a church deacon—he certainly talked like one!—and somehow I believed he would be dressed like the preachers in our church in Chicago, all in black with a fresh white shirt and a hat. And there was this man in *overalls!*

"Well, that was only the start. For when he took my suitcase and we went out of the waiting room, there was an old wagon waiting for us with two mules hitched to it! Not even horses, only those mules. You see, I was a proud little girl. I didn't know then that my Granddaddy Laird was a proud man, too, but proud over things that mattered, not show things, as I was."

Miss Lacey shook her head. "Oh me, how I hated it at first! But by the end of the summer I didn't want to go back to Chicago. I cried to stay, and I cried when I had to go home again to our apartment, which was so hot, and the noise of cars and children, and the dirty smells of the city. I dreamed about Hillsdale every night until I went back the next summer, and then I waited for the summer every year. Now there's no one left in Hillsdale for me to go back to, but I guess I'll dream about it until I die, even if I never go home there again."

While Nellie was listening, a strange thing happened to her. She stopped thinking about herself for a long time. It was almost as if she didn't even have a body to wriggle or feet that would fall asleep.

It had always seemed to her that everything other people said had to fit in with Nellie Cameron some way or another, either good or bad, mostly bad. But now Miss Lacey was talking about something separate. Her words came from the private center of her just as Nellie's words were a reaching out to others from her own hidden self.

She hated to think about the way she had stormed into this room after the Christmas vacation that made her sick. Why, she had no right to do that! Miss Lacey was a separate person; Sam was a separate person. Sometimes they met and sometimes they went away inside their own selves. It took a person to know a person. And that meant that Nellie was somebody, too.

Miss Lacey clapped her hands. "Well! Enough of that! Let's see what time we've got . . . five minutes. Want to try again? Why, Nellie! I don't believe I've ever seen such a big smile from you before!"

Claudia

Barbara Wallace

Claudia was perfectly happy climbing
trees with fourth-grader Duffy, but her
mother made her stop playing with him.
Janice, who once had been Claudia's best
friend, started acting terribly grown-up
and became Polly's best friend.
Claudia didn't really understand about
either Duffy or Janice, and before long,
she had something even more difficult
to try to understand.

Mrs. Harper was transferring some cold leftover soup from a larger to a smaller bowl the next morning while the rest of the family ate breakfast.

"That's the way Itty sounded," announced Claudia.

"That's the way Itty sounded doing what, dear?" inquired her mother.

"Throwing up," replied Claudia, calmly sipping her orange juice.

"Oh, honestly! Make her stop it! What next! She'll ruin our breakfast!"

"Barbara's right, dear," said Mrs. Harper. "That isn't exactly table conversation."

"Well, I don't care," Claudia shot back, more at Barbara than at her mother. "That's the way throwing up sounds in our school hall."

Mr. Harper set down his coffee cup. "Claudia, that is enough! We're not interested in either Itty or the way he . . . sounds in the school hall. Now, if you don't mind, the subject is closed."

Claudia retreated into gloomy silence. So many of her conversations with her family ended this way, by her being told to keep quiet or change the subject. At least it seemed that way at the moment. What was wrong with talking about somebody being sick? If she and Duffy had been on the subject, they would have had a very interesting conversation about it. In any event, Claudia left for school feeling cross and miserable.

The conversation was a bad beginning to a bad day. Claudia wondered later if that was what it was, or if she had forgotten to rub her finger around the newel-post three times when she forgot a book and had to go back after it.

A group of sixth-grade girls were clustered at the front door of the school when Claudia arrived. They looked at her with expressionless faces as she approached them, and then they turned their backs toward her. Claudia looked closer to see if Janice and Polly might be part of the group, but she could see that they weren't. She decided that she was imagining things and continued toward the girls. Without a word to her, but with several significant glances toward each other, the girls all began to drift away, leaving Claudia standing on the school steps alone.

She told herself firmly that she was not going to cry, and then pinched herself hard to make sure that she didn't. She wondered if she should go to the girls' room until she felt better but finally decided against it. She knew she would cry in the girls' room, and if she stayed there long enough, someone would be sent to find her. She would have to walk into the classroom looking like a wet, red-eyed rabbit.

What Claudia finally did do was run to the rings and swing herself across and back three times. It kept her from thinking about crying, and she could enter the school building without making a spectacle of herself.

She found another group meeting in the classroom, this one headed by Janice Irby and Polly McKisson. "Sh-sh-sh, here she comes!" someone hissed when Claudia appeared. After a good deal of nudging and several dark glances at Claudia, the group dissolved, melting away to individual desks in the best tradition of seasoned sixth-grade secret agents. Claudia felt like public school enemy number one.

For whatever it was worth, and that was not much at the moment, Sarah What's-her-name (Sarah's last name was Carvell, but Claudia wouldn't admit that she cared what it

was) had not been part of the meeting. She sat at her desk paying no attention to it and was, as usual, scribbling in her drawing tablet. She didn't even look up when Claudia came in.

Itty's desk was empty. Claudia hoped that whatever Itty had was catching and that, excluding herself, the whole class would get it, especially Janice and Polly. The disease might even turn out to be fatal. She stopped thinking this, however, when it occurred to her that it meant Itty would also have to die. She was miserable enough without thinking of Itty on his deathbed.

Things were no better at lunchtime. Claudia had always managed to find an empty seat at one of Mrs. Aiken's sixth-grade tables in the cafeteria, but today when she headed for one, someone next to it pulled the chair away from the table and shoved it into the middle of the floor. Then she saw another empty place next to Alice Clay and headed for that. Alice quickly slid into the empty chair and advised Claudia in a frosty voice that she was saving it for a friend. Claudia finally ended up at a fifth-grade table. Her throat felt so tight that she had to swallow three times to get one bite of peanut butter sandwich down.

Claudia didn't feel like braving the playground after that, so she returned to the classroom and sat staring out the window until the bell rang. Holy tomato! Holy tomato! She said that over and over again to keep herself from crying. Suddenly life had become one big round of finding things to do or say to keep from crying. Oh, holy tomato, anyway! Claudia took a big jab at her desk with her pencil, but all she did was break the lead.

Unfortunately, they had Miss Murdock that afternoon. Claudia was in no mood for Miss Murdock. Oddly enough, though, she didn't mind doing the warm-up exercises and even wished they would spend the whole time doing them. But Miss Murdock, eyeing them critically while they collapsed into their deep knee bends, told them that their leg muscles were completely out of shape. Tired legs, she called it. And it just so happened that she, Miss Murdock, had thought up a splendid game for putting the snap in their worn-out elastic. "The game," she said, "is called 'toad and frogs.'"

Even before hearing the rules, Claudia knew it was a terrible game. Any game with a name like that would have to be terrible.

"Now," continued Miss Murdock, "this is a game which is played in exactly the same manner as tag. The toad is 'it' and chases the frogs, except we will all get down on our hands and hop, hop, hop about as if we were a real little toad and real little frogs. Like this. . . ." She reached down to the ground and started leaping in one direction and then another, her whistle swinging madly about. Hop, hop, hop. Back and forth, around and around she went, looking less and less like a frog and more and more like a deranged hippopotamus with every leap.

All at once, almost by accident it seemed, she looked up at the girls. A startled look crossed her face and she turned a bright crimson. Then she stood up quickly and blew a sharp fweep on her whistle as if it was the *girls* who had been behaving like lunatics. "Now, is there anyone who doesn't understand how it's done?" she said briskly.

Claudia thought she might raise her hand and ask Miss Murdock to do it again, but then she decided she didn't feel like it. She didn't really feel like doing anything. All she wanted was to go home.

"Let me see," said Miss Murdock. "Whom shall we have

for our first toad?" The girls all looked around, considering each other's toadlike qualities.

Janice Irby raised her hand. "I have a good idea for a toad," she said. "I think Claudia Harper would make a good toad." Several of Mrs. Aiken's sixth-grade girls snickered.

"Splendid! A splendid suggestion!" said Miss Murdock, beaming at Claudia.

Claudia felt hot down through her toenails.

"Hop, frogs, hop! Chase, toad, chase!" sang Miss Murdock. Down went all the girls on their hands and off they hopped. Claudia, down on her hands, hopped after them.

She knew that she looked like an idiot, and the thought that they all looked like idiots didn't make her feel any better. The last thing she wanted to do at the moment was go leaping all over the playground, chasing people.

"Toad! Toad! Toad! You nasty old toad!" screamed Mrs. Aiken's sixth-grade girls, and the others picked up the chant. They stayed together in groups taunting Claudia until she hopped over; then they all broke up, chortling and screeching.

Ordinarily, Claudia would have loved being the toad. She liked being "it" in any game. But today her legs felt like melting rubber. It hurt to breathe and her eyes weren't focusing. The bunched-up girls would burst apart like bubbles in a witch's cauldron, leaving Claudia hopelessly flopping around after nothing, then always managing to choose the wrong person to chase. When the bell rang, Claudia hadn't caught anyone and was still the toad. All the way back to the classroom, the girls were snickering and staring, and whispering, "Toad! Toad!" in her direction. If she *had* been a toad, Claudia told herself, she would have squirted her poison juice all over them.

Nothing got much better after that day. The hardest part was not knowing why she had suddenly become the class creep. Claudia started thinking a lot about the kids she had considered class creeps in the past. There was, for instance, Amos Early in the fourth grade. Amos rarely took baths. He told someone once that water made his skin break out all over in purple warts. Nobody believed him, though, because who ever heard of water making your skin break out in purple warts? Claudia began to wonder if she smelled bad the way Amos did. She smelled herself secretly but then decided that *that* didn't do any good. You get so used to the way you smell, she told herself, that even if it was bad, you could never tell it. Look at skunks, for instance. But just in case, she started scrubbing herself so hard in her bath that her skin smarted and turned red.

Claudia found out, too, how it felt to be the last one chosen in sports. She had always known that it was terrible, but it turned out to be worse than terrible. She wondered how Sarah had lived through it all these years. Claudia made up her mind that if she ever had a turn at being team captain again, she was going to choose some people like Sarah first. Holy tomato, so what if your team *did* lose! It was terrible to be chosen last.

But the worst thing that happened, though, was the class election.

The only person who ever smiled at Claudia was Itty, and even he did it quickly, as if he might be caught and get killed. Claudia nearly died herself when Itty actually raised his hand and nominated her for vice-president on the day of the election. His face was white when he did it, and his hand looked, going up, as if it were about to dive into a pot of hot grease. Itty stared straight ahead at the blackboard, and the rest of the class was so still you could hear people breathing.

Unfortunately, Mrs. Aiken did not believe in sending people out of the room during the voting. Just before it was time to vote for vice-president, Bobby Paine leaned over and socked Itty on the arm because he was still staring at the blackboard and refused to look around when Bobby cleared his throat and coughed about ten times. The sock on the arm must have impressed Itty, because when Claudia's name was called out, he continued to stare at the blackboard but didn't raise his hand. Claudia got one vote and that was her own. Even that was because she put her hand up by accident and then was too proud to pull it down when someone snickered.

That was the worst thing that happened.

Claudia felt at times as if she wanted to jump up and scream, "I'm not it!" or "I didn't do it!" But not *what?* Or didn't *do* what? How can you say you're not something or didn't do something if you don't even know what you're talking about? It would be like going up to some policeman and saying, "Look, I didn't do it!" You would get arrested for just *saying* it.

Once Claudia was so desperate that she even considered discussing the situation with her family, her mother, her father, or even Barbara. But she couldn't. She found that she couldn't say anything at all about it at home. All she did was cry without being able to explain why she was crying.

One morning at breakfast, Barbara raised her nose in the air and started sniffing. "Phew! What's *that?*" Claudia had just walked into the room.

"I don't know," Mr. Harper said, "but I rather like it."

Claudia sat down at the table, saying nothing. She had

just helped herself to her father's shaving lotion in case her bath the night before hadn't been enough.

Barbara kept on sniffing. "Claudia, what have you done to yourself? You smell."

This was too much, and Claudia burst into tears right there at the table.

"Look here, Barbara. . . ." Mr. Harper began.

"I'm sorry. I didn't mean anything. It's just that she's got something on that smells, that's all."

"That is enough, Barbara!"

"I said I was sorry."

"It's all right, Barbara; I'm sure Claudia accepts your apology," said Mrs. Harper, putting her arm around Claudia and giving her a hug. "There, there, dear, Barbara didn't mean anything. Here, let me look at you." She raised Claudia's wet face and looked anxiously at one side and then the other. "Claudia, you feel all right, don't you? Are you feeling all right?" She put her hand on Claudia's forehead. "Dear, is anything the matter?"

Claudia shook her head and blew her nose into her paper napkin. The napkin scratched and made her eyes smart.

"I don't know. I wonder." Mrs. Harper sounded even more worried. "You know we never did have Dr. Bauman check you over before school this year. Maybe I'd better call him and make an appointment. Would you like that, dear?"

Claudia burst out sobbing again.

Her mother patted her on the head. "All right, dear, we won't make an appointment just yet."

"Look, Fran," Mr. Harper offered from behind his cup of coffee. "She'll be all right. She probably just had too much of her room last week. It'll blow over."

Her mother wanting to take her to the doctor. Her father saying it would all blow over. It was all more than Claudia could bear. Gasping and sobbing, she pushed her chair back and raced up to her room. Her mother followed her up, of course, and it all ended by Claudia climbing back into her pajamas and returning to bed. She happened to be wearing her favorite green pajamas with the goofy black whales all over them, but even that wasn't as comforting as it usually was.

Claudia hoped she would never burst into tears like that again. But she did.

Once was simply because her mother said one night that they were out of peanut butter and her father said he was too tired to go to the store for some. And Claudia had other crying spells that seemed just as pointless.

Mr. Harper kept right on saying that it would blow over. Mrs. Harper kept right on talking about going to the doctor, only they never went. And Claudia even overheard Barbara telling her mother that it was just Claudia's age, whatever that meant.

Claudia actually did get sick once and was spared a whole week of school. She came down with flu. Everyone at home was so nice, and in a way this made her feel even worse, because no one knew that they were being nice to someone who was this big creep at school. Still, Claudia knew that it pleased her mother to have something definite to work with, and she let herself be fed Jello and have her temperature taken a thousand times a day without complaining once.

In any event, now everyone was certain that Claudia's problem was that she had been coming down with the flu. Anything that happened later would be because she hadn't gotten over it yet.

The flu bug had solved everything for everyone but Claudia.

Afterthought   By reading just this much of Claudia's story, you can get some idea of how bewildered Claudia felt. You do not know why Claudia's classmates shut her out; neither does she. Can you recall a similar occurrence in your class? Try to imagine how the situation in Claudia's class came about. What might Claudia have done to cause it? Is it possible that she actually did nothing? What kind of a person does she appear to be? What can you see that Claudia is gaining from her experience? What are her classmates gaining?

Jane

Helen F. Daringer

Jane Douglas lived in an orphanage and
had never been to a "real" house until
Mrs. Thurman invited her to visit.
Mrs. Thurman even planned a party so
that Jane could meet other girls her age.
Jane refused a new party dress, afraid
that Mrs. Thurman couldn't afford to
buy it; Jane was used to thinking of
others. But you will discover, as
Jane did, that there are times when a
girl must think of herself.

They ate a cold snack at noon, because the dining room was ready for the party. The table had been stretched out almost as long as the one at the orphanage, and covered with a white cloth that practically touched the floor on both sides. In the center stood a deep oval bowl (it looked like silver, but Jane didn't suppose it really was), filled with sprays of blue larkspur and white stock and pink and white pinks. Even from the doorway she could smell the spicy stock and pinks. The larkspur had no smell at all.

Twenty places were laid, each with a fork and spoon and a fringed tissue-paper cylinder, pink and blue and yellow beside a folded linen napkin. Favors, Mrs. Thurman explained when she saw Jane inspecting them, her hands behind her back.

"I should have known." Jane sighed with satisfaction. "I've read about them in books."

They ate the snack in the kitchen, all except Abner, who preferred the back porch where there was a breeze. No one ate much. Jane had sampled the cake batter and icing too liberally to have an appetite, and Mrs. Thurman and Aggie both declared themselves too excited to be hungry. Jane

thought to herself that it was strange she did not feel excited. She felt very calm and collected. She felt as if she were not herself at all, but some other girl looking with her eyes and thinking with her mind.

Mrs. Thurman went to her room to lie down for a few minutes, but Jane dressed immediately. She rubbed her high shoes until they shone, the sides and back as well as the toes. She pulled up her long stockings until the ribs were straight lines, and fastened the hose supporters tight. Miss Fink maintained that there wasn't anything like wrinkles in a girl's stockings to take away her style. She maneuvered the freshly starched blue gingham carefully over her head and stood before the mirror to make sure her petticoat did not show.

Jane gazed with astonished pleasure when Mrs. Thurman appeared in the parlor. "You look lovely, Mrs. Thurman." Her eyes seconded the enthusiasm that spoke in her voice. "I know it's not polite to talk about people's clothes, but you look exactly like a fashion-book picture. I wish Miss Fink could lay eyes on you." Suddenly self-conscious and shy, she added in a subdued tone, "I hope you'll 'scuse me please for mentioning your dress."

"I'm glad you like it." Mrs. Thurman glanced down at her shell-pink voile, with its belt of twisted satin. "I was hoping you would. And you look as neat and fresh as if you had just stepped out of a bandbox."

Jane was pleased to be complimented.

"I wonder if you wouldn't like to wear a rosebud on your shoulder," Mrs. Thurman suggested. Jane stood very still, scarcely breathing, holding her head to one side—the wet comb marks were still showing in her brown hair—while the flower was pinned on. "There." Mrs. Thurman surveyed the blue gingham shoulder where the rosebud nestled. "Now everybody will be able to see who the hostess is."

It seemed a long wait until half-past two o'clock. Jane would have worried for fear nobody would come—they might forget or think it was tomorrow or their mothers mightn't let them—but Mrs. Thurman appeared so much at ease that Jane took her cue from her. If they just knew about the lemonade and peach ice cream and two kinds of cake with icing on, wild elephants couldn't keep them away.

The guests began to arrive, some on foot and others in carriages which wheeled leisurely around and went jogging off again. Mrs. Thurman stood beside Jane to introduce the guests—India Maud Meadows and Louise Craig, Florence and Alice Andrews, Cissie Matthews, who greeted Jane like an old friend, Mary Bryden, Sarah Williams, Annabelle Jones, Emily Welch, Jean Peirce, and all the others. They sat primly erect, skirts spread wide on the green velvet sofa and dark old chairs. They talked as politely to each other as if they were their own mothers and aunts.

When the last guest had arrived, panting and with hair ribbons askew because she had run most of the way, Mrs. Thurman excused herself. She might be needed in the kitchen, she said. They might play games in the house or on the lawn, as they preferred. If they enjoyed paper-and-pencil games, Jane would supply them with pencils and foolscap.

In certain ways Jane felt more sure of herself after Mrs. Thurman's departure. It was harder to think of things to say while she was there, because you kept thinking about your manners. And as everyone knows, too much thinking about manners often keeps people from becoming friends.

"Would you like to play charades?" she asked. There was silence. Some guests looked at Jane, some at each other. "Or riddles, like 'On top of a hill there's a mill, and under the mill there's a walk, and under the walk there's a key; what is it?'"

The silence spread and grew chilly. The guests were all looking at her. She had almost forgotten about the blue gingham, but now she remembered. She noticed that every girl, every single one, was wearing a white dress; yes, and a silk sash tied around her waist.

"Let's have somebody leave the room and we hide something and then she comes back and guesses where it's hidden."

Jane tried to sound as if what she was proposing were the most fun in the world.

Nobody answered. There was no friendliness, no flicker of kindness in the faces confronting her. They stared as if she were quite different from themselves and they were too well brought up to have anything to do with her. Jane felt herself turning red—not just her face, but her ears and neck. She could feel the burning color begin to move down her body. She held herself steady, although she could hardly keep her voice from wavering.

"Would you like to play 'drop the handkerchief' outdoors?"

Silence answered her. Nineteen pairs of eyes—blue, brown, hazel-colored—stared at her without blinking. For a moment Jane was frightened. Frightened and helpless. It was as though she were trapped in a solid piece of glass like the little sheep inside Matron's paperweight. She was not herself any longer; she was not Jane Douglas. She was a person to be stared at. The girls would go away and make fun of her behind her back. They would talk about her and make fun of her blue dress and her short hair.

Unexpectedly, something within her boiled up, seethed and bubbled, burst into flame like an exploding rocket. She threw back her head and stamped her foot. Her gray eyes were blazing.

"I'm going out to the stable and play 'pirate chief'," she announced loudly. "It's the most exciting game in the world. It's the kind that boys play when they won't let girls play with them. If anyone wants to play with me, come along. If you don't, you can just sit here forever for all I care!"

There was a stir, a shuffling of black patent-leather slippers

on the thick red carpet, a swishing of starched dimity and organdy and crisp taffeta sashes. The set faces relaxed; the eyes blinked.

Jane was quick to sense her advantage. "I'll explain about the game." It was no longer necessary to talk loudly, because everybody was paying attention. "There's a pirate chief and his band. They have to be awfully daring and venturesome because if they're not, they get caught and—" She paused dramatically. She was beginning to feel gay and excited and venturesome herself. But she mustn't let herself go; she had to keep her head. She had to think quickly, for she did not know what would happen to the pirates if they got caught. It was a new game that she was making up as she went along. "They have to pay a forfeit."

"Is that all there is to it? I thought it was something special. I've played lots of games like that." Cissie was superior, bored.

Others looked as if they were not particularly interested in "pirate chief" after all. Cissie's air of disdain had made an impression.

"Not like this one, you haven't!" Jane maintained stoutly. She braced herself to keep her courage from slipping. She

would fight to the end for her rights. She would not let Cissie take the party away from her; it wasn't Cissie's party, it was her own. Mrs. Thurman was giving it for her, Jane Douglas. She would not let Cissie have her way with the party and make Jane feel left out.

"Besides the pirates there's a rich family that has a box of treasure and a beautiful daughter," she continued, looking straight at Cissie.

"That sounds spiffy!" The deep, booming voice was India Maud's. She leaned forward eagerly from the sofa. "Does the pirate chief try to steal the treasure?"

The question served like a heady tonic. Jane's mind began to work faster and faster, more and more confidently. "Not just the treasure." She was speaking to India Maud, but she noted out of the corner of her eye that the others were all waiting to hear the answer too. "He tries to steal the daughter! He's in love with her."

"Does he get her?" This from Cissie, whose fancy was snared by the beauteous daughter.

India Maud turned upon her. "That's what the game is about, silly! I should think you could figure out that much for yourself." She walked over to Jane. "I'm going to be the girl's

father that fights to protect her. Jane, you can be the pirate chief."

"Let's not have it her father," objected Annabelle. "Fathers are too old. Let's have it a young man she's engaged to."

"Suits me," said India Maud. "I don't care who he is just so I'm him."

"I'll be the daughter," volunteered Cissie, quite carried away by enthusiasm now that India Maud and Annabelle approved the game.

"You? Don't be silly, Cissie. You're too big. You're half a head taller than I am. How'd it look to have the daughter bigger than the man that protects her?" There was no denying the soundness of India Maud's reasoning. "Mary'd make a good daughter. You can be the mother, Cissie." Mary, shy and small and beaming with pleasure, lined up beside her champion.

"Now, Jane, you and I'll choose the ones we want on our sides." India Maud was like a general marshaling his staff.

Deeply grateful to India Maud though she was, Jane was not quite willing to have her take charge. "Don't you think, India Maud," she proposed tactfully, "that we might let them choose which side they'd rather be on—pirates or protectors?"

"When everybody's running and hiding, how can we tell which are pirates?" questioned practical Sarah Williams. "I'll be sure to forget who is what."

"Pirates," commanded Jane, "take off your hair ribbons and leave them in the parlor."

"My sash too," said Florence, "and yours, Alice. Remember what Mamma said about being careful."

Similar injunctions must have been issued by other parents, for nineteen sashes were hastily draped over the sofa and outspread on chair backs. The parlor resembled a giant, rainbow-colored spider web.

"You didn't say what the forfeit is," Beth Topping reminded Jane.

For the fraction of a minute Jane was at a loss. While she groped hastily through her mind, her eyes focused on something outside the window—the fountain. Four silvery jets were arching through the shallow shade to break in sparkling spray against the iron umbrella. "The losers must take their shoes and stockings off and stick their feet into the fountain." She proclaimed the forfeit like a judge. Everybody giggled.

To have nothing at all
Is to have much still:
One's share in the sun,
And the winds that blow,
A right in the road
That swings over the hill,
And the far horizon
That lies below.

To have nothing at all
Does not take from the mind
Its free roving thoughts
Which still know their abode,
Nor the hope that's ahead,
Nor the sorrow behind,
Nor the future that lies
At the turn of the road.

Elizabeth Coatsworth

Chance

Ester Wier

After running away from seven foster
homes, Chance Reedy is sent to live
with his granny and brother Turpem,
who are strangers to him. Their house sits
on stilts near a Florida swamp.
Mr. Fairday, a naturalist who lives
nearby, teaches Chance about swamp
plants and about animals like old
One-Ear, a wild hog. Turpem gives
Chance a puppy but tells him the dog is a
skeer-cat—a coward; Turpem has no
use for cowards. Chance soon discovers
that Turpem takes stupid risks in order
to appear brave. The boys quarrel,
and Granny talks to Chance about
the situation.

Chance took Angus and the axe and walked toward the swamp. Granny's talk had surprised him, for he hadn't realized she had noticed how Turpem was always trying to lord it over him, using him as a measure for his own courage and plainly delighted every time his young brother failed to come up to that standard. It bothered him, too, for now he knew for certain that Granny didn't really respect or admire him the way she did Turpem, even though she complained about his brother's heedlessness.

"Looks like everyone thinks we're skeer-cats," he told Angus, "no matter what. Seems neither of us is ever really going to be a swamper. Seems we're always going to be outsiders."

There being no hurry to get back, and feeling like being alone, he took his time and followed the creek bank north for a long way. He was looking for the biggest cabbage palm he could find, something to make Granny especially pleased with him. Mr. Fairday had told him cabbage palms never died of old age. "Only way to get rid of them is to cut them down. Even fire won't kill them," he'd said. Well, Chance decided, he'd look for and get the oldest one there was in the whole swamp, figuring it would have to be the biggest.

Bald cypress rose a hundred feet in the air, their trunks swollen at the base to give them steadiness in the murky waters in which they grew. Already their small, rounded cones were beginning to form, revealing the progress of summer toward fall. On their trunks were patches of lichen, looking like smears of green, white, pink, or gray paint. Hearing a mewing sound, he stopped to watch a yellow-bellied sapsucker drill holes into the inner bark and gather the outflowing sap with its brushlike tongue. A blue-tailed skink, disturbed by his nearness, ran up a tree and disappeared. Following its upward flight with his eyes, he saw a barred owl regarding him from a branch, its head swiveling around so that its immovable eyes could hold him in their baleful gaze.

Lowering his body, he passed beneath a tangle of wild briers, following a dim trail made long ago. A few hundred feet along, he came upon a high spot where the stump of a dead cabbage palm stood. From its center there flowed a clear, sweet spring and, kneeling, he and the dog drank deep. Then Chance threw himself back upon the soft, dry earth. About him spider lilies shone white against the green growth, and giant red hibiscus bloomed on ten-foot stalks. High overhead, leafless ghost orchids clutched the trunks of trees like great spiders, their white flowers trailing long streamers.

With silence pressing close about him, the boy lay staring at the leafy canopy overhead, discouraged and downhearted. More than anything else in the world he had wanted to stay here in the swamp, to become part of the family. He had wanted to make Granny proud of him, to get along with Turpem and earn his respect and friendship. For once he had almost been able to believe that everything could go right for him, but now, suddenly, he found himself questioning and wondering, full of doubt and confusion. In the past when things hadn't gone the way he thought they should, or he had been disappointed by something, he had run away, as much to leave the uncertainty behind as to seek something else. Now he felt perplexed as to which was worse, running away to look for something you never found or to believe you'd found it and then have it turn out not to be what you'd expected at all.

He dug his fists into the earth. Losing his faith in Turpem was like it had been when he'd finally given up on his father ever coming back to claim him. It left an emptiness inside of him, and in a kind of panic he sat up and looked about him. If he was smart, he'd get out of this swamp now, before anything else happened. Tears slid down the furrow between his nose and cheek, and he brushed them off angrily.

Angus, who had been at the water's edge, watching the butterflies and grasshoppers and beetles, turned to come to him, but his puppy awkwardness caused him to lose his footing on the thick, slippery mass of lilies on the marshy bank, so that he slid into the water with a splash. Chance rushed to the water's edge and threw himself full length onto the earth, remembering the alligator that had been waiting when Chigger went overboard. He grasped the dog and pulled him up the rise.

The water, which was at its highest level in late summer and would drop through the fall and winter to reach its lowest in the spring, flowed imperceptibly southward, its progress almost impossible to see. To convince himself for the hundredth time that it actually did move, Chance turned over on his stomach and watched it, lazily. A delightful coolness, sweet and fresh, swept over him, and for the next half hour he lay there, absorbed in the minute life on the water's surface . . . the butterflies with beating wings hovering above it; the spiders spinning their webs from floating duckweed to nearby reeds; dragonflies darting through the grasses rising from the creek bottom; bees droning as they hovered among the saw grass, sipping from every bloom.

In a place where all is shadow, there are no shadows to reveal the passing of time, and Chance might have gone on lying there at the water's edge for another hour or two if Angus hadn't suddenly stiffened and begun to growl, the hair on his back standing up like hog bristles.

Slowly the boy turned his head to see what was troubling the dog. There, not more than fifteen feet away, stood a panther. It was a good seven feet from nose to tail tip, the gray of its coat blending into the shaggy bark of the cypress trunk against which it stood. Its yellow eyes rested upon the two of them curiously.

The axe still lay beside the spring. Chance knew if the cat meant to attack he would have no chance, for it outweighed him by far, and all he had were his two hands to use against it. To his amazement he found himself calm, feeling none of the panic he had experienced looking down from the tree to see old One-Ear on the ground beneath him.

He rose carefully, his mind working hard. Angus retreated behind him and stayed there. The big cat still watched but made no move, and the boy mentally checked off the actions open to him. He could turn and run, but if he did, the animal, which might not have been going to attack, might see him as a running target and pounce upon him. He could make a dash for the axe, but he knew that wouldn't work, for he could hardly hope to reach it before the panther reached him.

Do something! he told himself.

Do anything!

Without knowing what he meant to do, he threw his arms over his head and, stepping forward, shouted at the top of his voice, "Skat! Shoo! Get out of here, you skeer-booger!" Then he imitated the cry of the limpkin, it being the most frightening sound he knew. He made it as bloodcurdling and wild as he could, and the sound echoed and reechoed through the swamp.

The big cat was taken aback. Perhaps it had only just finished a meal of deer and wasn't hungry. Perhaps it had never before heard the sound of a human voice; but whatever it was, it kept the animal from attacking. Slowly it backed away, then took to its heels, fading into the grayness of the cypress swamp.

For a minute Chance stood motionless, watching it go. Now Angus, brave and bold, leaped and barked, running to where it had stood to examine the tracks and sniff the scent. All the boy could think of was what Granny had told him just a few hours ago about how Turpem had once come home telling tales no one would believe.

"She'd never believe this," he told Angus, and the thought of her face if he tried to show her how he had run a panther off brought such laughter bubbling up inside of him that he could hardly stand up straight. Grasping himself about the middle, he bent double, spasms of hysteria passing over him in waves, leaving him weak and helpless. When it was over, he wiped his eyes and gasped to the dog, "Nobody'll ever believe it. Turpem once said there were no panthers left in the swamp, and Granny'd say I went to sleep and dreamed it." Mr. Fairday had already told him never to expect anyone to believe what you said you'd seen in the swamp. The joke of it was that he would never be able to tell anyone about the bravest thing he had ever done in his life, something he could hardly believe himself. For once he hadn't run away from something unpleasant. He had stayed and faced up. That knowledge made all the difference in the world in his frame of mind, and it was all he could do to keep from busting out in song, he felt so happy.

Looking at Angus now, it occurred to him also that for the first time in his life something had depended upon him, had

believed in him and trusted him to take care of a situation.
He picked up the small dog and held it close, grateful for its
faith and loyalty.

Afterthought

The poem that begins this unit reminds you that you
are not just like any other person—you are unique. Yet the
world is full of people, and all of them must find ways to
get along together. Think about the characters in the unit.
What problems did each have to face? What did each one
have within himself to help him solve the problems of
living with others? How might these characteristics be
considered keys to the universe?

The Cay

Theodore Taylor

This long selection is for you to read alone—for your own pleasure. If you enjoy the selection, you may want to read the entire book.

The old man in the story speaks a beautiful language that may sound strange to you. Sometimes you may not understand a word he uses, but you can tell what he means.

We were torpedoed at about three o'clock in the morning on April 6, 1942, two days after leaving Panama.

I was thrown from the top bunk and suddenly found myself on my hands and knees on the deck. We could hear the ship's whistle blowing constantly, and there were sounds of metal wrenching and much shouting. The whole ship was shuddering. It felt as though we'd stopped and were dead in the water.

My mother was very calm, not at all like she was at home. She talked quietly while she got dressed, telling me to tie my shoes, and be certain to carry my wool sweater, and to put on my leather jacket. Her hands were not shaking.

She helped me put on my life jacket, then put hers on, saying, "Now, remember everything that we were told about abandoning ship." The officers had held drills every day.

As she was speaking, there was another violent explosion. We were thrown against the cabin door, which the steward had warned us not to lock because it might become jammed. We pushed it open and went out to the boat deck, which was already beginning to tilt.

Everything was bright red, and there were great crackling noises. The entire afterpart of the ship was on fire, and sailors were launching the lifeboat that was on our deck. Steam lines had broken, and the steam was hissing out. Heat from the fire washed over us.

When the lifeboat had been swung out, the captain came down from the bridge. He was a small, wiry white-haired man and was acting the way I'd been told captains should act. He stood by the lifeboat in the fire's glow, very alert, giving orders to the crew. He was carrying a briefcase and a navigation instrument I knew to be a sextant. On the other side of the ship, another lifeboat was being launched.

Near us, two sailors with axes chopped at lines, and two big life rafts plunged toward the water, which looked black except for pools of fire from burning fuel oil.

The captain shouted, "Get a move on! Passengers into the boats!" Tins of lubricating oil in the afterholds had ignited and were exploding, but the ones forward had not been exposed to the fire.

A sailor grabbed my mother's hand and helped her in, and then I felt myself being passed into the hands of a sailor on the boat. The other passengers were helped in, and someone yelled, "Lower away." At that moment, the *Hato* lurched heavily and something happened to the boat falls.

The bow tilted downward, and the next thing I knew, we were all in the water. I saw my mother near me and yelled to her. Then something hit me from above.

A long time later (four hours I was told), I opened my eyes to see blue sky above. It moved back and forth, and I could hear the slap of water. I had a terrible pain in my head. I closed my eyes again, thinking maybe I was dreaming. Then a voice said, "Young bahss, how are you feelin'?"

I turned my head.

I saw a huge, very old Negro sitting on a raft near me. He was ugly. His nose was flat and his face was broad; his head was a mass of wiry gray hair. For a moment, I could not figure out where I was or who he was. Then I remembered seeing him working with the deck gang of the *Hato*.

I looked around for my mother, but there was no one else on the raft. Just this huge Negro, myself, and a big black and gray cat that was licking his haunches.

The Negro said, "You 'ad a mos' terrible crack on d'ead, bahss. A strongback glanc' offen your 'ead, an' I harl you board dis raff."

He crawled over toward me. His face couldn't have been blacker, or his teeth whiter. They made an alabaster trench in his mouth, and his pink-purple lips peeled back over them like the meat of a conch shell. He had a big welt, like a scar, on his left cheek. I knew he was West Indian. I had seen many of them in Willemstad, but he was the biggest one I'd ever seen.

I sat up, asking, "Where are we? Where is my mother?"

The Negro shook his head with a frown. "I true believe

your mut-thur is safe an' soun' on a raff like dis. Or mebbe dey harl 'er into d'boat. I true believe dat."

Then he smiled at me, his face becoming less terrifying. "As to our veree location, I mus' guess we are somewhar roun' d'cays, somewhar mebbe fifteen latitude an' eighty long. We should 'ave pass dem til' dat mos' treacherous torpedo split d'veree hull. Two minute downg, at d'mos'."

I looked all around us. There was nothing but blue sea with occasional patches of orange-brown seaweed. No sight of the *Hato*, or other rafts, or boats. Just the sea and a few birds that wheeled over it. That lonely sea, and the sharp pains in my head, and the knowledge that I was here alone with a black man instead of my mother made me break into tears.

Finally the black man said, looking at me from bloodshot

eyes, "Now, young bahss, I mos' feel like dat my own self, Timothy, but 'twould be of no particular use to do dat, eh?" His voice was rich calypso, soft and musical, the words rubbing off like velvet.

I felt a little better, but my head ached fiercely.

He nodded toward the cat. "Dis is Stew, d'cook's cat. He climb on d'raff, an' I 'ad no heart to trow 'im off." Stew was still busy licking. " 'E got oi-ll all ovah hisself from d'wattah."

I looked closer at the black man. He was extremely old, yet he seemed powerful. Muscles rippled over the ebony of his arms and around his shoulders. His chest was thick and his neck was the size of a small tree trunk. I looked at his hands and feet. The skin was alligatored and cracked, tough from age and walking barefoot on the hot decks of schooners and freighters.

He saw me examining him and said gently, "Put your 'ead back downg, young bahss, an' rest awhile longer. Do not look direct at d'sun. 'Tis too powerful."

I felt seasick and crawled to the side to vomit. He came up beside me, holding my head in his great clamshell hands. It didn't matter, at that moment, that he was black and ugly. He murmured, "Dis be good, dis be good."

When it was over, he helped me back to the center of the raft, saying, " 'Tis mos' natural for you to do dis. 'Tis d'shock o' havin' all dis mos' terrible ting 'appen."

I then watched as he used his powerful arms and hands to rip up boards from the outside edges of the raft. He pounded them back together on cleats, forming two triangles; then he jammed the bases into slots between the raft boards. He stripped off his shirt and his pants, then demanded mine.

I don't know what happened to my leather jacket or my sweater. But soon, we had a flimsy shelter from the burning sun.

Crawling under it to sprawl beside me, he said, "We 'ave rare good luck, young bahss. D'wattah kag did not bus' when d'raff was launch, an' we 'ave a few biscuit, some choclade, an' d'matches in d'tin is dry. So we 'ave rare good luck." He grinned at me then.

I was thinking that our luck wasn't so good. I was thinking about my mother on another boat or raft, not knowing I was all right. I was thinking about my father back in Willemstad. It was terrible not to be able to tell him where I was. He'd have boats and planes out within hours.

I guess the big Negro saw the look on my face. He said, "Do not be despair, young bahss. Someone will fin' us. Many schooner go by dis way, an' dis also be d'ship track to Jamaica, an' on."

After a bit, lulled by the bobbing of the raft and by the soft, pleasant sounds of the sea against the oil-barrel floats, I went to sleep again. I was very tired and my head still ached. The piece of timber must have struck a glancing blow on the left side.

When I next awakened, it was late afternoon. The sun had edged down and the breeze across us was cool. But I felt very hot and the pain had not gone away. The Negro was sitting with his back toward me, humming something in calypso. His back was a great wall of black flesh, and I saw a cruel scar on one shoulder.

I asked, "What is your name?"

Hearing my voice, he turned with a wide grin. "Ah, you are back wit' me. It 'as been lonesome dese veree hours."

I repeated, "What is your name?"

"My own self? Timothy!"

"Your last name?"

He laughed, "I 'ave but one name. 'Tis Timothy."

"Mine is Phillip Enright, Timothy." My father had always taught me to address anyone I took to be an adult as "mister," but Timothy didn't seem to be a mister. Besides, he was black.

He said, "I knew a Phillip who feesh out of St. Jawn, but an outrageous mahn he was." He laughed deep inside himself.

I asked him for a drink of water.

He nodded agreeably, saying, "D'sun do parch." He lifted a hinged section of the raft flooring and drew out the keg, which was about two feet long. There was a tin cup lashed to it. Careful not to spill a drop, he said, " 'Tis best to 'ave only an outrageous smahl amount. Jus' enough to wet d'tongue."

"Why?" I asked. "That is a large keg."

He scanned the barren sea and then looked back at me, his old eyes growing remote. "D'large kag 'ave a way o' losin' its veree size."

"You said we would be picked up soon," I reminded him.

"Ah, yes," he said instantly, "but we mus' be wise 'bout what we 'ave."

I drank the tiny amount of water he'd poured out and asked for more. He regarded me silently a moment, then said, his eyes squinting, "A veree lil' more, young bahss."

My lips were parched and my throat was dry. I wanted a whole cup. "Please fill it up," I said.

Timothy poured only a few drops into the bottom.

"That isn't enough," I complained. I felt I could drink

three cups of it. But he pressed the wooden stopper firmly back into the keg, ignoring me.

I said, "I must have water, Timothy. I'm very hot."

Without answering, he opened the trap in the raft and secured the keg again. It was then that I began to learn what a stubborn old man he could be. I began to dislike Timothy.

"Young bahss," he said, coming back under the shelter, "mebbe before d'night, a schooner will pass dis way, an' if dat 'appens, you may drink d'whole kag. Mebbe d'schooner will not pass dis way, so we mus' make our wattah last."

I said defiantly, "A schooner will find us. And my father has ships out looking for us."

Without even glancing at me, he answered, "True, young bahss." Then he closed his eyes and would not speak to me anymore. He just sprawled out, a mound of silent black flesh.

I couldn't hold the tears back. I'm sure he heard me, but he didn't move a muscle of his face. Neither did he look up when I crawled out from under the shelter to get as far away from him as I could. I stayed on the edge of the raft for a long time, thinking about home and rubbing Stew Cat's back.

Although I hadn't thought so before, I was now beginning to believe that my mother was right. She didn't like them.

She didn't like it when Henrik and I would go down to St. Anna Bay and play near the schooners. But it was always fun. The black people would laugh at us and toss us bananas or papayas.

She'd say, when she knew where we'd been, "They are not the same as you, Phillip. They are different and they live differently. That's the way it must be." Henrik, who'd grown up in Curaçao with them, couldn't understand why my mother felt this way.

I yelled over at him, "You're saving all the water for yourself."

I don't think he was asleep, but he didn't answer.

When the sky began to turn a deep blue, Timothy roused himself and looked around. He said, with just an unfriendly glance at me, "If luck be, d'flyin' feesh will flop on d'raff. We can save a few biscuit by eatin' d'feesh. Too, wattah is in d'feesh."

I was hungry but the thought of eating raw fish didn't appeal to me. I said nothing.

Just before dark, they began skimming across the water, their short, winglike fins taking them on flights of twenty or thirty feet, sometimes more.

A large one shot out of the water, skimmed toward us, and then slammed into the raft flooring. Timothy grabbed it, shouting happily. He rapped its head with his knife handle and tossed it beneath the shelter. Soon another came aboard, not so large. Timothy grabbed it, too.

Before total darkness, he had skinned them, deftly cutting meat from their sides. He handed me the two largest pieces. "Eat dem," he ordered.

I shook my head.

He looked at me in the fading light and said softly, "We will 'ave no other food tonight. You bes' eat dem, young bahss." With that, he pressed a piece of the fish against his teeth, sucking at it noisily.

Yes, they were different. They ate raw fish.

I turned away from him, over on my stomach. I thought about Curaçao, warm and safe; about our gabled house in Scharloo, and about my father. Suddenly I blamed my mother because I was on the raft with this stubborn old black man. It was all her fault. She'd wanted to leave the island.

I blurted out, "I wouldn't even be here with you if it wasn't for my mother."

I knew Timothy was staring at me through the darkness when he said, "She started dis terrible wahr, eh, young bahss?" He was a shadowy shape across the raft.

Total darkness blotted out the sea, and it became cold and damp. Timothy took the shelter down, and we both pulled our shirts and pants back on. They were stiff from salt and felt clammy. The wind picked up, blowing fine chill spray across the raft. Then the stars came out.

We stayed in the middle of the raft, side by side, as it

drifted aimlessly over the sea. Stew Cat rubbed his back against the bottoms of my feet and then curled up down there. I was glad because he was warm.

I was thinking that it was very strange for me, a boy from Virginia, to be lying beside this giant Negro out on the ocean. And I guess maybe Timothy was thinking the same thing.

Once, our bodies touched. We both drew back, but I drew back faster. In Virginia, I knew they'd always lived in their sections of town, and us in ours. A few times, I'd gone down through the shacks of colored town with my father. They sold spicy crabs in one shack, I remember.

I saw them mostly in the summer, down by the river, fishing or swimming naked, but I didn't really know any of them. And in Willemstad, I didn't know them very well either. Henrick van Boven did, though, and he was much easier with them.

I asked, "Timothy, where is your home?"

"St. Thomas," he said. "Charlotte Amalie, on St. Thomas." He added, " 'Tis a Virgin Islan'."

"Then you are American," I said. I remembered from school that we had bought the Virgins from Denmark.

He laughed. "I suppose, young bahss. I nevar gave it much thought. I sail all d'islan's, as well as Venezuela, Colombo, Panama. . . . I jus' nevar gave it much thought I was American."

I said, "Your parents were African, Timothy?"

He laughed, low and soft. "Young bahss, you want me to say I true come from Afre-ca?"

"You say what you want." It was just that Timothy

looked very much like the men I'd seen in jungle pictures. Flat nose and heavy lips.

He shook his head. "I 'ave no recollection o' anythin' 'cept dese islan's. 'Tis pure outrageous, but I do not remember anythin' 'bout a place called Afre-ca."

I didn't know if he was telling the truth or not. He looked pure African. I said, "What about your mother?"

Now, there was deep laughter in his voice. " 'Tis even more outrageous I do not remember a fatha or my mut-thur. I was raise by a woman call Hannah Gumbs. . . ."

"Then you are an orphan," I said.

"I guess, young bahss, I guess." He was chuckling to himself, rich and deep.

I looked over toward him, but again, he was just a shadowy shape, a large mound. "How old are you, Timothy?" I asked.

"Dat fact is also veree mysterious. Lil' more dan sixty, 'cause d'muscle in my legs b'speakin' to me, complain all d'time. But to be true, I do not know exact."

I was amazed that any man shouldn't know his own age. I was almost certain now that Timothy had indeed come from Africa, but I didn't tell him that. I said, "I'm almost twelve." I wanted him to know I was almost twelve so that he would stop treating me as though I were half that age.

"Dat is a veree important age," Timothy agreed. "Now, you mus' get some natural sleep. Tomorrow might be a veree long day, an' we 'ave much to do."

I laughed. There we were on that bucking raft with nothing to do except watch for schooners or aircraft. "What do we have to do?" I asked.

His eyes groped through the darkness for mine. He came up on his elbows. "Stay alive, young bahss, dat's what we 'ave to do."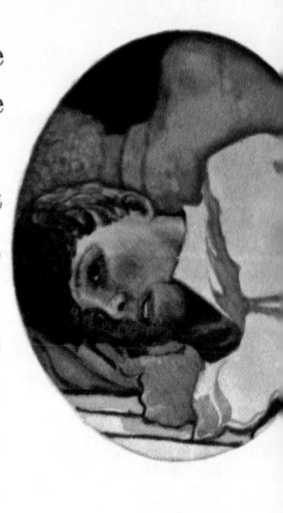

Soon, it became very cold and I began shivering. Part of it was coldness, but there was also fear. If the raft tipped over, sharks would slash at us, I knew.

My head was aching violently again. During the day, the pain had been dull, but now it was shooting along both sides of my head. Once, sometime during the early night, I felt his horny hand on my forehead. Then he shifted my body, placing it on the other side of him.

He murmured, "Young bahss, d'wind 'as shift. You'll be warmer on dis side."

I was still shivering, and soon he gathered me against him, and Stew Cat came back to be a warm ball against my feet. I could now smell Timothy, tucked up against him. He didn't smell like my father or my mother. Father always smelled of bay rum, the shaving lotion he used, and Mother smelled of some kind of perfume or cologne. Timothy smelled different and strong, like the black men who worked on the decks of the tankers when they were loading. After a while, I didn't mind the smell because Timothy's back was very warm.

The raft plunged on across the light swells throughout the long night.

I do not think he slept much during the night, but I'd been told that old people didn't sleep much anyway. I woke up when there was a pale band of light to the east, and Timothy said, "You fare well, young bahss? How is d'ead?"

"It still hurts," I admitted.

Timothy said, "A crack on d'ead takes a few days to go 'way." He opened the trap on the raft to pull out the water keg and the tin containing the biscuits, the chocolate squares, and dry matches.

I sat up, feeling dizzy. He allowed me half a cup of water and two hard biscuits, then fed Stew Cat with a wedge of leftover flying fish. We ate in silence as the light crept steadily over the smooth, oily sea. The wind had died and already the sun was beginning to scorch.

Timothy chewed slowly on half a biscuit. "Today, young bahss, a schooner will pass. I'd bet a jum on dat."

"I hope so," I said.

"I do tink we are not too far from Providencia an' San Andrés."

I looked hard at Timothy. "Are they islands?"

He nodded.

I kept looking at him. It seemed there was a film, a haze, separating us. I rubbed my eyes and opened them again. But the haze was still there. I glanced over at the red ball of sun, now clear of the horizon. It seemed dim. I said, "I think there is something wrong with my eyes."

Timothy said, "I warn you! You look direct at d'sun yestiddy."

Yes, that was it! I'd looked at the sun too much.

"Today," Timothy said, "do not eben look at d'wattah. D'glare is bad too."

He went about setting up the triangles for our shelter, and I took off my clothes. After he had draped my pants and shirt, I got under the shelter. The pain in my head was almost unbearable now, and I remember moaning. Timothy tore off a piece of his shirt from the shelter roof, soaked it in fresh water, and placed it over my eyes. There was worry in his voice as he talked.

Awhile later, I took the cloth off my eyes and looked up. The inside of our shelter was shadowy and dark, but the pain had begun to go away. "It doesn't hurt as much anymore," I said.

"Ah, see, it jus' takes time, young bahss."

I put the cool cloth back over my eyes and went to sleep again. When I woke up, it was night. Yet the air felt hot, and the breeze that came across the raft was warm. I lay there thinking.

"What time is it?" I asked.

" 'Bout ten."

"At night?"

There was puzzlement in his voice. " 'Tis day."

I put my hand in front of my face. Even in the very blackest night, you can see your own hand. But I could not see mine.

I screamed to Timothy, "I'm blind, I'm blind."

"What?" His voice was a frightened roar.

Then I knew he was bending over me. I felt his breath in my face. He said, "Young bahss, you cannot be blin'." He pulled me roughly from the shelter.

"Look at d'sun," he ordered. His hands pointed my face. I felt the strong warmth against it, but everything was black.

The silence seemed to last forever as he held my face toward the sun. Then a long, shuddering sigh came from his great body. He said, very gently, "Now, young bahss, you mus' lie downg an' rest. What 'as happen will go 'way. 'Tis all natural temporary." But his voice was hollow.

I got down on the hot boards, blinking my eyes again and again, trying to lift the curtain of blackness. I touched them. They did not feel any different. Then I realized that the pain had gone away. It had gone away but left me blind.

I could hear my voice saying, far off, "I don't feel any pain, Timothy. The pain has gone away."

I guess he was trying to think it all out. In a few minutes, he answered, "Once, ovah 'round Barbados, a mahn 'ad an outrageous crack on d'ead when a sailin' boom shift. Dis mahn was blin' too. Tree whole day 'e saw d'night. Den it true went away."

"Do you think that is what will happen to me?"

"I tink dat be true, young bahss," he said.

Then he became very quiet.

After a moment, lying there in darkness, hearing the creak of the raft and feeling its motion, it all hit me. I was blind and we were lost at sea.

I began to crawl, screaming for my mother and my father, but felt his hard hands on my arms. He held me tight and said, low and soft, "Young bahss, young bahss." He kept repeating it.

I'll never forget that first hour of knowing I was blind. I was so frightened that it was hard for me to breathe. It was as if I'd been put inside something that was all dark and I couldn't get out.

I remember that at one point my fear turned to anger. Anger at Timothy for not letting me stay in the water with my mother, and anger at her because I was on the raft. I began hitting him and I remember him saying, "If dat will make you bettah, go 'ead."

After a while, I felt very tired and fell back on the hot boards.

I guess it was toward noon on the third day aboard the raft that Timothy said tensely, "I 'ear a motah."

"A motah?"

"Sssssh."

I listened. Yes, there was a far-off engine sound coming in faintly above the slap of the sea. Then I could hear Timothy moving around. " 'Tis an aircraft," he said.

My heart began to pound. *They were looking for us.* I felt around, then crawled from beneath the shelter to look toward the sound. But I could see nothing.

I heard the hinges on the trapdoor creak. Timothy said quietly, as though afraid to chase the sound away, "It knowin' what we doin' 'ere by seein' smoke, I do believe."

He ripped down one of the triangle legs, and I heard cloth tearing. Soon he said, "We made d'torch, young bahss. D'mahn up dere be seein' d'smoke all right, all right."

The faint drone of the aircraft seemed closer now. In a moment, I smelled cloth burning and knew he was holding the wrapped piece of wood toward the sky.

He shouted, "Look downg 'ere."

But already the drone seemed to be fading.

Timothy yelled, "I see it, I see it! Way to port!"

I tried to make my eyes cut through the darkness. "Is he coming our way?"

"Don' know, don' know, young bahss," Timothy replied anxiously.

I said, "I can't hear it now." There was nothing in the air but the sea sounds.

Timothy shouted, "Look downg 'ere! Dere is a raff wit a lil' blin' boy, an' old mahn, an' Stew Cat. Look downg 'ere, I tell you."

The drone could not be heard. Just the slap of the water and the sound of the light wind making our shelter flap.

We were alone again on the ocean.

After a moment of silence, I heard the sizzle of the water

as Timothy doused the torch. He sighed deeply, "I be ready next time for true. Let d'torch dry, den I be ready."

Soon he sat down beside me. " 'Tis a good ting not to harass d'soul ovah dis. We are edgin' into d'aircraft track, same as d'ship dey run."

I said nothing but put my head down on my knees.

"Do not be dishearten, young bahss. Today, we will be foun', to be true."

But the long, hot day was passing without sight of anything. I knew Timothy was constantly scanning the sea. It was all so calm now that the raft didn't even seem to be drifting. Once, I crawled over to the edge to touch the warm water and felt Timothy right behind me.

He said, "Careful, young bahss. D'sharks always hungry, always waitin' for d'mahn to fall ovahboard."

Drawing back from the edge, I asked, "Are there many here?"

"Yes, many 'ere. But long as we 'ave our raff, they do not meliss us."

Standing on the seawall at Willemstad, sometimes I'd seen their fins in the water. I'd also seen them on the dock at the Ruyterkade market, their mouths open and those sharp teeth grinning.

I went back under the shelter, spending a long time rubbing Stew Cat. He purred and pushed himself along my body. I was glad that I had seen him and had seen Timothy before going blind. I thought how awful it would have been to awaken on the raft and not know what they looked like.

Timothy must have been standing over us, for he said,

410

"D'cot not good luck." After a moment he added, "But to cause d'death of a cot is veree bad luck."

"I don't think Stew Cat is bad luck," I said. "I'm glad he is here with us."

Timothy did not answer, but turned back, I guess, to watch the sea again. I could imagine those bloodshot eyes, set in that massive, scarred black face, sweeping over the sea.

"Tell me what's out there, Timothy," I said. It was very important to know that now. I wanted to know everything that was out there.

He laughed. "Jus' miles o' blue wattah, miles o' blue wattah."

"Nothing else?"

He realized what I meant. "Oh, to be sure, young bahss, I see a feesh jump way fo'ward. Dat mean large feesh chase 'im. Den awhile back, a turtle pass us port side, but too far out to reach 'im back. . . ."

His eyes were becoming mine. "What's in the sky, Timothy?"

"In d'sky?" He searched it. "No clouds, young bahss, jus' blue like 'twas yestiddy. But now an' den, I see a petrel. While ago, a booby. . . ."

I laughed for the first time all day. It was a funny name for a bird. "A booby?"

Timothy was quite serious. "Dis booby I saw was a blue face, mebbe nestin' out o' Serranilla Bank, mebbe not. Dey be feedin' on d'flyin' feesh. I true watchin' d'birds 'cause dey tell us we veree close to d'shore."

"How does a booby look, Timothy?"

"Nothin' much," he replied. "Tail like our choclade, sharp beak, mos' white on 'is body."

I tried to picture it, wondering if I'd ever see a bird again.

In the early morning (I knew it was early because the air was still cool and there was dampness on the boards of the raft), I heard Timothy shout, "I see an islan', true."

In wild excitement, I stumbled up and fell overboard.

I went under the water, yelling for him, then came up, gasping. I heard a splash and knew he was in the water too.

Something slapped up against my leg, and I thought it was Timothy. I knew how to swim but didn't know which way to go. So I was treading water. Then I heard Timothy's frightened roar, "Sharks," and he was thrashing about near me.

He grabbed my hair with one hand and used his other arm to drag me back toward the raft. I had turned on my face and was trying to hold my breath. Then I felt my body being thrown, and I was back on the boards of the raft, gasping for air. I knew that Timothy was still in the water, because I could hear splashing and cursing.

The raft tilted down suddenly on one side. Timothy was back aboard. Panting, he bent over me. He yelled, "Fool mahn! I tol' you 'bout d'shark!"

I knew Timothy was in a rage. I could hear his heavy breathing and knew he was staring at me. "Shark all 'round us, all d'time," he roared.

I said, "I'm sorry."

Timothy said, "On dis raff, you crawl, young bahss. You 'ear me?"

I nodded. His voice was thick with anger, but in a moment, after he took several deep breaths, he asked, "You all right, young bahss?"

I guess he sat down beside me to rest. His breathing was still heavy. Finally, he said, "Mahn die quick out dere."

We'd both forgotten about the island. I said, "Timothy, you saw an island!"

He laughed. "Yes, d'islan'! Dere 'tis. . . ."

I said, "Where?"

Timothy answered scornfully, "Dere, look, mahn, look. . . ."

Angrily, I said to him, "I can't see." He kept forgetting that.

His voice was low when he said, "Yes, young bahss. Dat be true! In all dis harassment wid d'shark, I did forget."

Then I felt his hands on my shoulders. He twisted them. "Dat direction, young bahss."

Straining to look where he had me pointed, I asked, "Are there any people on it?"

" 'Tis a veree smahl islan', outrageous low."

I repeated, "Are there any people on it?" I thought they could contact my father and then send for help.

Timothy answered honestly, "No, young bahss. No people. People not be libin' on d'islan' dat 'as no wattah."

No people. No water. No food. No phones. It was not any better than the raft. In fact, it might be worse. "How far away are we?"

" 'Bout two mile," Timothy said.

"Maybe we should stay on the raft. A schooner will see us, or an airplane."

Timothy said positively, "No, we bettah off on lan'. An' we driftin' dat way. D'tide be runnin' wid us." His voice was happy. He wanted to be off the sea.

I was certain my father had planes and ships out looking for us. I said, "Timothy, the Navy is searching for us. I know."

Timothy did not answer me. He just said, " 'Tis a pretty ting, to be sure. I see a white beach, an' behin' dat, low sea-grape bushes; den on d'hill, some palm. Mebbe twenty, thirty palm."

I was sure he couldn't even see that far.

I said, "Timothy, wouldn't it be better if we stayed on the raft and found a big island with people on it?"

He ignored me. He said, "Bidin' d'night, I saw surf washin' white ovah banks off to port but did not awaken you, young bahss. But knew we be gettin' near d'cays. . . ."

I said, "I don't want to go on that island."

I don't think there was anyone on earth as stubborn as old Timothy. There was steel in his voice when he answered, "We be goin' on dat islan', young bahss. Dat be true."

But he knew how I felt now, because he added, "From dis islan', we will get help. Be true, I swear. ! . ."

It seemed hours but it was probably only one until Timothy said, "Do not be alarm now, young bahss. I am goin' to jump into d'wattah an' kick dis raff to d'shore. Widout dat, we'll pass d'islan', by 'n' by."

In a moment, I heard a splash on one side of the raft and then Timothy's feet began drumming the water. I guess he was not afraid of sharks this close in. Soon, he yelled, "Boddam, young bahss, boddam." His feet had touched sand. In another few minutes, the raft lurched and I knew it had grounded.

I listened for sounds from shore, hoping there would be a cheerful "hello," but there were none. Just the wash of the low surf around the raft.

Timothy said, "'Ere, young bahss, on my shoulders an' I'll fetch you to d'lan'." He helped me to his back.

I said, "Don't forget Stew Cat."

He laughed back heartily. "One at a time, young bahss."

With me on his back, he splashed ashore, and judging from the time it took, the raft wasn't very far out. Then he lifted me down again.

"Lan'," he shouted.

The warm sand did feel good on my feet, and now I was almost glad that we wouldn't have to spend another night on the hard, wet boards of the raft.

He said, "Touch it, young bahss. Feel d'lan'; 'tis outrageous good."

I reached down. The grains of sand felt very fine, almost like powder.

Timothy said, "'Tis a beautiful cay, dis cay. Nevah hab I seen dis cay." Then he led me to sit under a clump of bushes. He said, "You res' easy while I pull d'raff more out of d'wattah. We mus' not lose it."

I sat there in the shade, running sand through my fingers, wondering where, among all those many islands in the Caribbean, we were.

Timothy shouted up from the water, "Many feesh 'ere. *Langosta*, too, I b'knowin'. We ros' dem."

Langosta, I knew, was the native lobster, the one without claws. I heard Timothy splashing around down by the surf and knew he was pulling the raft up as far as he could get it.

A moment later, puffing hard, he flopped down beside me. He said, "Cotch me breath, den I will tour d'islan', an' select a place for d'camp. . . ."

He put Stew Cat into my lap.

"Camp?" I asked, stroking big Stew.

Timothy replied, "We mebbe 'ere two, tree days. So we be libin' comfortable."

He could tell I was discouraged because we had come to the island and there were no people on it. He said confidently, "We be rescue, true. Before d'night, I build a great fire pile o' brush an' wood. So d'nex' aircraft dat fly ovah, we set it off."

"Where are we, Timothy? Near Panama?"

He answered slowly, "I cannot be sure, young bahss. Not veree sure."

"But you said you knew about the banks and the cays that are near the banks." I wondered if he knew anything, really, or if he was just a stupid old black man.

Timothy said, "Lissen, I know dat many banks an' cays are roun' fifteen north an' eighty long. Dere is Roncador an' Serranno; Quito Sueño an' Serranilla an' Rosalind; den dere is Beacon an' North Cay. Off to d'wes', somewhere, is Providencia an' San Andrés. . . ." He paused a moment and then said, "Far 'way, up dere, I tink, is d'Caymens, an' den Jamaica."

"But you are not sure of this island?"

Timothy answered gravely, "True, I am not sure."

"Do the schooners usually come close by here?" I asked.

Again very gravely, Timothy said, "D'mahn who feeshes follows d'feesh. Sartainly, d'feesh be 'ere. I be seein' wid my own self eyes."

I kept feeling that Timothy was holding something back from me. It was the tone of his voice. I'd heard my father talk that way a few times. Once, when he didn't want to tell me my grandfather was about to die; another time was when a car ran over my dog in Virginia.

Of course, both times happened when I was younger. Now, my father was always honest with me, I thought, because he said that in the end that was better. I wished Timothy would be honest with me.

Instead he got up to take a walk around the cay, saying he'd be back in a few minutes. Then Stew Cat wandered away. I called to him but he seemed to be exploring too. Realizing that I was alone on the beach, I became frightened.

I knew how helpless I was without Timothy. First I began calling for Stew Cat, but when he didn't return I began shouting for Timothy. There was no answer. I wondered if he'd fallen down and was hurt. I began to crawl along the beach and ran head on into a clump of low-hanging brush.

I sat down again, batting at gnats that were buzzing around my face. Something brushed against my arm, and I yelled out in terror. But I heard a meow and knew it was only Stew Cat. I reached for him and held him tight until I heard brush crackling and sang out, "Timothy?"

"Yes, young bahss," he called back from quite a distance.

When he was closer, I said harshly, "Never leave me again. Don't you ever leave me again!"

He laughed. "Dere is nothin' to fear 'ere. I walked roun' d'whole islan', an' dere is nothin' but sea grape, sand, a few lil' lizzard, an' dose palm tree. . . ."

I repeated, "Never leave me alone, Timothy."

"All right, young bahss, I promise," he said.

He must have been looking all around, for he said, "No wattah 'ere, but 'tis no problem. We still 'ave wattah in d'kag, an' we will trap more on d'firs' rain."

Still believing he wasn't telling me everything, I said, "You were gone a long time."

He answered uneasily, "Thirty minutes at mos'. D'islan' is 'bout one mile long, an' a half wide, shaped like d'melon. I foun' a place to make our camp, up near d'palm. 'Twill be a good place for a lookout. D'rise is 'bout forty feet from d'sea."

I nodded, then said, "I'm hungry, Timothy."

We were both hungry. He went back to the raft, took out the keg of water and the tin of biscuits and chocolate.

While we were eating, I said, "You are worried about something, Timothy. Please tell me the truth. I'm old enough to know."

Timothy waited a long time before answering, probably trying to choose the right words. Finally he said, "Young bahss, dere is, in dis part of d'sea, a few lil' cays like dis one, surround on bot' sides by hombug banks. Dey are cut off from d'res' o' d'sea by dese banks. . . ."

I tried to make a mental picture of that. Several small islands tucked up inside great banks of coral that made navigation dangerous was what I finally decided on.

"You think we are on one of those cays?"

"Mebbe, young bahss, mebbe."

Fear coming back to me—I knew he'd made a mistake in

bringing us ashore—I said, "Then no ships will pass even close to us. Not even schooners! We're trapped here!" We might live here forever, I thought.

Again he did not answer directly. I was beginning to learn that he had a way of being honest while still being dishonest. He said, "D'place I am tinking of is call Debil's Mout'. 'Tis a U-shaped ting, wit dese sharp coral banks on either side, runnin' maybe forty, fifty mile. . . ."

He let that sink in. It sounded bad. But then he said, "I do hope, young bahss, dat I am outrageous mistaken."

"If we are in the Devil's Mouth, how can we be rescued?" I asked angrily. It was his fault we were there.

"D'fire pile! When aircraft fly above, dey will see d'smoke an' fire!"

"But they might just think it is a native fisherman. No one else would come here!"

I could picture him nodding, thinking about that. Finally, he said, "True, but we cannot fret 'bout it, can we? We'll make camp, an' see what 'appens."

He poured me a half cup of water, saying happily, "Since we 'ave made lan', we can celebrate."

I drank it slowly and thoughtfully.

During the afternoon, Timothy was busy and we did not talk much. He was making a hut of dried palm fronds. I sat near him under a palm. Now that we were onshore, I again

began to think about what had happened to my mother. Somehow, I felt she was safe. I was also sure that a search had been started for us, not fully understanding that a war was on and that all the ships and aircraft were needed to fight the U-boats. I even thought about Henrik van Boven and what a story I would have to tell when I saw him again.

I tried not to think about my eyes, sitting there under the palm, listening to Timothy hum as he made the camp. I trusted him that my sight would return within a few days. I also trusted him that an aircraft would spot our fire pile.

In late afternoon, he said proudly, "Look, our hut!"

I had to remind him again, stupid old man, that I couldn't see, so he took my hands and ran them over the fronds. It was a hut, he said, about eight feet wide and six feet deep, with supports made of wood he'd picked off the beach. The supports were tied together with strong vines that covered the north end of the island.

The roof, which sloped back, he said, was about six feet off the ground. I could easily stand up in it, but Timothy couldn't. Not quite.

Timothy said, "Tomorrow, we be gettin' mats to sleep on, weave our own, but tonight we mus' sleep on d'sand. 'Tis soft."

I knew he was very proud of the hut. It had taken him only a few hours to build it.

"Now," he said, "I mus' go downg to d'reef an' fetch langosta. We'll ros' it, to be true."

I became frightened again the minute he said it. I didn't want to be left alone, and I was afraid something might happen to him. "Take me with you, Timothy," I pleaded.

"Not on d'reef," he answered firmly. "I 'ave not been dere before. If 'tis safe, tomorrow I will take you." With that, he went down the hill without saying another word.

My mother was right, I thought. They had their place and we had ours. He did not really like me, or he would have taken me along. He was different.

It seemed as though he were gone for a very long time. Once, I thought I heard an aircraft, but it was probably just my imagination. I began yelling for Timothy to come back, but I guess he couldn't hear because of water noise on the reef.

The palm fronds above me rattled in the breeze, and there were other noises from the underbrush. I knew Stew Cat was around somewhere, but it didn't sound like him.

I wondered if Timothy had checked for snakes. There were also scorpions on most Caribbean islands, and they were deadly. I wondered if there were any on our cay.

During those first few days on the island, the times I spent alone were terrible. It was, of course, being unable to see that made all the sounds so frightening. I guess if you are born blind, it is not so bad. You grow up knowing each sound and what it means.

Suddenly, the tears came out. I knew it was not a manly thing to do, something my father would have frowned on, but I couldn't stop. Then from nowhere came Stew Cat. He rubbed along my arms and up against my cheek, purring hard. I held him close.

Soon, Timothy came up the hill, shouting, "Young bahss, tree nice langosta."

I refused to speak to him because he had left me for such a long time.

He stood over me and said, "'Ere, touch dem; dey are still alive." He was almost crowing over his lobster.

I turned away. Sooner or later, Timothy would have to understand that he could not ignore me one minute and then treat me as a friend the next.

He said softly, "Young bahss, be an outrageous mahn if you like, but 'ere I'm all you got."

I didn't answer.

He roasted the langosta over the fire, and later we crawled into the hut to spend our first night on the silent island.

Timothy seemed very tired and groaned a lot. Before we went to sleep, I asked him, "Tell me the truth, Timothy, how old are you?"

He sighed deeply, "More dan seventy. Eben more dan seventy. . . ."

He was very old. Old enough to die there.

In the morning, Timothy began making the fire pile down on the beach. He had a plan. We'd always keep a small fire smoldering up by the hut, and if an airplane came near, he'd take a piece of burning wood from our small fire to ignite the big one. That way, he said, we could save the few matches that we had.

It didn't take him long to stack driftwood over dried palm fronds. Then he said, "Now, young bahss, we mus' say somethin' on d'san'."

Sometimes it was difficult to understand Timothy. The soft and beautiful West Indian accent and way of speaking weren't always clear.

"Say something on the sand?" I asked.

"So dey be knowin' we are downg 'ere," he explained patiently.

"Who?"

"D'mahn in d'sky, of course."

"Oh." Now I understood.

I guess Timothy was standing there looking at me, waiting for me to say something or do something. I heard him say, "Well, young bahss."

"What do we do now?" I asked.

His voice now impatient, he said, "Say somethin' wid d'rock, wid many rock; eeevery rock be sayin' somethin'. . . ."

I frowned at him. "I don't think I can help you, Timothy. I can't see any rocks."

Timothy groaned. "I can see d'rock, young bahss. But what do we say?"

I laughed at him, enjoying it now. "We say 'help.'"

He grunted satisfaction.

For the next twenty or thirty minutes, I could hear Timothy dropping rocks against each other, singing softly to himself in calypso. It was a song about "fungee an' feesh." I'd had "fungi" in Willemstad down in the blacks' market at Ruyterkade. It was just plain old cornmeal. But most food has different names in the islands.

Soon, he came to stand over me. "Now, young bahss," he said. He seemed to be waiting.

"Yes?"

There was a silence until Timothy broke it with anguish. "Wid d'rock, say 'help.' "

I looked up in his direction and suddenly understood that Timothy could not spell. He was just too stubborn, or too proud, to admit it.

I nodded and began feeling around the sand for a stick.

He asked, "What you reachin' for?"

"A stick to make lines with."

He placed one in my hands, and I carefully lettered H-E-L-P on the sand while he stood above me, watching. He kept murmuring, "Ah-huh, ah-huh," as if making sure I was spelling it correctly.

When I had finished, Timothy said approvingly, "I tell you, young bahss, dat do say 'help.' " Then he happily arranged the rocks on the sand, following my lines.

I felt good. I knew how to do something that Timothy couldn't do. *He couldn't spell.* I felt superior to Timothy that day, but I let him play his little game, pretending not to know that he really couldn't spell.

In the afternoon, Timothy said we'd make a rope.

On the north end of the island, tough vines, almost as

large as a pencil, were laced over the sand. It took us several hours to tear out a big pile of them. Then Timothy began weaving a rope that would stretch all the way down the hill to the beach and fire pile.

The rope was for me. If he happened to be out on the reef, and I heard a plane, I could take a light from our campfire, follow the rope down, and touch off the big fire. The vine rope would also serve to get me safely down to the beach.

After we'd torn the vines out, and he was weaving the rope, he said, "Young bahss, you mus' begin to help wid d'udder wark."

We were sitting up by the hut. I had my back to a palm and was thinking that back in Willemstad, at this moment, I'd probably be sitting in a classroom, three desks away from Henrik, listening to Herr Jonckheer talk about European history. I'd been tutored in Dutch the first year in Willemstad so I could attend the regular school. Now I could speak it and understand it.

My hands were tired from pulling the vines, and I just wanted to sit and think. I didn't want to work. I said, "Timothy, I'm blind. I can't see to work."

I heard him cutting something with his sharp knife. He replied softly, "D'han' is not blin'."

Didn't the old man understand? To work, aside from pulling up vines or drawing something in the sand, you must be able to see.

Stubbornly, he said, "Young bahss, we need sleepin' mats. You can make d'mats."

I looked over in his direction. "You do it," I said.

He sighed back, saying, "D'best mat maker in Charlotte Amalie, downg in Frenchtown, b'total blin'."

"But he's a man, and he has to do that to make a living."

"B'true," Timothy said quietly.

But in a few minutes, he placed several lengths of palm fiber across my lap. He really was a black mule. "D'palm mat is veree easy. Jus' ovah an' under. . . ."

Becoming angry with him, I said, "I tell you, I can't see."

He paid no attention to me. "Take dis' han', hol' d'palm like dis; den ovah an' under, like d'mahn in Frenchtown; den more palm."

I could feel him standing there watching me as I tried to reeve the lengths, but I knew they weren't fitting together. He said, "Like dis, I tell you," and reached down to guide my hand. "Ovah an' under. . . ."

I tried again, but it didn't work. I stood up, threw the palm fibers at him, and screamed, "You ugly black man! I won't do it! You're stupid, you can't even spell. . . ."

Timothy's heavy hand struck my face sharply.

Stunned, I touched my face where he'd hit me. Then I turned away from where I thought he was. My cheek stung, but I wouldn't let him see me with tears in my eyes.

I heard him saying very gently, "B'gettin' back to wark, my own self."

I sat down again.

He began to sing that "fungee and feesh" song in a low voice, and I could picture him sitting on the sand in front of the hut; that tangled gray hair, the ugly black face with the thick lips, those great horny hands winding the strands of vine.

The rope, I thought. It wasn't for him. It was for me.

After a while, I said, "Timothy. . . ."

He did not answer, but walked over to me, pressing more palm fronds into my hands. He murmured, " 'Tis veree easy, ovah an' under. . . ." Then he went back to singing about "fungee and feesh."

Something happened to me that day on the cay. I'm not quite sure what it was even now, but I had begun to change.

I said to Timothy, "I want to be your friend."

He said softly, "Young bahss, you 'ave always been my friend."

I said, "Can you call me Phillip instead of young boss?"

"Phill-eep," he said warmly.

During our seventh night on the island, it rained. It was one of those tropical storms that comes up swiftly without warning. We were asleep on the palm mats that I'd made, but it awakened us immediately. The rain sounded like bullets hitting on the dried palm-frond roof. We ran out into it, shouting and letting the fresh water hit our bodies. It was cool and felt good.

Timothy yelled that his catchment was working. He had taken more boards from the top of the raft and had made a large trough that would catch the rain. He'd picked up bamboo lengths on the beach and had fitted them together into a short pipe to funnel the rainwater into our ten-gallon keg.

It rained for almost two hours, and Timothy was quite angry with himself for not making a second catchment, because the keg was soon filled and overflowing.

We stayed out in the cool rain for twenty or thirty minutes and then went back inside. The roof leaked badly but we didn't mind. We got on our mats and opened our mouths to the sweet, fresh water. Stew Cat was huddled in a miserable ball over in a corner, Timothy said, not enjoying it at all.

I liked the rain because it was something I could hear and feel; not something I must see. It peppered in bursts against the frond roof, and I could hear the drips as it leaked through. The squall wind was in the tops of the palms and I could imagine how they looked in the night sky, thrashing against each other high over our little cay.

I wanted it to rain all night.

We talked for a long time when the rain began to slack off.

Timothy asked me about my mother and father. I told him all about them and about how we lived in Scharloo, getting very lonesome and homesick while I was telling him. He kept saying, "Ah, dat be true?"

Then Timothy told me what he could remember from his own childhood. It wasn't at all like mine. He'd never gone to school, and was working on a fishing boat by the time he was ten. It almost seemed the only fun he had was once a year at carnival when he'd put frangipani leaves around his ankles and dress up in a donkey hide to parade around with *mocki jumbis*, the spirit chasers, while the old ladies of Charlotte Amalie danced the *bambola* around them.

He chuckled. "I drink plenty rhum dose tree days of carnival."

I could picture him in his donkey skin, wheeling around to the music of the steel bands. They had them in Willemstad too.

Because it had been on my mind, I told him that my mother didn't like black people and asked him why.

He answered slowly, "I don' like some white people my own self, but 'twould be outrageous if I didn' like any o' dem."

Wanting to hear it from Timothy, I asked him why there were different colors of skin, white and black, brown and red, and he laughed back, "Why b'feesh different color, or flower b'different color? I true don' know, Phill-eep, but I true tink beneath d'skin is all d'same."

Herr Jonckheer had said something like that in school, but it did not mean quite as much as when Timothy said it.

Long after he'd begun to snore in the dripping hut, I

thought about it. Suddenly, I wished my father and mother could see us there together on the little island.

I moved close to Timothy's big body before I went to sleep. I remember smiling in the darkness. He felt neither white nor black.

Key to Pronunciation

Listed below are diacritical symbols and key words. The boldface letters in the key words represent the sounds indicated by the symbols.

/ā/	c**a**ke	/h/	**h**ome	/ō/	r**o**pe	/th/	**th**in
/a/	h**a**t	/(h)w/	**wh**ite	/o/	t**o**p	/th/	**th**is
/ä/	f**a**ther	/ī/	p**ie**	/ô/	s**aw**	/u/	n**u**t
/är/	c**ar**	/i/	p**i**g	/oi/	**oi**l	/ûr/	f**ur**
/âr/	c**are**	/ir/	d**ear**	/ōō/	m**oo**n	/v/	**v**ine
/b/	**b**oy	/j/	**j**ump	/ŏŏ/	b**oo**k	/w/	**w**ill
/ch/	**ch**urch	/k/	**k**ite	/ôr/	f**or**k	/y/	**y**es
/d/	**d**uck	/ks/	bo**x**	/ou/	**ou**t	/yōō/	**u**se
/ē/	b**ea**n	/kw/	**qu**it	/p/	**p**et	/z/	**z**oo
/e/	p**e**t	/l/	**l**ook	/r/	**r**un	/zh/	a**z**ure
/f/	**f**un	/m/	**m**an	/s/	**s**ee	/ə/	**a**bove
/g/	**g**o	/n/	**n**ot	/sh/	**sh**ip		circ**u**s
/gz/	e**x**act	/ng/	si**ng**	/t/	**t**op	/ər/	butt**er**

Abbreviations Used for Parts of Speech

adj.—adjective
adv.—adverb
conj.—conjunction

interj.—interjection
n.—noun
pl.—plural

prep.—preposition
pron.—pronoun
v.—verb

Aa

a·bra·sive [ə·brā′siv] *n.* A hard material, as sand, used to rub or wear softer materials down.

a·broad [ə·brôd′] *adv.* Out of one's country; in or into foreign lands.

ac·ti·vate [ak′tə·vāt] *v.* 1. To make active. 2. To start, as machinery.

a·cute [ə·kyōōt′] *adj.* 1. Extremely important; critical; grave. 2. Reaching a crisis quickly; severe, as a disease.

ad [ad] *n.* A shortened form of the word ADVERTISEMENT.

ad·ja·cent [ə·jā′sənt] *adj.* Lying near or close by; adjoining.

ag·grieved [ə·grēvd′] *adj.* Having cause for complaint; ill-treated; wronged: The *aggrieved* tenants complained to their landlord.

aisle [īl] *n.* A passageway, as in a theater or church, that separates one section of seats from another section.

al·a·bas·ter [al′ə·bas′tər] *n.* A smooth white or tinted stone, often carved into vases or small statues.

al·cove [al'kōv] *n.* A recess or small section of a room opening out from the main section.

Alcove

al·ly [ə·lī' *or* al'ī] *n.* A person or country joined with another for a particular purpose.

al·ma·nac [ôl'mə·nak] *n.* A yearly calendar giving the days, weeks, and months of the year with facts about the weather, sun, moon, etc.

am·a·teur [am'ə·chŏor *or* am'ə·t(y)ŏor] *n.* A person who does something without sound training or skill.

am·bi·tious [am·bish'əs] *adj.* 1. Moved by or possessing an eager desire to succeed or to achieve something, as wealth or power. 2. Requiring great skill or much effort for success; challenging; difficult: The historian's book was an *ambitious* undertaking.

an·a·lyze [an'ə·līz] *v.* To examine critically or closely.

an·nex [an'eks] *n.* An addition to a building, or another building used along with the main one.

ap·pre·hen·sion [ap'rə·hen'shən] *n.* A worried expectation of something bad; dread or fear.

ar·chi·tect [är'kə·tekt] *n.* A person who designs and draws up plans for buildings or other structures and sees that the plans are carried through by the builders.

ar·ti·fi·cial [är'tə·fish'əl] *adj.* Made by man rather than by nature.

a·skew [ə·skyōo'] *adj.* On or to one side; disarranged: The kitchen curtains were all *askew.*

as·sas·si·nate [ə·sas'ə·nāt] *v.* To murder by a secret or surprise attack.

as·sault [ə·sôlt'] *n.* Any sudden, violent attack.

as·sent [ə·sent'] *n.* Consent or agreement.

as·sert [ə·sûrt'] *v.* 1. To say in a clear, firm way; declare. 2. To claim; insist on: He *asserted* his right to speak.

as·sume [ə·sōom'] *v.* To take on (a shape, role, look, etc.): The embarrassed speaker *assumed* the attitude of a comedian.

as·ter·oid [as'tə·roid] *n.* Any of several hundred small planets between Mars and Jupiter.

at·tire [ə·tīr'] *n.* Dress; apparel.

au·thor·i·ta·tive [ə·thôr'ə·tā'tiv] *adj.* Showing special knowledge; commanding.

au·to·ma·tion [ô'tə·mā'shən] *n.* The automatic operation of a process, machine, etc., under the control of electronic or mechanical devices instead of human beings.

aux·il·ia·ry [ôg·zil'yər·ē] *adj.* 1. Giving help. 2. Available if needed; extra: An *auxiliary* engine may be used if the power fails. 3. Less important; not major.

Bb

baf·fle [baf'əl] *v.* To confuse; bewilder; perplex: The question *baffled* me.

bale·ful [bāl'fəl] *adj.* Evil or threatening; malicious: The wolves stared at each other with *baleful* eyes.

bal·er [bāl′ər] *n.* A machine that tightly packs bundles of hay, cotton, or other bulky material.

bank·rupt [bangk′rupt] *n.* A person who has been declared unable to pay his debts by a court, his property being taken from him and distributed among his creditors.

ba·sin [bā′sən] *n.* A sink or a bowl for washing.

be·grudge [bi·gruj′] *v.* To envy another's enjoyment or possession of: The townspeople *begrudged* the newcomers their good luck.

bi·na·ry [bī′nər·ē] *adj.* Made up of or having to do with two parts or elements: A *binary* number system uses two as a base and therefore has two numerals, 0 and 1.

bi·og·ra·phy [bī·og′rə·fē] *n.* An account of a person's life.

blight [blīt] *n.* 1. Any disease that harms or destroys plants. 2. Anything that harms or destroys: Crime is a *blight* on our nation.

boat fall. A tackle used to raise or lower a ship's boat to or from the water.

bow·er [bou′ər] *n.* A shady spot, as in a garden.

brave [brāv] *v.* To meet or face with courage; defy: The team *braved* cold winds until they could rescue the survivors.

brood [brood] *v.* To think deeply in a worried manner: He *brooded* over his low marks.

buff·er [buf′ər] *n.* Anything that lessens or cushions the shock of a blow.

bunt [bunt] *v.* To bat (a baseball) very lightly and low, so that it only reaches the infield.

bu·reau [byŏŏr′ō] *n.* 1. A chest of drawers, usually with a mirror. 2. A government department.

Cc

ca·det [kə·det′] *n.* 1. A young man in training to become an officer in any of the armed forces. 2. A student attending a military school.

cal·i·ber [kal′ə·bər] *n.* Excellence, ability, etc.

cal·i·brate [kal′ə·brāt] *v.* To mark, check, or adjust the scale of (a measuring instrument).

ca·lyp·so [kə·lip′sō] *n.* A type of West Indian song in which the singer gives the latest news or tells a story, making up the words as he sings.

cam·bric [kām′brik] *n.* 1. A fine white linen. 2. A cotton cloth made to look like linen.

cane·brake [kān′brāk′] *n.* A thick growth of cane, any of various plants with slender, woody stems.

can·o·py [kan′ə·pē] *n.* 1. A covering hung over a throne, bed, entrance, etc., or carried on poles over high officials or sacred objects. 2. Any covering overhead, as the sky or a tree.

ca·reen [kə·rēn′] *v.* To lurch from side to side while moving, as if out of control: The truck *careened* around the curve.

car·om [kar′əm] *v.* To strike and bounce off: The car *caromed* off the wall.

cas·tor [kas′tər] *n.* One of a set of small, swiveling wheels fastened under each leg or corner of a piece of furniture to make it easier to move about.

cat·call [kat′kôl′]. 1. *n.* A shrill call or whistle made in public to show dislike or impatience. 2. *v.* To make catcalls.

caul·dron [kôl′drən] *n.* A large kettle or pot.

cay [kā *or* kē] *n.* A low island, usually small.

cen·sor·ship [sen′sər·ship] *n.* The act, method, or system of examining books, letters, news, plays, etc., and cutting out what is felt ought not be read, heard, or seen.

char·ac·ter·is·tic [kar′ik·tə·ris′tik] *n.* A very special feature, quality, or trait: A great curiosity was one of his *characteristics*.

cha·rades [shə·rādz′] *n.pl.* A game in which the players try to guess what words or phrases are being acted out in pantomime, often syllable by syllable.

châ·teau [sha·tō′] *n.* 1. A French castle. 2. A large country house resembling a French castle.

cir·cuit [sûr′kit] *n.* 1. A route or path that turns back to where it began. 2. The path taken by an electric current.

cir·cuit·ry [sûr′kit·rē] *n.* A particular arrangement or design of electrical circuits.

clap·board [klab′ərd *or* klap′bôrd′] *n.* A thin board having one edge thinner than the other, used as siding on wooden buildings.

clap·trap [klap′trap] *n.* Nonsense.

clas·sic [klas′ik] *adj.* 1. Being in the first class or highest rank, as in literature or art. 2. Of or characteristic of the art, literature, or culture of ancient Greece and Rome.

cleft [kleft] *n.* A division between two parts; a crack or dent, as in the chin.

clin·ic [klin′ik] *n.* A place where advice on specific problems is given.

cock·ad·ed [kok·ād′əd] *adj.* Decorated with ribbons and rosettes, especially on the hat, lapel, etc.

cock·eyed [kok′īd′] *adj.* An informal term meaning "ridiculous."

com·pact [kəm·pakt′ *or* kom′pakt] *adj.* Closely and firmly put together: The magazines were stacked in a *compact* pile.

com·pe·tent [kom′pə·tənt] *adj.* Having enough ability; capable: The volunteers were *competent* in administering first aid.

con·cept [kon′sept] *n.* A general idea or notion.

conch [kongk *or* konch] *n.* A small marine animal that lives in a large, spiral shell.

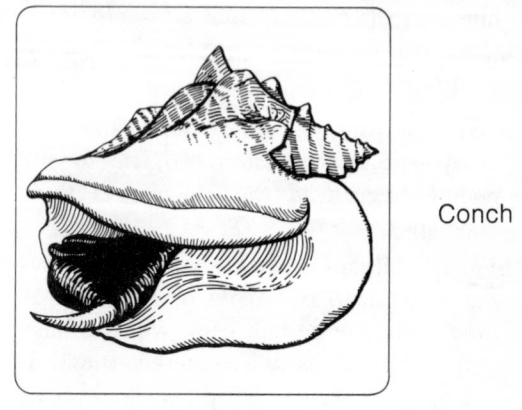

Conch

con·de·scend [kon′di·send′] *v.* To behave as if superior; patronize.

con·jur·er [kon′jər·ər *or* kun′jər·ər] *n.* A magician.

con·spir·a·tor [kən·spir′ə·tər] *n.* A person involved with others in a secret plan to do an evil or unlawful act; plotter.

con·sult [kən·sult′] *v.* To turn to for advice, aid, or information: The writer *consulted* a dictionary for the meaning of a word.

con·trac·tor [kon′trak·tər] *n.* A person or firm that agrees to supply materials or perform services for a stated price.

con·vene [kən·vēn′] *v.* To come together; assemble: Congress *convenes* every year.

con·verge [kən·vûrj′] *v.* To move toward one point or place; come together: The rails seemed to *converge* in the distance.

con·vert [kən·vûrt′] *v.* To win over or change to a new religion or belief.

cop·y·right [kop′ē·rīt] *n.* The exclusive right to publish or sell any part or all of a literary, musical, or art work. In the United States, copyright lasts for twenty-eight years with the right of renewal for another twenty-eight years.

corps [kôr] *n.* A large section or special group of people united in some special work or activity.

cor·rode [kə·rōd'] *v.* To become eaten away; rust: Iron *corrodes* in damp air.

cow·ard [kou'ərd] *n.* A person who lacks the courage to meet pain, danger, or difficulty.

cres·cent [kres'ənt] *n.* Anything having the curved shape of the quarter moon.

cro·chet·ing [krō·shā'ing] *v.* Making or trimming (sweaters, afghans, etc.) by forming connected loops of thread or yarn with a hooked needle.

cue [kyōō] *n.* A helpful hint or indication, as when one is uncertain what to do.

cull [kul] *v.* To sort out and take the poor or worthless ones from.

cur·so·ry [kûr'sər·ē] *adj.* Not thorough; hasty: The man gave the newspaper a *cursory* reading.

czar [zär] *n.* One of the former emperors of Russia.

Dd

da·ta [dā'tə] *n.pl.* Facts or figures; information.

dea·con [dē'kən] *n.* 1. A clergyman who is next below a priest in rank. 2. A church official who helps a clergyman in things not connected with actual worship.

den·im [den'əm] *n.* 1. A strong twilled cotton cloth used for overalls, play clothes, etc. 2. (*pl.*) Clothes made of this material.

dense [dens] *adj.* Having its parts crowded together; thick: The *dense* jungle was uninhabited.

de·pressed [di·prest'] *adj.* Gloomy or sad.

de·ranged [di·rānjd'] *adj.* Crazy; insane.

de·sert [di·zûrt'] *v.* To leave one's military duty or post without leave and without intending to return.

des·o·late [des'ə·lit] *adj.* Dreary; barren.

de·spon·dent [di·spon'dənt] *adj.* In low spirits; discouraged or depressed: He was *despondent* over his bad health.

de·tect [di·tekt'] *v.* To discover, as something hidden or hard to perceive.

dis·ci·pline [dis'ə·plin] *v.* To train to obedience, self-control, and order.

dis·close [dis·klōz'] *v.* 1. To expose to sight; uncover. 2. To make known.

dis·com·bob·u·late [dis'kəm·bob'yə·lāt] *v.* To confuse; upset.

dis·con·so·late [dis·kon'sə·lit] *adj.* Full of sadness or despair; unhappy; forlorn.

dis·dain [dis·dān'] *n.* Scorn or haughty contempt, especially toward someone or something considered inferior.

dis·in·te·grate [dis·in'tə·grāt] *v.* To break apart into small pieces or fragments; crumble: Rain *disintegrated* the children's mud pies.

dis·mal [diz'məl] *adj.* 1. Dark, gloomy, and depressing. 2. Sad and miserable.

dis·po·sal [dis·pō'zəl] *n.* Freely available for one's use or service: He had time at his *disposal*.

dis·po·si·tion [dis·pə·zish'ən] *n.* A person's usual mood or spirit; nature; temperament.

dis·tract [dis·trakt'] *v.* To draw (the mind, etc.) from something claiming attention: The TV *distracts* her from her homework.

don [don] *v.* To put on (a piece or pieces of clothing).

dor·mi·to·ry [dôr'mə·tôr'ē] *n.* 1. A building, as at a school or college, that has many rooms for sleeping. 2. A large room with many beds for sleeping.

driv·el [driv'əl] *n.* Foolish talk or writing.

drone [drōn]. 1. *v.* To make a deep humming or buzzing sound. 2. *n*. Such a sound.

du·pli·cate [d(y)oo′plə·kit] *n*. An exact copy: His secretary made a *duplicate* of the letter.

Ee

eaves·drop·per [ēvz′drop′ər] *n*. One who listens secretly to things being said in private.

eb·on·y [eb′ə·nē] *n*. A hard, heavy wood, usually black.

e·clipse [i·klips′] *n*. 1. A complete or partial hiding of the sun (**solar eclipse**) as the moon passes between the sun and an observer on the earth. 2. A complete or partial hiding of the moon (**lunar eclipse**) as the moon passes through the earth's shadow.

e·di·tion [i·dish′ən] *n*. The total number of copies of a publication issued at any one time and printed from the same plates.

ef·fi·cient [i·fish′ənt] *adj*. Producing results with the least effort or waste; capable: The reader made *efficient* use of the glossary.

egg [eg] *v*. To urge or coax into doing something: We *egged* him on to jump.

e·go [ē′gō] *n*. The part of a person's mind or self by which he is aware that he is different from all other people in his thoughts, feelings, and actions.

elbow grease. Physical effort; hard work: Use some *elbow grease* on that dirty pan.

e·lu·sive [i·loo′siv] *adj*. Escaping or avoiding capture.

em·phat·ic [em·fat′ik] *adj*. 1. Spoken or done with emphasis. 2. Striking; decisive: The festival was an *emphatic* success.

em·ploy [im·ploi′] *v*. To make use of: Seat belts were *employed* for safety.

en·gag·ing [in·gā′jing] *adj*. Pleasing; charm-ing: Our visitors had *engaging* manners.

er·rat·ic [i·rat′ik] *adj*. 1. Uneven or irregular in action, progress, etc. 2. Unusual; odd: Her classmates discussed her *erratic* behavior.

eth·ics [eth′iks] *n*. The rules of right behavior, especially with reference to a particular profession, way of life, etc.

ex·cep·tion·al [ik·sep′shən·əl] *adj*. Not ordinary; unusual.

ex·er·tion [ig·zûr′shən] *n*. Great effort.

ex·ot·ic [ig·zot′ik] *adj*. 1. Belonging to or growing in another part of the world; foreign. 2. Strangely different and fascinating.

ex·port [ik·spôrt′ *or* eks·pôrt] *v*. To send to other countries for sale or trade: Germany *exports* many cars.

Ff

fan·fare [fan′fâr′] *n*. Any noisy or showy display: The candidates arrived with a great deal of *fanfare* from bands, photographers, and shouting people.

fa·tigue [fə·tēg′] *n*. A tired condition resulting from hard work, effort, or strain; weariness.

feat [fēt] *n*. A remarkable act or deed, as one showing great skill, endurance, or daring.

fer·ment [fər·ment′] *v*. To undergo or bring about the slow decomposition of organic substances by the action of yeast, bacteria, or enzymes: Wine is formed when grape juice *ferments*.

fife [fif] *n*. A small flute having a shrill tone, used with drums in military music.

fleet·ing [flēt′ing] *adj*. Passing quickly; swift.

fo·cus [fō′kəs]. 1. *n*. In physics, a point at which light rays, sound waves, radio waves, etc., come together after passing through something that bends them, as a lens, or after bouncing off a curved reflector. 2. *v.* To bring (light rays, sound waves, etc.) to a focus.

fools·cap [fōōlz′kap] *n.* A size of writing paper about thirteen inches wide and sixteen inches long.

for·feit [fôr′fit] *n.* 1. The giving up or loss of something as a penalty. 2. Something that is forfeited; penalty.

fra·ter·ni·ty [frə·tûr′nə·tē] *n.* A group of people sharing the same interests, profession, activities, etc.

free·style [frē′stīl′] *n.* An event in which a contestant, as a swimmer or skater, may use any style he chooses.

frig·id [frij′id] *adj.* Lacking warmth of feeling; formal and unfriendly: *The candidates gave each other a* frigid *greeting.*

fru·gal [frōō′gəl] *adj.* 1. Avoiding waste; using thrift. 2. Costing little money; meager.

fun·da·men·tal [fun′də·men′təl] *n.* Anything basic to a system; an essential part.

fu·tile [fyōō′təl] *adj.* Done in vain; useless.

Gg

ga·ble [gā′bəl] *n.* The triangular top part of an outer wall, under a ridged roof and above its eaves.

gal·ax·y [gal′ək·sē] *n.* 1. A large system of celestial bodies. 2. The Milky Way. 3. Any brilliant group.

gen·ial [jēn′yəl] *adj.* Friendly and kind; cheerful.

ge·ol·o·gist [jē·ol′ə·jist] *n.* A person who specializes in the study of the history and structure of the earth's crust, especially as recorded in rocks.

ghast·ly [gast′lē] *adj.* 1. Horrible; terrifying. 2. Deathlike in appearance; pale; wan.

ghet·to [get′ō] *n.* Any section of a city or town crowded with a minority group or the very poor.

glen [glen] *n.* A small secluded valley.

glib·ly [glib′lē] *adv.* In the manner of one who speaks easily without much thought or sincerity: *The coach spoke* glibly *about the faults of the opposing team.*

glob·u·lar [glob′yə·lər] *adj.* 1. Shaped like a globe; round; spherical. 2. Made up of tiny spheres of matter or drops of liquid.

gourd [gôrd *or* gōōrd] *n.* 1. A fruit related to the pumpkin, with a hard outer shell. 2. The plant bearing this fruit.

graph·ic [graf′ik] *adj.* Giving an exact picture or report; vivid; detailed: *Today's paper contains a* graphic *news story about dinosaur fossils.*

grif·fin [grif′ən] *n.* In Greek myths, a beast with the head and wings of an eagle and the body of a lion.

Griffin

grist [grist] *n.* Grain that is to be ground into meal.

grog [grog] *n.* Any alcoholic drink.

gru·el·ing [grōō′əl·ing] *adj.* Very tiring or exhausting.

guff [guf] *n.* An informal term that means "meaningless chatter or talk."

guil·lo·tine [gil′ə·tēn] *n.* A device for beheading condemned persons by means of a heavy blade that falls between vertical guides.

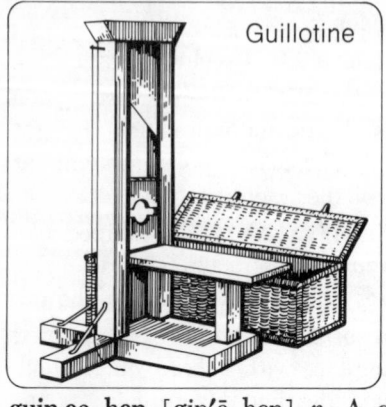
Guillotine

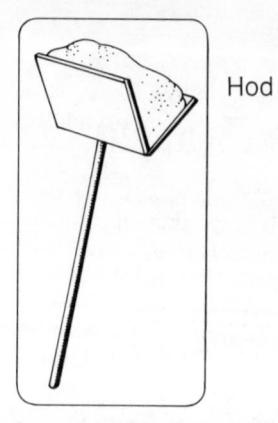
Hod

guin·ea hen [gin′ē hen] *n.* A chickenlike fowl raised for food, having gray feathers with white specks.

Hh

har·ass [har′əs *or* hə·ras′] *v.* To annoy with small, repeated attacks.

head·strong [hed′strông′] *adj.* Stubbornly set upon having one's own way: The *headstrong* boy insisted on leaving school early.

head·y [hed′ē] *adj.* 1. Apt to make one lightheaded or dizzy; intoxicating: The waitress wore a *heady* perfume. 2. Rash; headstrong: The newsman's *heady* report cost him his job.

herb [(h)ûrb] *n.* A plant that withers and dies away after its yearly flowering, especially such a plant used as a seasoning, medicine, etc.

hip·po·griff [hip′ə·grif] *n.* In Greek myths, an animal with the body of a horse and the foreparts of a griffin.

hod [hod] *n.* 1. A trough set on a long handle, used to carry bricks, cement, etc. 2. A pail or scuttle for carrying coal.

hop·per [hop′ər] *n.* A container for coal, grain, etc., that narrows toward the bottom, through which the contents can be dropped or fed slowly.

hor·i·zon·tal [hôr′ə·zon′təl] *adj.* Parallel to the horizon; level.

hos·til·i·ty [hos·til′ə·tē] *n.* An unfriendly feeling; dislike or hate.

hov·er [huv′ər *or* hov′ər] *v.* 1. To remain in or near one place in the air, as birds, etc. 2. To linger or remain nearby.

hu·mid·i·ty [(h)yōō·mid′ə·tē] *n.* Moisture; dampness, especially of the air.

hyp·no·sis [hip·nō′sis] *n.* An artificially induced condition like sleep in which a person responds to suggestions or instructions made by the person who has induced the condition.

Ii

ig·nite [ig·nīt′] *v.* To set on fire; make burn.

im·per·cep·ti·ble [im′pər·sep′tə·bəl] *adj.* Too small or slight to be noticed.

imp·ish [imp′ish] *adj.* Full of mischief.

im·ple·ment [im′plə·mənt] *n.* A thing used in work; utensil; tool.

im·pro·vise [im′prə·vīz] *v.* To make offhand from whatever material is available: The survivors *improvised* a shelter from old boards.

im·pulse [im′puls] *n.* The transference of a stimulus through a nerve fiber.

im·pul·sive [im·pul′siv] *adj.* Acting suddenly and without careful thought: The *impulsive* girl bought six hats.

in·ca·pac·i·tate [in′kə·pas′ə·tāt] *v.* To make unfit, especially for normal physical activity; disable: The player was *incapacitated* with a sprained ankle.

in·cline [in′klīn *or* in·klīn′] *n.* A sloping surface; slope: The old car could not be driven up the steep *incline*.

in·cred·i·ble [in·kred′ə·bəl] *adj.* So strange, unusual, or extraordinary as to be unbelievable.

in·de·cent [in·dē′sənt] *adj.* 1. Not proper. 2. Not moral or modest; obscene.

in·fe·ri·or [in·fir′ē·ər] *adj.* Not so good in quality, worth, usefulness, etc.

in·flate [in·flāt′] *v.* To swell or puff out by filling with air or gas.

in·i·ti·a·tion [in·ish′ē·ā′shən] *n.* A meeting of a club or society at which new members are put through special ceremonies or tests in order to be admitted into the club.

in·junc·tion [in·jungk′shən] *n.* An order, issue, or command requiring someone to do something.

in·stan·ta·ne·ous [in′stən·tā′nē·əs] *adj.* Happening, done, or over in an instant: The accident victim's death was *instantaneous*.

in·te·grate [in′tə·grāt] *v.* In the United States, to make the use or occupancy of (a school, park, neighborhood, etc.) available to persons of all races.

in·ter·est [in′tər·ist *or* in′trist] *n.* The money paid, as by a bank or borrower, for the use of money: He gets 5% *interest* on his savings account.

in·te·ri·or [in·tir′ē·ər] *n.* The part of a country back from a border or coastline.

in·ter·val [in′tər·vəl] *n.* 1. From time to time: The driver spoke at *intervals*. 2. The time between two events.

in·trigue [in·trēg′] *v.* To arouse the interest or curiosity of; fascinate.

in·trud·er [in·trood′ər] *n.* Someone or something that comes in without being invited or wanted.

in·ver·sion [in·vûr′zhən] *n.* Something opposite to or reversed in order, direction, or effect.

in·vest [in·vest′] *v.* 1. To put (money) to use in order to make a profit: Buying a business, a property, or stocks is a way of *investing*. 2. To use or spend with the hope of getting some later advantage or profit: Time *invested* in one's education is well spent.

in·volve [in·volv′] *v.* 1. To associate; implicate: His abrupt departure *involved* him in the mystery. 2. To absorb; engross: Soon the class became *involved* in a discussion of the subject.

i·rate [ī′rāt *or* ī·rāt′] *adj.* Angry.

i·tem·ize [ī′təm·īz] *v.* To list each item of: Please *itemize* the bill.

Jj

jaunt·y [jôn′tē] *adj.* Having a lively or self-confident air or manner.

Kk

kilt [kilt] *n.* A short pleated skirt.

Kilt

ki·va [kē′və] *n.* A Pueblo Indian building usually used only by men for recreation, work, and religious ceremonies.

Ll

lar·ynx [lar′ingks] *n.* The upper part of the windpipe, containing the vocal cords.

lat·i·tude [lat′ə·t(y)ōōd] *n.* Distance north or south of the equator, measured as an angle at the earth's center and expressed in degrees.

leach [lēch] *v.* 1. To make water or other liquid run or filter through (something) in order to remove certain materials. 2. To remove or be removed by such a filtering action: The device was designed to *leach* alkali out of ashes.

lev·el [lev′əl] *v.* To destroy or knock down.

light-year [līt′yir′] *n.* The distance traveled by light in one year, about six trillion miles.

li·no·type [lī′nə·tīp] *n.* A machine used for setting type, operated by a keyboard. A full line of type is cast in a single piece of metal.

lu·bri·cate [lōō′brə·kāt] *v.* To apply a substance, as oil or grease, to moving parts of a machine so that they will slide smoothly against each other and not wear out so quickly.

Mm

main [mān] *n.* The principal pipe in a system conveying gas, water, etc.

ma·neu·ver [mə·n(y)ōō′vər] *v.* 1. To use planned moves skillfully. 2. To force or trick by skillful moves.

ma·nip·u·la·tion [mə·nip′yə·lā′shən] *n.* An instance or example of operating or working with to manage or control (someone, something, some idea, etc.).

ma·son·ry [mā′sən·rē] *n.* Something built of concrete, stone, brick, etc.

ma·te·ri·al·ize [mə·tir′ē·əl·īz′] *v.* To take on visible form; appear: The mountaintop *materialized* from behind the clouds.

max·im [mak′sim] *n.* A brief statement of a rule of conduct or a general principle.

mea·sly [mēz′lē] *adj.* Scornfully small; petty.

me·di·e·val [mē′dē·ē′vəl *or* med′ē·ē′vəl] *adj.* Of, relating to, or belonging to the Middle Ages, extending from about A.D. 400 to 1400.

med·ley [med′lē] *n.* A mixture of unlike or unrelated things; jumble: The garden was a *medley* of rocks, flowers, colored glass, and driftwood.

me·te·or [mē′tē·ər] *n.* A small fragment of matter from outer space that is heated white-hot by friction with the earth's atmosphere and appears briefly as a streak of light; shooting star.

me·te·or·ite [mē′tē·ə·rīt′] *n.* A part of a meteor that is not burned up and strikes the earth as a lump of stone or metal.

me·te·or·oid [mē′tē·ə·roid′] *n.* One of the pieces of matter in outer space that forms meteors upon entering the earth's atmosphere.

mim·ic [mim′ik] *v.* 1. To imitate the speech or actions of, usually in order to make fun of someone. 2. To copy closely; ape.

mis·fit [mis′fit′] *n.* A person who gets on badly with those around him or in a given situation.

mod·er·ate [mod′ər·it] *adj.* Not extreme or excessive: These are *moderate* prices.

mod·i·fy [mod′ə·fī] *v.* 1. To change moderately. 2. To make less extreme or severe: The mayor *modified* his views when he saw how much the project would cost.

mo·men·tum [mō·men′təm] *n.* Force, speed, or impetus, usually growing in strength or intensity: The uprising of the peasants gained *momentum* with the king's death.

mon·o·syl·la·ble [mon′ə·sil′ə·bəl] *n.* A word of one syllable.

mort·gage [môr′gij] *n.* A claim on property, given as security for a loan.

mo·tive [mō′tiv] *n.* A reason or cause that makes a person act.

mug [mug] *v.* To assault and rob.

murk·y [mûr′kē] *adj.* Dark, gloomy, or obscure.

myr·i·ad [mir′ē·əd] *n.* A vast indefinite number.

Nn

nat·u·ral·ist [nach′ər·əl·ist] *n.* A person who is trained in the study of nature, especially as related to the earth and living things.

new·el·post [n(y)ōō′əl·pōst′] *n.* The post that supports an end of the handrail of a staircase.

niche [nich] *n.* A recess or hollow in a wall, as for a statue.

nim·ble [nim′bəl] *adj.* Light and quick in movement; lively.

nit·wit [nit′wit′] *n.* A silly or stupid person.

nov·el [nov′əl] 1. *adj.* New, strange, or unusual: Using the elbows is a *novel* way to play the piano. 2. *n.* A long piece of fiction, usually of book length.

nov·el·ty [nov′əl·tē] *n.* The quality of being new and unusual; newness: The *novelty* of sending rockets into space has not worn off.

nymph [nimf] *n.* In Greek and Roman myths, any of a group of lesser goddesses who lived in woods, fountains, trees, etc.

Oo

ob·liv·i·ous [ə·bliv′ē·əs] *adj.* Not conscious or aware: He was *oblivious* to his surroundings.

ob·long [ob′lông] *adj.* Longer in one dimension than in another: A football field is *oblong*.

ob·scure [əb·skyŏŏr′] *v.* To make dim or indistinct: Fog *obscured* the mountains.

on·er·ous [on′ər·əs] *adj.* Hard to bear; burdensome; oppressive: After the flood the townspeople began the *onerous* task of cleaning up.

op·press [ə·pres′] *v.* To burden or keep down by unjust use of force or authority: The king *oppressed* the people.

op·ti·cian [op·tish′ən] *n.* A person who makes or sells optical goods, as eyeglasses, etc.

out·ra·geous [out·rā′jəs] *adj.* 1. Very rude or insulting. 2. Fantastic; unbelievable.

Pp

pan·de·mo·ni·um [pan′də·mō′nē·əm] *n.* Great disorder and uproar.

pa·pa·ya [pə·pä′yə] *n.* 1. An edible, yellow melonlike fruit that grows in tropical America. 2. The tree that bears this fruit.

parch [pärch] *v.* 1. To make or become dry with heat; shrivel. 2. To make or become thirsty.

pa·tent·ly [pāt′(ə)nt·lē] *adv.* Clearly; obviously: That statement is *patently* untrue.

peas·ant [pez′ənt] *n.* In Europe, a person of humble birth, as a small farmer.

per·plex [pər·pleks′] *v.* To cause to hesitate or doubt; confuse; bewilder; puzzle: The arithmetic problem *perplexed* the entire class.

phan·tom [fan′təm] *n.* Something that

exists only in the imagination but seems to be real.

plaque [plak] *n.* A flat piece of metal, wood, porcelain, ivory, etc., having designs or lettering on one side.

pla·teau [pla·tō′] *n.* A broad stretch of high, level land; a high plain.

plum·met [plum′it] *v.* To fall straight down; plunge.

pock·mark [pok′märk′] *n.* A pit or scar, as may be left on the skin by smallpox or a similar disease.

pre·ven·tive [pri·ven′tiv] *adj.* Intended or used to prevent harm, disease, etc.: *Preventive* medicine helps check many diseases.

pro·dig·ious [prə·dij′əs] *adj.* 1. Enormous in size, quantity, or degree. 2. Marvelous; amazing.

prof·fer [prof′ər] *v.* To offer: He *proffered* a bouquet of roses.

pro·file [prō′fil] *n.* The outline of a human face as seen from the side.

pro·gram [prō′gram]. 1. *n.* A series of instructions directing an electronic computer to perform certain operations in a certain order. 2. *v.* To work out or make up a program for: The bank *programed* a computer to bring all accounts up to date.

pro·por·tion·al [prə·pôr′shən·əl] *adj.* Of or having to do with things related in size, number, or degree: Your reward will be *proportional* to your effort.

prop·o·si·tion [prop′ə·zish′ən] *n.* 1. A scheme or plan put forth for consideration or approval; proposal. 2. A statement to be discussed or debated.

pub·lish·er [pub′lish·ər] *n.* A person or company that prints and issues books, magazines, newspapers, etc., for sale to the public.

pun [pun] *n.* The humorous use of two or more words having the same or similar

sounds but different meanings, as in, "When the cub shed its coat, it was all bare (bear)."

Rr

ra·di·a·tion [rā′dē·ā′shən] *n.* 1. The sending out of radiant energy, as from radioactive substances. 2. The energy sent out.

ra·ma·da [rə·mä′də] *n.* An open-roofed structure, especially Spanish American, usually shaded by trees or vines; arbor.

ran·dom [ran′dəm] *adj.* Not planned or organized; chance: The class alphabetized a *random* selection of words.

rash·ly [rash′lē] *adv.* Carelessly; too hastily; recklessly.

re·ha·bil·i·tate [rē′hə·bil′ə·tāt] *v.* To restore to good condition, health, appearance, etc.

re·in·state [rē′in·stāt′] *v.* To put back into a former condition or situation.

re·lay race [rē′lā rās]. A running or swimming race in which each member of a team races a certain distance and is then replaced by a teammate.

rem·nant [rem′nənt] *n.* A remaining trace; something left over.

re·mote [ri·mōt′] *adj.* Distant: We spent our vacation in a *remote* fishing village.

re·o·ri·en·ta·tion [rē·ôr′ē·en·tā′shən] *n.* The act of readjusting or setting right again according to the facts or a particular situation: The soldier's *reorientation* to civilian life was difficult.

re·press [ri·pres′] *v.* To hold back or down; check: The speaker *repressed* a desire to sneeze.

re·prieve [ri·prēv′] *v.* To give temporary relief to; delay.

re·search [ri·sûrch′ *or* rē′sûrch] *n.* Careful, patient investigation and study.

re·sign [ri·zīn′] *v.* To give up (an office,

position, job, etc.): The judge *resigned* because of poor health.

re·splen·dent [ri·splen′dənt] *adj.* Splendid; gorgeous.

re·treat [ri·trēt′] *v.* To go back or backward; withdraw.

rid·dle [rid′(ə)l] *v.* To corrupt; permeate: The crew was *riddled* with plotting mutineers.

rig·or mor·tis [rig′ər môr′tis] *n.* The stiffness or rigidity of muscles after death.

rite [rīt] *n.* 1. A formal, solemn, or religious ceremony performed in a set way. 2. The words or acts that make up such a ceremony.

roy·al·ties [roi′əl·tēz] *n.pl.* Money earned by a song, play, invention, novel, etc., and paid to the author or creator for the right to use, sell, or perform his work.

rud·dy [rud′ē] *adj.* 1. Tinged with red. 2. Having a healthy glow; rosy.

ru·mor [roo′mər] *n.* A story or report that has not yet been proven true but is being told from person to person.

Ss

salve [sav] *n.* A soothing or healing ointment for wounds, burns, sores, etc.

san·i·ta·tion [san′ə·tā′shən] *n.* The preservation of good health by sanitary methods and measures: Garbage disposal is a method of *sanitation*.

schol·ar·ship [skol′ər·ship] *n.* 1. A grant of money awarded to a student to help pay for his education. 2. The methods or quality of a student's study: Her poor *scholarship* improved with better study habits.

scope [skōp] *n.* 1. The area covered; range; extent. 2. Room or chance for expression,

development, etc.: The job gave full *scope* to his talents.

scrim·mage [skrim′ij] *n.* A rough, disorderly struggle.

seam·stress [sēm′stris] *n.* A woman skilled at sewing or earning her living by sewing.

seg·re·gate [seg′rə·gāt] *v.* 1. In the United States, to set apart and force to use separate schools, housing, parts of parks, buses, etc., because of racial, religious, or social differences. 2. To regulate use of (a school, park, etc.) so as to separate racial, religious, or ethnic groups.

seis·mic [sīz′mik] *adj.* Of, having to do with, or caused by earthquakes: The tunnel collapsed after a severe *seismic* shock.

sem·a·phore [sem′ə·fôr] *n.* A system of sending messages by means of the arms, flags, etc., held in different positions.

set·ter [set′ər] *n.* One of a breed of hunting dogs trained to point out game by standing rigid.

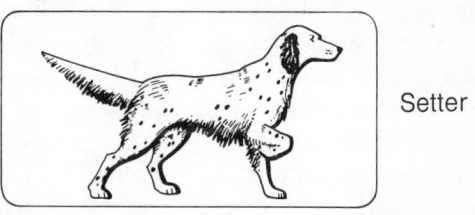

Setter

sex·tant [seks′tənt] *n.* An instrument for measuring the angular distance between two objects, as between the sun and the horizon, used especially to determine a ship's position at sea.

shaft [shaft] *n.* 1. In a machine, a rotating rod that transmits power. 2. The long, narrow rod of an arrow, spear, etc. 3. An opening through the floors of a building, as for an elevator.

sheep·ish [shē′pish] *adj.* 1. Awkwardly shy, embarrassed, or abashed: The milkman had a *sheepish* expression after he dropped the milk. 2. Foolish, meek, or timid, as a sheep.

sig·nif·i·cant [sig·nif'ə·kənt] *adj.* 1. Having or carrying a hidden meaning: The lawyer gave the jury a *significant* look when he asked for a just verdict. 2. Important; noteworthy.

sin·is·ter [sin'is·tər] *adj.* Threatening evil, trouble, or bad luck; ominous: There was something *sinister* about the old house.

smart [smärt] *n.* A sharp, stinging sensation.

smog [smog] *n.* A combination of smoke and fog.

som·ber [som'bər] *adj.* 1. Having little light or brightness; dark. 2. Gloomy and melancholy; sad.

sor·cer·y [sôr'sər·ē] *n.* The use of magic or witchcraft, usually for some evil purpose.

spasm [spaz'əm] *n.* 1. Any sudden, brief burst of energy or activity. 2. A sudden, involuntary contraction of a muscle or muscles.

spec·ta·cle [spek'tə·kəl] *n.* 1. Something exhibited to the public, especially something grand and showy. 2. (*pl.*) A pair of eyeglasses.

spec·u·late [spek'yə·lāt] *v.* 1. To form theories; meditate; ponder; think: People *speculated* about living beings on Mars. 2. To invest money where there is a considerable risk of loss but the possibility of large profits.

spi·ral [spī'rəl] *adj.* Winding or curving like the thread of a screw.

ster·e·op·ti·con [ster'ē·op'ti·kon *or* stir'ē·op'·ti·kon] *n.* A device that projects pictures onto a screen by means of a powerful light; magic lantern.

stew·ard [st(y)oo'ərd] *n.* A servant on a ship, airplane, etc.

still [stil] *n.* An apparatus for distilling liquids, especially alcoholic liquors.

sub·dued [sub·d(y)ood'] *adj.* Made less intense; held down or back: I like *subdued* colors.

sub·se·quent [sub'sə·kwənt] *adj.* Following in time, place, or order: *Subsequent* events proved us wrong.

sub·side [səb·sīd'] *v.* To become less violent or active.

sub·sti·tute [sub'stə·t(y)oot]. 1. *n.* A person or thing that takes the place of someone or something else. 2. *v.* To be a substitute.

suc·ces·sion [sək·sesh'ən] *n.* A group of persons or things that follow one after another: The team enjoyed a *succession* of victories.

suf·fi·cient [sə·fish'ənt] *adj.* Equal to what is needed; enough; adequate.

sulk·y [sul'kē] *adj.* Sullenly cross or ill-humored.

su·per·nat·u·ral [soo'pər·nach'ər·əl] *adj.* Outside the known laws or forces of nature: A witch is supposed to have *supernatural* powers.

su·per·son·ic [soo'pər·son'ik] *adj.* Being or traveling faster than the speed of sound.

sur·geon [sûr'jən] *n.* A doctor whose practice is largely limited to surgery, operations dealing with the repair or removal of diseased or injured organs or parts of the body.

sus·tain [sə·stān'] *v.* To provide nourishment or necessities for: They had hardly enough food to *sustain* life.

swine [swīn] *n.* A pig, hog, or boar.

sym·bol [sim'bəl] *n.* 1. Something chosen to stand for or represent something else. 2. A mark or sign used to indicate something, as a plus sign, a numeral, a dollar sign, etc.

Tt

tact·ful [takt′fəl] *adj.* Showing or having ability to speak and behave so as not to hurt or offend others.

tac·tics [tak′tiks] *n.* Any means to win an advantage; methods: He changed his *tactics* and stopped shouting.

tap·i·o·ca [tap′ē·ō′kə] *n.* A starchy substance obtained from the dried root of the cassava plant, used in puddings and to thicken liquids.

tech·ni·cal [tek′ni·kəl] *adj.* Having to do with, according to, or strictly following the rules or special techniques of a game, art, science, etc.

tech·nol·o·gist [tek·nol′ə·jist] *n.* A person who puts scientific and industrial skills to practical use.

tem·po·rar·y [tem′pə·rer′ē] *adj.* Lasting or meant to be used for a short time only; not permanent.

ten·e·ment [ten′ə·mənt] *n.* 1. An apartment house that is poorly built or maintained, usually overcrowded, and often in a slum. 2. A room or set of rooms for a single tenant or family.

the·o·ret·i·cal [thē′ə·ret′i·kəl] *adj.* Of, having to do with, or existing in theory.

throat·y [thrō′tē] *adj.* Having or producing a deep, husky sound; gutteral: She has a *throaty* voice.

throes [thrōz] *n.pl.* A difficult struggle or ordeal: The country was in the *throes* of a civil war.

top·per [top′ər] *n.* A man's tall hat, used with formal wear.

tor·pe·do [tôr·pē′dō] *n.* A large, underwater projectile that moves under its own power. It is shaped like a cigar and is filled with high explosives that blow up when it strikes a ship.

tor·til·la [tôr·tē′yä] *n.* In Mexico, a flat cake made of coarse cornmeal baked on a sheet of iron or a slab of stone.

tra·di·tion [trə·dish′ən] *n.* 1. The passing down of customs, beliefs, tales, etc., from one generation to the next. 2. A custom, belief, set of practices, etc., passed down in this way.

trans·fer [trans′fər *or* trans·fûr′] *v.* To move or send from one place or person to another.

trans·fix [trans·fiks′] *v.* To make motionless, as with horror or fear.

trans·late [trans·lāt′] *v.* To change (something spoken or written) into another language.

trans·mit [trans·mit′] *v.* To send or pass on from one person or place to another; transfer: Dirty hands *transmit* disease.

trans·par·ent [trans·pâr′ənt] *adj.* So clear or sheer as to be seen through easily.

treach·er·ous [trech′ər·əs] *adj.* 1. Likely to betray; disloyal; unreliable. 2. Not as good or safe as it appears.

tread [tred] *n.* The part of an automobile tire that touches the ground.

tri·pod [trī′pod] *n.* A three-legged stand for a camera, transit, etc.

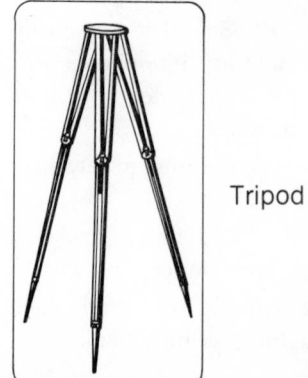

Tripod

tus·sle [tus′əl] *n.* A rough struggle.

tu·tor [t(y)ōō′tər]. 1. *v.* To give private

instruction. 2. *n.* A person who teaches another, usually privately.

Uu

un·com·pre·hend·ing·ly [un′kom·pri·hend′-ing·lē] *adv.* Without understanding: We listened *uncomprehendingly* to the German teacher.

u·ni·corn [yōō′nə·kôrn] *n.* An imaginary animal said to look like a horse with one long horn projecting from its forehead.

u·nique [yōō·nēk′] *adj.* 1. Being the only one of its type; without an equal or like; singular. 2. Unusual, rare, or notable.

un·mys·tic [un·mis′tik] *adj.* Without mystery or confusion; clear.

un·nerve [un·nûrv′] *v.* To cause to lose strength, firmness, self-control, or courage: The pistol shots *unnerved* us.

un·per·turbed [un′pər·tûrbd′] *adj.* Not alarmed or agitated; undisturbed: The traffic officer was *unperturbed* by the tie-up.

un·ru·ly [un·rōō′lē] *adj.* Difficult to control or discipline; disobedient.

Vv

va·cant [vā′kənt] *adj.* Being or appearing to be without thought, intelligence, or interest: The usher had a *vacant* look as he collected the tickets.

vague [vāg] *adj.* Not definite, clear, precise, or distinct.

van·i·ty [van′ə·tē] *n.* Too much pride in oneself or in one's appearance; conceit.

vault [vôlt] *n.* A strongly protected place for keeping valuables, as in a bank.

vise [vīs] *n.* A clamp having two jaws that can be closed together with a screw, used to grasp and hold objects as they are worked on.

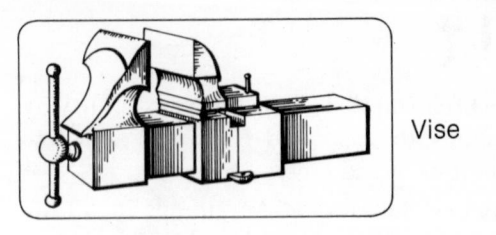

Vise

vi·tals [vīt′(ə)lz] *n.pl.* 1. The parts or organs necessary to life, as the lungs, heart, brain, etc. 2. The essential parts of anything.

vo·cal·ize [vō′kəl·īz] *v.* To sing, speak, or make vocal sounds.

Ww

warp [wôrp] *v.* To turn or twist out of shape.

war·rant [wôr′ənt *or* wor′ənt] *v.* To be sufficient grounds for; justify: The situation *warrants* bold action.

weath·er [weth′ər] *v.* To undergo changes from exposure to the weather: The carpenter replaced the siding that had *weathered*.

weight·y [wā′tē] *adj.* Of great importance, influence, or significance: A *weighty* discussion about ecology followed the meeting.

wench [wench] *n.* In earlier times, a female servant; maid.

wince [wins] *v.* To shrink or draw back, as from a blow or a pain; flinch.

wry [rī] *adj.* 1. Bent, twisted, or turned to one side: The joke brought a *wry* smile to his face. 2. Grim, bitter, or ironic: His comments are full of *wry* humor.

Zz

zeal·ous [zel′əs] *adj.* Filled with or caused by a great interest and devotion, as when working for a cause; having enthusiasm.